PRIMARY EMBRYONIC INDUCTION

LOGOS PRESS

SCIENTIFIC MONOGRAPHS
ON
EXPERIMENTAL BIOLOGY

Editorial Committee

Professor D. R. Newth
Professor H. Abercrombie F.R.S.
L. Brent Ph.D.
J. Maynard Smith B.A., B.SC.

PRIMARY EMBRYONIC INDUCTION

LAURI SAXÉN, M.D., M.A.
Lecturer in Pathology,
University of Helsinki

SULO TOIVONEN, Ph.D.
Professor in Experimental Zoology,
University of Helsinki

LOGOS PRESS GREAT JAMES STREET, LONDON
PRENTICE-HALL, INC. ENGLEWOOD CLIFFS, N.J.

Printed in Great Britain by J. W. Arrowsmith Ltd., Bristol 3

Contents

Foreword

Taken in a somewhat schematic fashion, research concerned with embryonic induction could be divided into different periods: first, the hopeful 'twenties, then the rather confused 'thirties, the depressed and inactive 'forties, and finally the 'fifties, filled with a new optimism and activity. Despite the many noteworthy results achieved during this most recent period of active study, the problem still remains open, even in some of its most essential aspects, so that it might be questioned whether this is an appropriate time for a monograph such as this. As yet, it is hardly possible to make major syntheses, and in many respects our work will perforce stand as just a collection of scattered information, assuming to some extent the characteristics of a catalogue. However, there is something to be said for this form of procedure. In fact, it is quite obvious that the early 'sixties will mark the introduction of a new period of research in embryonic induction. New methods of study have brought in their train numerous new objectives in this field of work, have afforded new instances of embryonic induction, and have often led to new lines of investigation which will without doubt give good results. In this connection we wish especially to mention the remarkable work and stimulating ideas of Dr. Clifford Grobstein; one of the present authors (L.S.) derived a great deal of pleasure from an opportunity to visit his laboratory and see the work being done there. As these studies will perhaps result in research on primary induction losing its leading position, and in the major interest being directed towards other fields of induction, it might not be without interest to compile, on the threshold of this new phase of development, what knowledge we have of primary induction.

We undertook our work with our eyes fully open to the difficulties presented by the dispersed character of this knowledge and the nature of this particular field of research; it is certainly not an easy task to try to compile and to analyze the abundant material connected with a new branch of study still in course of development, and in which no general and uniform line of progress can be found. We are fully aware that the way in which the material has been presented in our work is but one of many, and in our endeavours to divide its contents into rather definite groups, we have at times perhaps been too schematic. Normal development and its chemistry, the chemistry of the inductive agents and the different conceptions of the induction process, form quite certainly a coherent group, and it is only in order to bring clarity to our text that we have set them in different chapters.

In our work, we derived especial profit from two broad surveys published recently, and to which frequent reference is made (Holtfreter and Hamburger in: *Analysis of Development*, 1955; and Dalcq in: *Fundamental Aspects of Normal and Malignant Growth*, 1960). In addition, Tuneo Yamada has recently published two reviews which amply summarize the highly important work done in his laboratory (in: *The Chemical Basis of Development*, 1958, and in: *Advances in Morphogenesis*, 1961). We would also mention that the research work carried out prior to 1936 was dealt with in detail in the monograph published in that year by Hans Spemann, the pioneer in the field.

May we express our gratitude to our publishers and to the members of their scientific advisory committee, Professor D. R. Newth and Professor M. Abercrombie, for very pleasant collaboration. Our fellow workers, Dr. Taina Kuusi, Dr. Tapani Vainio, and Mr. Juhani Kohonen, have read our manuscript, and we are grateful to them for many important suggestions and remarks. The "Subject Index" was prepared by Mr. Kohonen and the list of references by Miss Aino Nikupaavo, M.A., Librarian. We wish also to thank Mrs. Anja Tuomi, Miss Ann-Kristin Thors, Mr. Tauno Pirinen and Mr. Paavo Korhonen for their valuable technical help.

During our work, we have had many fruitful and stimulating discussions at the "Wetterkulla Medical Centre", a farm house in Central Finland where a small group of scientists sometimes meets for a week for very informal discussions. We have greatly appreciated these discussions and the objective criticisms made by the other members of the group, Professor Erkki Saxén, Dr. Kari Penttinen, and Dr. H. R. Nevanlinna.

We are very much obliged to Mr. Fred A. Fewster, who read through the manuscript with a view to correcting inaccuracies in the English. We also extend our thanks to our colleagues and to those publishers through whose courtesy we obtained abundant pictorial material for our work.

Our studies whose findings are given in this work have for many years been supported by grants from the Sigrid Juselius Foundation and, more recently, by a grant from the National Cancer Institute, U.S. Public Health Service (C–5347).

Helsinki, July 1961.   L.S.   S.T.

I

Historical Background of the Induction Problem

1. *Weismann's theory*

Before the end of last century, when the main features of vertebrate ontogeny had become known, the question arose as to why embryonic cells, originally all of similar appearance, were later differentiated into various types of tissue, in other words how the normal development of an individual was regulated. A number of theories were proposed at that time in an effort to solve the problem. Of these theories, that proposed by Weismann (1892) was to prove the most fruitful in furthering scientific knowledge, although subsequently it appeared that this theory was incorrect in its essential features.

According to Weismann's theory, ontogeny was determined in advance, at as early a stage as the fertilized egg. This meant, for example, that in every blastula each cell would have a positive fate in the future development. The young embryo would be similar to a mosaic in which every piece had its own ineluctable significance in the whole.

2. *Roux' hot needle experiment*

Weismann's theory was purely and simply an idea which had no empirical background. We have to be grateful to Roux (1888) for placing the examination of the problem of differentiation on an experimental basis. He made the classic experiment of drilling one of the blastomeres in an amphibian two-cell stage with a hot needle, in order to follow what he believed would be the independent development of the other blastomere, the living one.

As a result of this experiment, support was given to Weismann's theory, as the living cell did in fact give rise to one half of the embryo; but later this was explained as being merely the consequence of the remnant of the killed cell preventing the free development of the living one.

3. *Embryo-dividing experiments*

When the cells of the two-cell stage were separated one from the other by means of a gradually tightening loop of hair (Endres 1895; Herlitzka 1897), it was realized that at this stage each cell was still totipotent, that is to say each of them was capable of developing into a whole embryo (figure 1), and even into an adult individual. Subsequently, it has by this means been found possible to divide the blastula and the gastrula into two parts; similar results being achieved if the ligature is placed along the middle line of the grey crescent (Spemann, 1901, 1903).

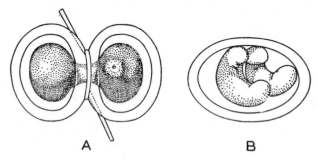

                    A   B

Figure 1. Constriction of the two-cell stage of a newt embryo with a hair loop (*A*) results in two normally developing embryos (*B*) if the ligature lies along the presumptive median plane. (After Spemann, 1936.)

4. *Testing the time of determination*

The dividing experiments prove that determination has not occurred at the beginning of development, but that the cells in a young embryo have more developmental potency than would seem to be implied by their source.

Once this fact became clear, new questions were posed; *when* and *how* does the final determination of the tissues take place?

The answer to the question of "When?" was explained at the beginning of this century by Spemann (1916, 1918) and his school; grafting experiments, or transplantations, were made between amphibian embryos. When, for example, a piece of presumptive neural plate was removed from an early gastrula, and grafted on to the belly side of a new "host" of the same age, the graft developed in a way similar to that of its new surroundings, and not in accordance with the region of origin (figure 2A). Thus the tissue of the neural plate could not have been determined prior to the operation; its fate must have been determined by some factor connected with its new position. When the experiment was carried out between two late gastrula or young neurula stages, the result was the opposite. The graft developed in its new surroundings, on the belly, into formations of the central nervous system such as would have arisen in the original position, and the piece of the presumptive neural plate could not do otherwise than to self-differentiate in accordance with its origin (figure 2B).

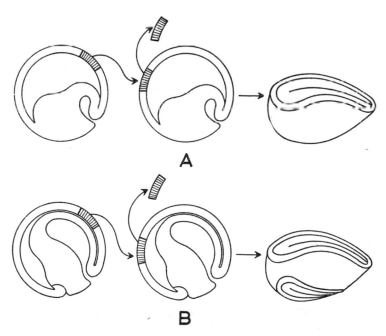

A

B

Figure 2. *A*. Piece of presumptive neural plate removed from an early newt gastrula, and grafted on to the ventral side of another of the same age; no induction occurs, but it develops in accordance with its new surroundings. *B*. A corresponding piece removed from a late gastrula develops in the new surroundings according to its original fate. (Orig.)

These results served to establish that the neural plate had been given its determination during gastrulation, and had lost its ability to develop in any other direction but into nervous structures.

This provided the answer to the question of "when" determination occurs. But the other question, that of "how", proved to be more complicated and difficult of solution.

5. Discovery of some secondary induction systems

It is true that Spemann, simultaneously with his other experiments, was able to trace something of the mechanism which guides the development of some organs. For instance, mention may be made of his discovery of the correlation of the development of the eye and the lens (Spemann, 1901, 1912). The eye cup, which comes into being as an outpushing of the brain, is in very close proximity to the ectoderm, which forms the lens and fits the opening of the eye cup. If the ectoderm which normally develops into the lens is removed, and replaced with a piece of the ectoderm from another part of the embryo, this foreign ectoderm is also capable of forming the lens. If the eye cup were cut from its original position, and grafted under the ectoderm in another part of the embryo, then the lens also would be formed there. If some foreign tissue were grafted between the eye cup and the presumptive lens-ectoderm, then the formation of the lens would be prevented.

It became obvious that the development of the eye is guided by a system with two components: the eye cup is the active component, later known as the action system or the inductor, which determines the development of the ectoderm: the ectoderm is the reaction system which obeys the orders of the inductor. Taken together, these two systems are termed the induction system. At that time nobody knew the way in which the eye cup could determine the differentiation of the lens.

It became evident that there were other secondary induction systems, very similar to that involved in the formation of the eye, in the development of some other organs. However, these different systems seem to operate in mutual independence, and it was not possible to detect any general system which connected them.

6. Discovery of the primary organizer

In the spring of 1921, in Spemann's laboratory, one of his pupils, Hilde Mangold, was engaged in carrying out transplantation with a view to defining the exact time of determination of different parts of the early gastrula (Spemann, 1921). She transplanted a piece from the blastoporal lip into the belly side of another embryo of the same age. The result was very striking. A second neutral plate was formed on the belly of the host; this developed into neural groove, and later into neural tube. On each side, ear vesicles and rows of somites were to be seen. In other words, a secondary dorsal axis came into being on the belly of the host.

The experiment was performed with embryos of two different species of Triturus, one of which (*T. cristatus*) had pale eggs, and the other (*T. vulgaris*) much darker ones. It was observed that only a very small part of the secondary neural plate had formed from the graft, the main part of it originating in host tissues which had differentiated in directions other than normal (figure 3).

Meanwhile, Vogt (page 11) had in his experiments with vital stains shown that the blastoporal lip would form in normogenesis the mesoderm mantle whose middle part lies under the presumptive neural plate. It became evident that the blastoporal lip, later the archenteron roof, acts as the inductor of the medullary plate, and the transplant taken from this part of the embryo is able to induce a secondary dorsal axis also on the belly of the new host (Spemann and H. Mangold, 1924).

When the action of the blastoporal lip was discovered, it was obvious that this primary inductor, or primary organizer as Spemann entitled it, linked the earlier known secondary induction systems whose importance lay only in the development of different organs into a main system which guided the whole development and differentiation of the embryo. The primary inductor directly determines the differentiation of the neural plate, but at the conclusion of this stage of development, secondary inductors are formed in different parts of the neural plate, and these are identical with the action systems whose presence was known previously. Directly or indirectly, different parts of the central nervous system give rise to the development of eyes, nasal pits, ear vesicles, and so on. The main system acts as a chain reaction, in which every step in development is the result of an earlier occurrence, and is the prerequisite for those following. This chain reaction is initiated by the action of the blastoporal lip, that is to say by the middle part of the grey crescent, the primary organizer (Bautzmann, 1926).

If the whole of the organizer was grafted on the ventral side of a gastrula, it would cause a very complete embryonic axis to be formed. In successful experiments, such secondary formations may be very similar to the axis of the host (Holtfreter, 1933d; Ekman, 1937).

B

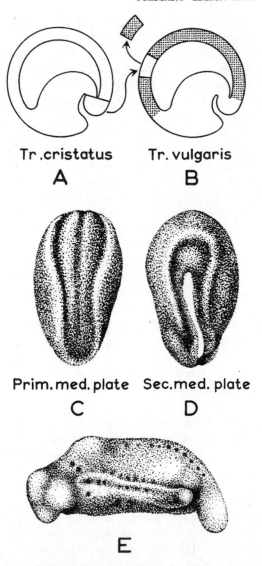

Figure 3. Heteroplastic transplantation of the blastopore lip of *Triturus cristatus* gastrula (colourless) (*A*) to the ventral side of *Triturus vulgaris* gastrula (pigmented) (*B*) induces a secondary neural plate (*D*) and subsequent development of a secondary embryo on the belly of the host (*E*). (After Spemann and H. Mangold, 1924.)

(a) *Head and trunk organizer.* Subsequently it was established in Spemann's laboratory (Spemann, 1927, 1931) that the blastoporal lip of an early gastrula, and that part of an older one, have qualitatively different inductive properties. The region at the margin of the blastopore in a young gastrula, that is the presumptive anterior part of the archenteron roof ("head organizer"), tends to induce head structures whereas the presumptive posterior part ("trunk organizer") is able to induce trunk and tail structures (Plate 1.1).

(b) *Discovery of the chemical nature of the inductors.* Until 1932, the real nature of the inductive action presented an enigma. How is the organizer able to influence the competent ectoderm so that its development will be determined in a certain direction only? In that year, a preliminary report was issued (Bautzmann, Holtfreter, Spemann and O. Mangold, 1932), in which it was stated that organizers which have been killed are also capable of inducing secondary formations if they are brought into contact with competent ectoderm. The organizer may be killed by one means or another, by crushing, by freezing or by heating; by treatment with different kinds of solvents, alcohol, ether, chloroform, and so on. But nevertheless, it can primarily induce a neural plate, and secondly all kinds of derivatives. It became evident that the nature of the inductive action could no longer be regarded as mechanical irritation by the inductor alone. It was obviously chemical in nature.

(c) *The importance of the methods of operation.* The question might be posed as to why this experiment with killed inductors had not been previously carried out. Why had time been lost for ten years after the discovery of the primary organizer without such empirical investigation? The main transplantation method employed in experiments made had involved investigation of the living organizer only. The piece of organizer tissue was grafted on to the surface of the host gastrula, from which a corresponding piece of the ectoderm was first removed (figure 2; plate 1.2). In addition, the donor from which the transplant originated had to be of approximately the same age, as otherwise the grafted piece would not be capable of growing with the host tissues.

Meanwhile, O. Mangold had found a new method of operation (Mangold and Spemann, 1927). The inductor was inserted in the blastocoel through a cut made in its roof (Plate 1.1). As gastrulation progressed, the inductor was pressed against the inner surface of the ectoderm, and could act on the ectoderm from the same direction as that normally taken by the archenteron roof. The wound in the ectoderm healed in a matter of minutes, and the inductor was now in a closed cavity from which it could not be expelled. By this "implantation" or "insertion" method, it became possible to test the action of a tissue older than the host, even of the differentiated tissues of adult animals, and furthermore of animals of any other species. This new method also allowed the testing of the action of killed inductors, and even that of chemical substances, if they were first impregnated in agar or some other absorptive substance.

Subsequently, Holtfreter (1933b) applied a third principal method, that of explantation, or the "sandwich method", for the investigation of the inductive activity of various kinds of living or killed inductors. The inductor for examination was placed in a vesicle formed from the isolated presumptive epidermis of two young gastrula stages (Plate 1.3). This method is more reliable than the others cited, as it excludes the action of the organizers of the host embryo. All the differentiations which are discernible in the reacting material are occasioned by the action of the inductor. With no inductive action, the epidermal explant is unable to differentiate at all, although multiplication of the cells is continued, but a proliferating clump of undifferentiated cells will be formed.

(d) *First attempts at solution of the biochemistry of the induction process.* As the findings of Spemann's laboratory had hinted at the nature of the inductive action possibly being chemical in nature, real "teams" were formed, in which embryologists were associated with biochemists, with a view to determining the active agent, the "evocator". Within a short period, many reports were published, with accounts of the progress achieved in the work undertaken by these teams (see Chapter VII).

A great deal of work was done, thousands of amphibian embryos were operated on, but unfortunately the results obtained in the various laboratories were very different, and often in direct conflict. After some years, the teams abandoned their task, no decisive results having been obtained.

It is now possible to understand why they failed to attain their objective. In this first attempt to solve the riddle of the inductive principle, the background to the problem was not sufficiently clear for a final solution. For some reason, it was then expected first and foremost that the inductive action would be found to be caused by one substance alone. It has subsequently been shown that this is unlikely to be the case. Furthermore, the small size of the eggs occasioned many difficulties; when tissues from embryos were treated in various solvents, the fractions obtained were always too minute for examination by the usual biochemical methods, and this naturally involved much trouble. In addition, we know today that some of the inductive principles are thermolabile, and that a moderately high temperature inactivates them. Nevertheless, the research work done at that time was by no means labour in vain. Afterwards, when investigation of the induction problem was carried out at a slower tempo, many of the facts discovered earlier proved of great value to those who have made further efforts in this field.

(e) *The subsequent progress of the problem.* Subsequently, many new methods have been applied to the investigation of the embryonic induction problem. Scientists in different laboratories have modified the main methods of operation mentioned above for the specification of different features of the induction phenomen. By radio-autographic technique it has been possible to follow the movements of substances from the inductor to the reacting material. Immunological methods make it possible to obtain minute amounts of substances which are present in the cells. Tissue culture methods have been applied with many modifications in experimental embryology, and new analytical methods of biochemistry have also been used in the determination of inductive principles.

In what follows, the authors attempt to present the main points of subsequent progress in the investigation of this problem, together with an account of its present state.

The authors have in this monograph concentrated on dealing with work carried out since 1936; as regards older works, the reader is referred to the extensive monograph by Hans Spemann printed in 1936 and translated into English in 1938.

II

The Early Development of the
Amphibian Embryo

1. Cleavage

If one wishes to achieve comprehension of the problem we intend to deal with, it is necessary to call to mind the main features of the early development of the embryo. As efforts to solve the inductor problem are almost invariably based upon experiments carried out with amphibian embryos, what follows refers exclusively to the amphibians.

As is the case with all mesolecithal eggs, that is to say eggs with a moderate amount of yolk, in amphibians cleavage is total, or holoblastic, and unequal. This results in a blastula with a thinner animal wall and a thicker vegetative one, as can be seen in a cross-section (see figure 5A). In view of the subsequent characteristics, and also some morphological differences, it is possible to distinguish three main regions in the blastula: (1) the upper part around the animal pole, (2) the lower part around the vegetative pole, and (3) the intermediate zone, between the others, which is also known as the marginal zone, going round the equator of the blastula. In many species of Amphibia, there is a clear difference of colour between these regions. The animal region is most deeply pigmented. The marginal zone, which is broader on one side of the equator, is also pigmented, but not so deeply, and is generally of a greyish colour. Its shape and colour result in its also being known as the grey crescent. The vegetative region is the one most devoid of colour; in some species it is milk-white.

These three regions are in approximate correspondence to the subsequent three main germ layers: the animal region will constitute the outer germ layer or ectoderm, the vegetative the inner germ layer or endoderm, and the marginal zone will develop into the middle germ layer or mesoderm. The segregation of the different area of the blastula into these germ layers is a very complicated step of embryonic development, that of gastrulation.

2. Gastrulation

(a) The "vital dye method" of Vogt. There are many difficulties involved in a full comprehension of gastrulation, and a final understanding was not obtained until the "vital dye method" was applied. This method entails pressing small lumps of agar, impregnated with various kinds of vital dye, against the outer surface of the blastula. Generally speaking, the two dyes utilized for this purpose are neutral red and Nile blue sulphate (Plate 2.1).

This method was discovered by Vogt (1923a, 1923b, 1924, 1925, 1926, 1929). His findings have not since been subjected to any substantial changes, although a number of other embryologists have introduced revisions with a view to application to Vertebrata other than Amphibia (Birds: Gräper, 1929; Wetzel, 1929a and 1929b; Pasteels, 1936, 1937b; Reptiles: Pasteels, 1935, 1937a, Fishes: Pasteels, 1933, 1934; Cyclostomes: Weissenberg, 1929a; 1929b).

The pieces of agar colour the cells of the outer surface of the blastula without thereby causing any damage to them. The coloured patches can then be followed through the later stages of development, and their position located after gastrulation.

(b) The fate map of an amphibian embryo. By utilizing this vital stain method, Vogt (1926) was able to determine the future fate of different parts of the blastula. From the results obtained, he worked out the fate map of an amphibian embryo in which were exactly located all the presumptive anlagen of future differentiated tissues and organs.

In Vogt's map, there can be seen (figure 4) the three areas of the blastula: the future ectoderm, the mesoderm and the endoderm. The future ectoderm comprises two main areas: the presumptive central nervous system and the presumptive epidermis. In the anlage of the mesoderm, we find the material for the notochord, which occupies an extensive area in the middle part of the grey crescent. On each side of this, the presumptive materials for myotomes are located. In the middle line between the presumptive notochord and the blastopore is the future prechordal plate, which will later lie under the forebrain. The lateral and the ventral parts of the marginal zone section correspond to the mesodermal lining of the body cavity (somatopleure and splanchnopleure), the kidneys, etc.

The endoderm will form the primitive gut, later the lining of the gut, and the large glands of the digestive system, such as the liver

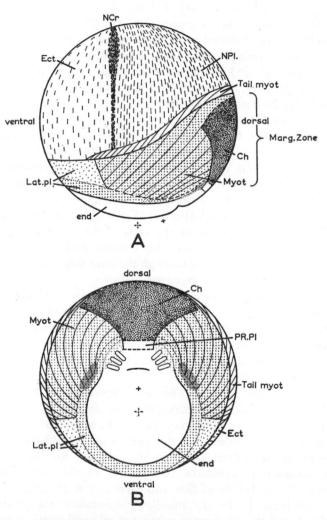

Figure 4. Fate maps of Vogt. *A*. The left side of a newt embryo, with the different presumptive areas indicated. *B*. The map seen from the vegetal pole. Ch, notochord; Ect, ectoderm; end, endoderm; Lat. pl., lateral plate; Myot, myotomes; NCr, neural crest; NPl., Neural plate; PR.Pl., prechordal plate. (After Vogt, 1925, 1929 and Pasteels, 1942, somewhat modified.)

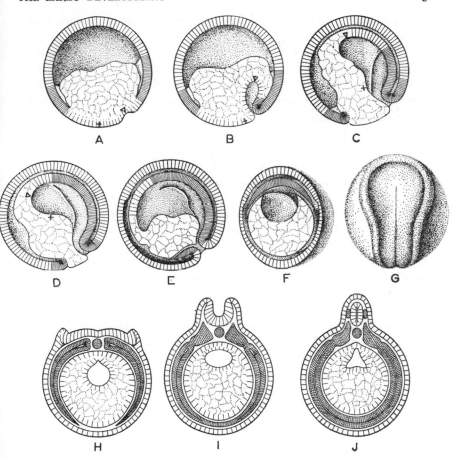

Figure 5. Scheme of the early development of amphibian (*Urodela*) embryo. *A*. Sagittal section of an early gastrula. *B*. Sagittal section of the middle gastrula. *C*. Sagittal section of a gastrula with large yolk plug. *D*. Sagittal section of a gastrula with small yolk plug. *E*. Sagittal section at the end of gastrulation. *F*. The same stage sectioned transversally. *G*. Neurula with open neural plate seen dorsally. *H*. The same stage sectioned transversely. *I*. Transverse section of the middle neurula with open neural furrow. *J*. Transverse section of the neurula after the closing of the neural tube. In figures *A–F*: The presumptive ectoderm indicated by thin hatching, presumptive mesoderm by dense hatching, presumptive endoderm by dotted cell boundaries. In figures *H–J*: The neural crest, dense hatching, the mesoderm dense and dots. (*A–H*: After Spemann, 1936; *I–J*: original.)

and pancreas. The branchial pouches will be formed on each side, close to the prechordal plate anlage.

The broadest part of the marginal zone and the presumptive neural plate correspond to the future dorsal side of the embryo (in figure 4A, on right) while the presumptive epidermis and the narrowest part the marginal zone correspond to the future ventral side (figure 4A, left).

(c) *The outer topography of gastrulation.* By utilizing the vital dye method, Vogt also found it possible to trace with precision the events of the complicated process of gastrulation.

One indication of the beginning of the gastrulation, the blastopore, is first to be observed as a shallow depression situated on the surface of the late blastula. It is on the borderline of the vegetative region, exactly below the broadest part of the grey crescent. Subsequently, it becomes a horizontal slit. The blastopore soon becomes deeper, and the presumptive notochord, situated on the upper lip of the blastopore, begins to move around the edge of the lip into the inner part of the embryo. The presumptive endoderm, below the blastopore, follows the notochord primordium into the embryo.

This movement of the tissues is known as invagination. Strictly speaking, this term is not absolutely accurate, as the connotation is a substantial in-folding of sheets of tissue. In reality, the movement of the mesodermal and the endodermal primordia is no infolding at all, but rather a flowing or streaming movement of the cells. This is to be seen from the elongation of the dye spots, which were originally round in shape (Plate 2.1, D, E).

The invaginating stream of presumptive mesodermal cells starts in the middle of the blastoporal lip, where the presumptive notochord is situated, but gradually broadens to both corners of the blastopore. Simultaneously, both corners grow along the border line between the presumptive mesoderm and the endoderm. After a while, the blastopore assumes a sickle shape, and later takes the form of a horseshoe; finally, it is circular, and surrounds the part of the presumptive endoderm known as the yolk-plug which has remained on the outer surface of the embryo. In the following stage, the blastopore circle diminishes in size, the yolk-plug is completely engulfed, and eventually the blastopore is merely a narrow vertical slit.

In the meantime, the presumptive mesoderm has continued its progress round the margin of the blastopore. The final result is that the whole of the grey crescent has disappeared from the outer surface into the embryo.

The developmental stage from the appearance of the first small blastopore depression to the disappearance of the yolk-plug is termed the gastrula. At the end of gastrulation, the ectoderm alone covers the outer surface of the embryo.

(d) *The inner topography of gastrulation.* Vogt (l.c.) followed the dots of dye into the inner part of the gastrula, and by this means was able to learn how the mesodermal and endodermal primordia gradually move into their final position.

When the cells of the presumptive prechordal plate and the notochord have begun their movement round the blastoporal lip, the first slight depression of the blastopore (figure 5A) deepens, and the primitive gut or archenteron is formed (figure 5B). During the process of invagination, the archenteron lengthens, and finally its blind wall touches the inner surface of the ectoderm opposite the blastopore. Subsequently, in the early larval stage, the mouth breaks through here, and later the blastopore is replaced by the anal opening.

When the primitive gut begins the process of elongation from the young blastopore, its roof is formed by the presumptive material of the prechordal plate, and later on also by the presumptive mesoderm; its floor consists of endoderm. On each side are the border-lines between the mesoderm and the endoderm. Very soon after the beginning of prolongation of the primitive gut, the mesodermal roof splits away from the endodermal floor on both lateral margins (figure 5C). The connection between the mesoderm and the endoderm remains a permanent feature only at the anterior end of the archenteron, where the prechordal plate effects a junction between these two germ layers.

Once the lateral margins of the mesoderm have separated from the endoderm, they grow downwards between the covering ectoderm and the free margin of the endoderm. In the late stage of gastrulation, with a circular blastopore, the mesoderm completely surrounds the entodermal yolk-plug at the posterior end of the endoderm (figure 5D). The endoderm now resembles an open trough over which a mantle is thrown, the mesodermal cell layer (figure 5F). Thus at the termination of gastrulation the three cell layers are in their definitive positions; the innermost layer is the endoderm, outside this is the mesoderm, and the ectoderm covers the whole of the gastrula.

3. Neurulation

(a) *The outer topography of neurulation and the development of the ectoderm.* When the yolk-plug has finally disappeared from view, the embryo is still almost spherical in shape; it is also evenly coloured by a dark pigment which is characteristic of the ectoderm. Shortly after this, there can be observed from the outside of the embryo the first signs of differentiation of the ectoderm. On the dorsal side, starting from the blastoporal slit, a slight longitudinal furrow can be seen: around this will be formed a somewhat flattened pear-shaped rea which is slightly darker in colour (figure 5G). This is the first primordium of the central nervous system, known as the neural or medullary plate.

The ectodermal epithelium of the neural plate thickens; its cells become elongated and arrange themselves into a columnar epithelium, whereas the cells of the epidermis remain more or less flattened, and are arranged in a stratified epithelium which is usually two or three cells in thickness.

The edges of the neural plate soon become elevated in ridges, the neural folds. Meanwhile, the spherical shape of the whole of the embryo has changed; it is now inclined to be oval in shape, or slightly pear-shaped. With the elapse of time, the neural plate narrows and the neural folds become higher, until it would be more appropriate to refer to the whole of the neural area as the neural groove rather than plate (figure 5I). Finally, the folds touch each other at the middle line and fuse, beginning from the future occipital region of the embryo and progressing forwards and backwards. The neural tube is formed. Eventually, this is lying beneath the ectoderm, which covers it without a break (figure 5J).

The neural tube is broadest at its anterior end. This part later forms the brain with its cavities. In the posterior part of the neural tube the cavity is narrow; it will later form the central canal of the spinal cord.

The most posterior fifth or seventh of the original neural plate has a different fate in the development. It will form the somites in the future tail (Bijtel, 1931, 1936; Nakamura, 1942; Spofford, 1948; Smithsberg, 1954, see page 44), although somites in the rest of the body originate from the dorsal part of the mesoderm mantle (see below).

The developmental stage from the first appearance of the neural plate until the closure of the neural tube is known as the neurula.

(b) *Neural crest.* When the neural folds have fused in the dorsal middle line, and the neural tube and the covering epidermis have become isolated from each other, there is formed a thin mantle of cells between the neural tube and the dorsal epidermis which belongs to neither of them. This flattened mass is called the neural crest.

The origin of the neural crest can be traced back to the early gastrula stage (figure 4). In the edges of the neural folds is a strip of cells which runs like a peripheral band round the whole neural plate. This was first described in the Amphibia by A. Brachet (1908), but its importance to the development of the different kinds of tissues was not found out until very much later. The problem of the neural crest has been subjected to more intensive investigation since 1931, when a detailed survey was presented by Raven (1931); subsequently, many others have devoted attention to this problem (for details of literature, see Hörstadius, 1950).

When the neural folds touch one another in the dorsal middle line, the neural material fuses to the neural, and the epidermis to the epidermis. The material of the neural crest is isolated from both of them (figure 6), and both of the rudiments join at the middle

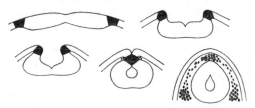

Figure 6. The formation of the neural crest (black) in amphibians.
(After Balinsky, 1960, modified.)

line. Subsequently, the cells of the neural crest start to migrate in a lateral and ventral direction from their original location. In fact, the neural crest cells form streams along the inner side of the epidermis, and between it and the lateral layer of the mesoderm. They penetrate into each space between the other tissues, and the streams make contact with each other at the mid-ventral line of the body.

The neural crest constitutes the origin of many kinds of cell, as has been proved by many different methods:

(1) The stream of cells has been followed by means of local vital staining (Detwiler, 1937).

(2) To this end, Raven (1931, 1936) applied xenoplastic transplantation between animals belonging to different genera of amphibians, in which the cells are of different size and colour, and the sizes of nuclei differ.

(3) By extirpations of parts of the neural crest, deficiencies were caused (Harrison, 1924; van Campenhout, 1930; DuShane, 1938; Hörstadius and Sellman, 1946) and a partial lack of pigmentation noted.

(4) New surroundings for the cells were produced by homoplastic transplantation, i.e. by rotation of the neural crest or the neural plate (Hörstadius and Sellman, 1946).

(5) Following transplantation of the neural crest cells between various species with different patterns of melanophores, an investigation was made into the change of pigmentation (Twitty, 1936; Twitty and Bodenstein, 1939, etc.).

These methods resulted in an alteration of the old concept concerning the "mesodermal tissues". It has been discovered that a considerable number of cells once believed to have their source in the mesoderm mantle develop instead from the neural crest. A part of the mesechyme, the "ectomesechyme" with melanophores, is a neural crest derivative, and the other originates from the "endomesoderm" or mesoderm mantle. A part of the skeleton, the major part of the visceral skull, also has the same source. Furthermore, the spinal ganglia with centripetal nerve-roots, the cells of Schwann's sheath, the meninges (at least as far as the pia mater and the arachnoidea are concerned), the entire sympathetic nervous system, the cells of the adrenal medulla and other cromaffine tissue, and other parts, might also find their origin in the neural crest.

(c) The development of the mesoderm. When the neural plate starts to differentiate, the mesoderm mantle splits into five cell strips: the rudiments for the notochord, the somites and the lateral plates.

Beneath the dorsal middle longitudinal furrow of the medullary plate, the rudiment of the notochord separates from the mesodermal mantle as a narrow rod of cells. Its anterior end lies beneath the future mesencephalon, and does not reach under the future forebrain, where the thin layer of the prechordal plate underlies the floor of the brain. The hind end of the notochord rudiment reaches the blastopore. Primarily, the notochord rudiment is seen as a vertical cell column in transverse sections, and its cells do not differ

from those of the mesoderm mantle. A short time later, the notochord becomes of roundish shape in cross section, its cells now
being somewhat larger and filled with fluid. The cytoplasm and
the nucleus are pressed against the border of the cell.

Meanwhile, thickening occurs in the strips of the mesoderm
mantle to the right and to the left of the notochord. Subsequently,
these parts subdivide, starting from the anterior end, into rows of
cube-shaped cell lumps, the somites. Each somite is separated from
the adjoining ones, but remains connected to the remaining lateral
plate mesoderm by means of a stalk, the source of the kidney.
Later, parts of the somites close to the notochord become separated
from it, and form the skeletogenous sheet around the notochord.
The major part of each somite, the myotomes, is the source of the
somatic muscles. The cells in a myotome become elongated in the
longitudinal direction of the body. These cells will subsequently
differentiate into striated muscle fibres. The remaining part of
every somite forms mesenchyme, and afterwards a part of the
connective tissue of the skin and of the body.

At about the same time as there takes place the segmentation of
the somites, each of the margins of the mesoderm mantle, the lateral
plates, splits into two layers. An external layer applied to the ectoderm is known as the parietal layer or somatopleure, and an internal
layer applied to the entoderm is the visceral layer or splanchnopleure.
The narrow cavity between these two layers is the coelomic cavity
or coelom. First of all, the cavities on each side are isolated from
each other, but when the margins of the lateral plates have joined
ventrally, the cavities also join. At a later stage, when the cavity
has been expanded into the body cavity of the adult animal, the
parietal layer is joined to the somites, which have grown downwards
to form the inner lining of the wall of the cavity, the peritoneum
parietale. A part of the connective tissue has also the same origin.
The splanchnopleure forms the outer surface of the digestive tract
and the other viscera, the peritoneum viscerale, and also the layers
of the smooth muscles and the connective tissue of the gut. The
blood and the blood vessels also have this as their source.

(d) *The development of the endoderm.* During the late gastrula
stage, the endoderm was still a trough open dorsally. At the beginning of neurulation, the free margins of the endoderm join each
other under the notochord, and the primitive gut or the archenteron
is formed. This is known to be a cranially blind tube with a very

thin roof; however, the floor, with large cells rich in yolk, is singularly thick. At the cranial end of the primitive gut is a break in the mesodermal layer, and the endoderm is in contact with the ectoderm. Later, in the larval stage, the ectoderm sinks in here to form a pocket-like depression, the stomodeum. Subsequently, the ectoderm and the endoderm here fuse into the pharyngeal membrane, which afterwards perforates.

The lungs, the large glands connected with the digestive tract, the liver and the pancreas, are also derived from the endoderm, as is the entire inner surface of the digestive tract, the mucous membrane, with its glands.

4. *Morphogenetic movements during early development*

During gastrulation, large parts of the earlier blastula, the presumptive mesoderm and the endoderm, disappear into the inner part of the embryo. This "invagination" comprises folding of some sheets of tissue, the stretching of others, streaming of the cells, and so on. During these morphogenetic movements every part, every cell, of the embryo, participates. During neurulation, the movements of the tissues are continued in the rolling up the neural plate, in the segregation of the notochord and the somites, and in closing the archenteron. The question now arises—How are these movements of the tissues and the individual cells achieved?

This is an old question and one that has been the subject of much investigation; unfortunately, it must be admitted that no fully satisfactory answer has been found.

(*a*) *The movements of future germ layers.* The morphogenetic movements during gastrulation might roughly be divided into three simultaneous occurrences—the behaviour of each of the three germinal layers.

As was mentioned above (page 10), at the blastula stage the future ectoderm forms the animal region. During gastrulation, it has to expand and stretch in order to cover the whole surface at the gastrula stage. The increase in the surface is achieved by rapid division of the cells, but especially by means of thinning of the epithelial-layer.

This expansion has been shown to be an active process. Isolated future ectoderm also acts in the same way. If the ectoderm is transplanted into a place where stretching is impossible, the expansion of its surface area causes folds (Mangold, 1923, 1925; Spemann,

1921, 1931). In exogastrulated embryos the ectoderm is, if there are not other underlying tissues, wrinkled and full of folds (Holtfreter, 1933e).

The future mesodermal area of the blastula experiences an extremely complicated movement when it invaginates and stretches to its final position between the ectoderm and endoderm of the late gastrula. It rolls over the margin of the blastopore, starting at the dorsal middle line, continuing laterally and ventrally. At the end of gastrulation, when the yolk plug disappears and the blastopore has narrowed to a slit, the hind part of the mesoderm mantle contracts to a narrow ring around the blastopore.

Vogt (1923b) showed by the vital stain method that the movement of the future mesoderm also entails a stretching of the tissue, especially along the dorsal midline. Subsequently, the same was shown by Schechtman (1942) by the utilization of isolated pieces of the blastopore lip. The invagination movement of the tissue is autonomous and independent of its surroundings, as was first shown by Spemann and H. Mangold (1924). The direction and the extent of the stretching are determined (Spemann, 1931; Lehmann, 1932; Schechtman, 1942). The contraction of the final blastoporal ring is similarly independent and autonomous, as reported by Vogt (1922); gastrulation is to some extent inhibited by removing the presumptive epidermis from a blastula. Schechtman (1942) showed that it is possible to inhibit the contraction of the final blastoporal ring by transplantation of narrow strips of presumptive epidermis at the corners of the blastopore. This brings about more or less total exogastrulation.

As one follows gastrulation, it could well be imagined that the passing of the future endoderm into the interior of the gastrula is, to a greater or lesser extent, a passive movement, caused by the invagination of the mesoderm and the contraction of the blastoporal margin. As can be seen below, however, this movement also depends, even if to a less marked extent, on the "dynamic determination" (Vogt, 1923b), or on the "kinetic properties" of the germ layer itself, as is the case with the other germ layers.

(b) *The behaviour of cells of the different germ layers during gastrulation.* The causality of the movements of the different germ layers has become better understood by following the behaviour of the cells originating from the various germ layers.

Holtfreter (1939a, 1939b, 1944a; Townes and Holtfreter, 1955)

c

combined explants from different germ layers of different stages of development. They discovered that combinations of some tissues show considerable mutual affinity, and fuse into a single mass of cells, but that the others repel each other. Such processes are evidently important during the course of gastrulation when the tissues move towards and away from each other.

By treatment in an alkaline isotonic saline (Holtfreter, 1943a), or by trypsinizing, it is possible to disaggregate the different embryonic tissues into single cells, which can be combined to form mixtures containing cells of different origin and fate, and also from different species. From the dissociated aggregates, each type of cell is capable of becoming "sorted out" and thus able to form quite well organized organs or parts of them (Townes and Holtfreter, 1955; Moscona and Moscona, 1952, 1953; Moscona, 1956, 1957a, 1957b, 1960, 1961; Trinkaus and Groves, 1955; Trinkaus, 1961). In combinations of amphibian endodermal and ectodermal cells, no ability to form normal differentiations is shown, but some sorting out of cells occurs. However, combinations of cells originating from the germ layers which will enter into a close relationship during normogenesis, accept each other, and do not self-isolate. The ectodermal and the endodermal cells are able to behave harmoniously by the mediation of the mesodermal cells (Townes and Holtfreter, 1955) (figure 7).

Following alkaline disaggregation, it is also possible to continue the study of the behaviour of different kinds of isolated cells (Holtfreter, 1944c, 1946, 1947a, 1948b; Twitty, 1945; Twitty and Niu, 1948; Weiss, 1945). These experiments led to the conclusion that the cells of different germ layers have more or less marked kinetic tendencies. Some cells, such as those of the blastoporal lip and the medullary plate, move in one direction only, and are polarized in their kinetic tendencies.

The reaggregation of the isolated cells in a homogeneous disaggregation differs both with the origin of the cells, and with the stage of development of cells of one and the same germ layer. Those cells which are to form the epidermis have strong adhesive properties, and resolve into thin sheets of cells if they are growing on glass, whereas the others, that is to say, for example, the cells of the blastoporal lip, and especially those of the medullary plate, assume bottle-like, cylindrical or even vermiform shapes (figure 8). In such cells, the adhesiveness disappears from the distal ends; here

EPIDERMIS+ENDODERM   MESODERM+ENDODERM   EPIDERMIS+MESODERM   EPIDERMIS+MESODERM
                                                                                  +ENDODERM

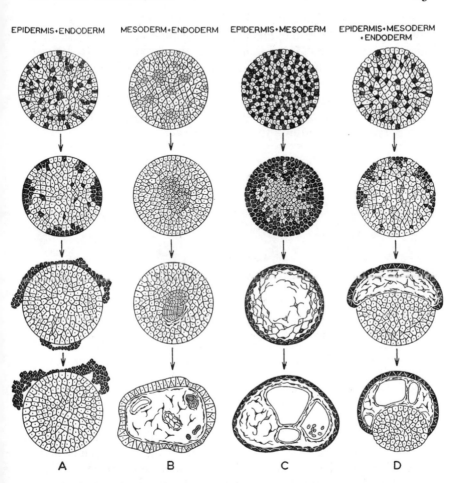

A   B   C   D

Figure 7. Disaggregated cells of the three germ layers mixed in
various combinations. *A*. The combination of epidermal and endodermal cells leads to a sorting out and self-isolation of homologous
tissues. *B*. A combination of endodermal and mesodermal cells
results in centripetal migration of the mesodermal cells, the endodermal cells forming an epithelial layer on the surface. *C*. A combination of epidermal and mesodermal cells leads to outward
movement of epidermal cells and inward movement of the mesodermal cells, the latter eventually forming mesenchyme, coelomic
cavities and blood cells. *D*. Cell segregation and formation of
tissues in a combination of epidermal, mesodermal and endodermal
cells. (After Townes and Holtfreter, 1955.)

they form a hyaline bulge like the pseudopodium of an amoeba. They are capable of moving with the hyaline cap as their anterior end; the movement is similar to an amoeboid one. In longish, vermiform cells there have been observed waves of constriction, as in peristaltic movement (Holtfreter, 1946, 1947a). The anterior end of the cell possessing the hyaline cap corresponds to that part of the cell which in the original tissue faces the interior of the blastula, the posterior end forming the outer surface.

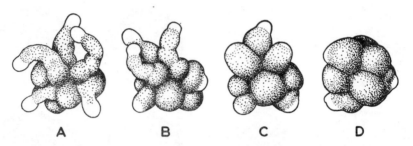

A   B   C   D

Figure 8. Behaviour of isolated cells of urodelan neural plate. *A*. The cells have adopted a cylindrical shape. The winding cell bodies are united by their coated ends alone; the free ends do not fuse together, even though they are touching each other. *B–D*. The elongated cells shorten and the hyaline tips reduce in size or disappear completely. At the same time, the adhesiveness of the cells is restored leading to the formation of a tightly packed aggregation. (After Holtfreter, 1947a.)

While the cells are in process of lengthening, the adhesiveness diminishes or disappears at the anterior end, but remains at the posterior end, the cells here being as though glued together. Even this adhesiveness finally diminishes, and the cells are free to move in accordance with their kinetic tendency. It is possible to imagine that this autonomous kinetic tendency makes the cell capable of gliding into the spaces between neighbouring cells in the inner part of the embryo (Plate 2.2). When all the cells in a part of the embryo have the same tendencies, a stream of cells is formed which brings about invagination.

The force of the migrating cell stream has been measured by Waddington (1939) by means of a steel ball and an electro-magnet: he observed it to be 0·34 mg/mm^2 in the invaginating mesoderm.

The cells are attached to each other by their adhesive properties at the extremely narrow posterior end, which originally constitutes the outer surface of the blastula. There is assumed to be a "coat" (cf. Holtfreter, 1943a) by which the cells are held together. Balinsky (1960) observed no special coat in his electron micrographs, and concluded that the posterior ends of the cells are attached closely together perhaps by some form of cementing substance alone. In an electron micrograph by Karasaki (1959a) (Plate 2.3), irregular papillae are to be seen on the surface of the presumptive neural area, but somewhat deeper there is a thin but dense layer which separates the cortical zone from the endoplasmic area. According to Karasaki, this layer might have the function of the hypothetical "surface coat". The best evidence for the existence of such a coat is the observation of Bell (1960). By means of focused ultrasonic treatment, he succeeded in isolating a coat from the surface of a young embryo of *R. pipiens*. Until stage 14 (Harrison), it is a thin filmy membrane with little or no structure visible under the electron microscope. Later, it is no longer possible to isolate the coat without attached cells. Minute coiled fibrils can now also be seen, not only on the surface of the cells, but continuing from the coat into the intercellular spaces. According to Bell, the intercellular matrix may have its source in the surface coat.

With different kinds of "dynamic determination" or "kinetic tendencies", comprehension might be possible of all the movements during gastrulation and neurulation, but complete obscurity still shrouds the problem of why cells take the appropriate steps in normal development, and how the polarity of the movements is determined, and what factors give the cells these tendencies and subsequently change them.

5. *Structural changes in the cytoplasm during gastrulation and neurulation*

As was learnt above, considerable changes occur in the localization and in the shape of the different kinds of cell during the course of gastrulation and neurulation. On the other hand, little is known of what changes take place in the cytoplasm of differentiating cells. In particular, as far as amphibian development is concerned, but few investigations have been devoted to the "cytoarchitecture" of the differentiation based upon observations made with the aid of the electron microscope (Eakin, 1957; Eakin and Lehmann, 1957; Yamada and Karasaki, 1958; Karasaki, 1957a, 1959a, 1959b).

Although these investigations were confined to some species only (*Xenopus laevis, Triturus pyrrhogaster, T. alpestris*), and although some differences were discovered between the various species, the results achieved in Nagoya, Berne and Berkeley were in such close correspondence with each other that some generalization should be possible.

In the ectoderm cells, the endoplasmic reticulum seems to be very loose and coarse until the gastrula stage is reached. There are large vesicles connected by cytoplasmic fibres. The mitochondria are globular, with few but thick ridges, and between them are to be observed large spaces. When the chordamesoderm is invaginating under the presumptive neural plate, there is a rapid change in the structure of the future neural cells. The endoplasmic reticulum becomes more complex, the mitochondria grow into rod-like bodies with many thin ridges and narrow inter-communicating spaces. At the end of neurulation, the number and size of the mitochondria have very much increased. The development of the intrinsic structure of the presumptive epidermis is slower, and the structure of its cells does not reach such a point of differentiation as is attained by the cells of the neural plate.

It has been known for a considerable time, from observations by light microscope, phase-contrast microscope, centrifugal fractionation, etc., that in amphibians, other vertebrates and some evertebrates, the number, size and enzyme production of the mitochondria increase during early development (Meves, 1908; Duesberg, 1910; Gustafson and Lenicque, 1952; Boell and Weber, 1955).

The yolk platelets are ellipsoid bodies scattered throughout the cytoplasm. The platelet is a compact body with a superficial layer of fine particles. Up to the gastrula stage, this superficial layer retains its original thickness in the presumptive epidermis cells. In the future neural cells, this superficial layer diminishes gradually in thickness, and disappears completely at the tail-bud stage; this was observed by Karasaki (1959a) in electron microscope studies of yolk platelets. He also found that the structure of the outer surface of the platelet itself changes at the tailbud stage.

With the differentiation of the endoplasmic reticulum, there is also an increase in the number of micro-particles which furnish the surface of the reticulum—this is particularly true as regards the neural plate cells. Following Palade's (1955) description of these granules (recently reviewed exhaustively by Haguenau, 1958) they have been termed Palade's granules, RNA-granules (because of their high content of RNA—see below, page 31) or ribosomes.

Electron microscope observations indicate (e.g. Karasaki, 1959a) that structural changes also occur in the nucleus during the differentiation. The contents of the interphase nucleus of the ectoderm cell have, up to the early gastrula stage, a granular appearance. The number of granules, and consequently the density of the nucleoplasm, increases gradually until the tail-bud stage, when the cell is comparable with that of the adult animal. At first the nucleolus is absent. This first makes its appearance at the gastrula stage as a clump of particles; the typical structure of the nucleolus is not formed until the tail-bud stage.

The functional changes in the nucleus during development have been the subject of much study during recent years, the method used being that of nuclear transplantation. This method was applied by Briggs and King (1952) to amphibian eggs. Later, they showed (King and Briggs, 1955) that the functional properties of the nucleus undergo substantial changes during gastrula stages. The method of nuclear transfer appears to provide a means of investigating the problem of differentiation from a new angle.

6. *Metabolism during gastrulation and neurulation*

The differentiation of the cytoplasm, the increase both in the number and the complexity of the mitochondria, along with the structural development of the endoplasmic reticulum, indicate that there could also be expected to be considerable changes in the metabolism of the embryo during gastrulation and neurulation. This biochemical side of the early development has attracted much attention, and in this connection it is impossible to provide a detailed account of the results which have been achieved. Here, concentration must be centred upon the main features alone; reference is made to the exhaustive reviews undertaken by Brachet (1944, 1950a, 1957, 1960a), Barth and Barth (1954) and Needham (1931, 1950).

(a) *Oxygen consumption and carbohydrate metabolism.* Woerdeman (1933a, b, c and d) and Raven (1933, 1935a) observed that the animal half of an early amphibian embryo (axolotl) contained more glycogen than did the vegetal. In reality, Woerdeman discovered that the glycogen content forms an animal-vegetable and a dorso-ventral gradient in the late blastula. This fact has since been confirmed by many other investigators in various other species. The distribution of glycogen in the late blastula and in the gastrula was determined in detail by Heatley and Lindahl (1937). They divided a median zone of blastula and gastrula of axolotl into six pieces (figure 9B), and determined the glycogen content of each of them. By this means they succeeded in confirming the gradients observed by Woerdeman, and furthermore, the decrease in the amount of glycogen in the invaginating parts of the embryo. Subsequently, it has been demonstrated (e.g. Gregg, 1948; Løvtrup, 1953) that there is no measurable decrease in glycogen content during cleavage, but that glycolysis starts as soon as gastrulation begins.

Simultaneously with measurement of the glycogen content, experiments have also been made with a view to determining the consumption of oxygen during the different stages of early development. Many authors have shown that the cleavage of frogs' eggs can proceed in anaerobic conditions and in the presence of metabolic inhibitors (Brachet, 1934; Barnes, 1944; Spiegelman and Moog, 1945) but that from the start of gastrulation a supply of oxygen is necessary. This obviously depends on the circumstance that during cleavage oxygen uptake is very low, but that it later progressively increases (Atlas, 1938; Moog, 1944; Barnes, 1944; Spiegelman and Steinbach, 1945; Boell, 1945; Barth, 1946; Ten Cate, 1953). In correspondence with the glycogen distribution, the respiration in the dorsal blastoporal lip is higher than in the more ventral regions; this was first observed by Brachet (1935), and has subsequently been confirmed by a number of investigators employing other methods (Fischer and Hartwig, 1938; H. Lehmann, 1938; Barth, 1939b, 1942; Boell, 1948; Gregg and Løvtrup, 1950). The most accurate results obtained were those of Sze (1953), who divided the early gastrula of the axolotl in a way similar to that utilized by Heatley and Lindahl (1937), and determined the oxygen consumption in different regions. In experiments conducted with the Cartesian diver, he found that the dorso-ventral and animal-vegetal gradients in oxygen consumption corresponded with the distribution of glycogen (figure 9A). Meanwhile, Fischer and Hartwig (1936), Piepho (1938) and Child (1948) followed the reduction of vital dyes under anaerobic conditions in amphibian blastulae, gastrulae and neurulae. In the reduction of the dye, they found the same gradients, both dorso-ventral and animal-vegetal, as those discovered by other methods (figure 10). Later, Flickinger and Blount (1958)

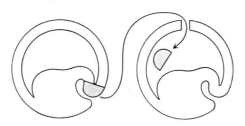

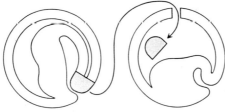

Plate 1.1. Implantation of the margin of the blastopore lip from an early newt gastrula (head inductor) into another of the same age causes development of a secondary head (above), whereas the margin of the blastopore lip of a late gastrula (trunk inductor) induces a secondary trunk and tail in an early gastrula (below).

(Orig.)

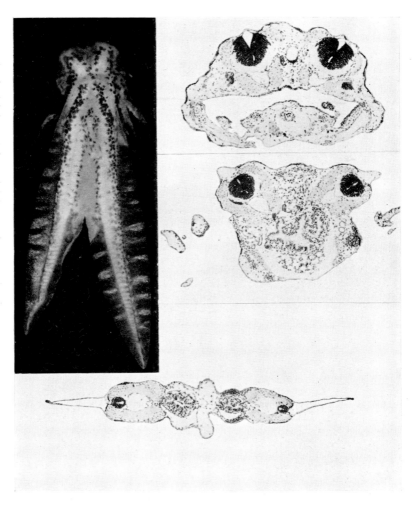

Plate 1.2. Dorsal blastopore lip of an early newt gastrula transplanted into the blastocoele of another has induced a secondary embryo. (Orig.)

Plate 1.3. (*opposite*) *Above:* Scheme of the explantation ("sandwich") method of Holtfreter (1933b). Pieces of presumptive epidermis of two early newt gastrulae are joined together around the inductor (in this case living "head"-inductor). All the differentiations which will take place in the epidermal vesicle are caused by the action of the inductor. Without an inductor, no differentiation will occur. *Below:* The dorsal blastopore lip of an early newt gastrula has induced differentiations of head, trunk and tail in an epidermis explant. (Orig.)

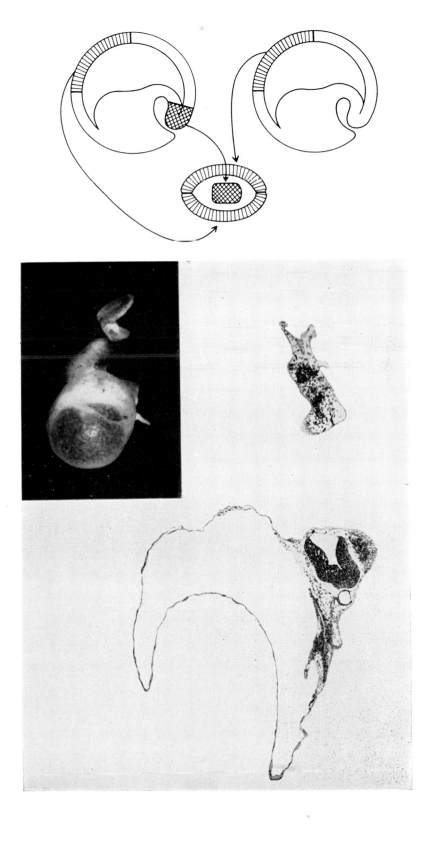

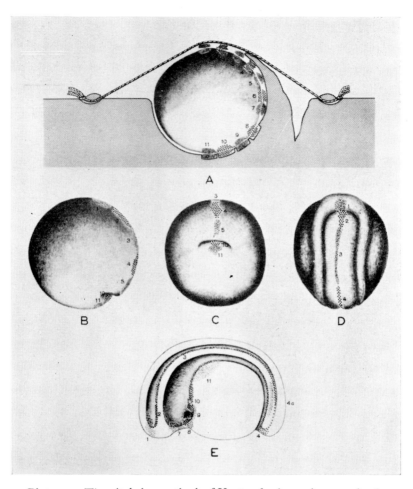

Plate 2.1. The vital dye method of Vogt. *A*. Agar pieces, stained with two different vital dyes, stamp dye spots on the surface of newt embryo (1–11). *B–E*. The movements of the spots are followed during gastrulation (*B–C*) and neurulation (*D*) until the tail bud stage (*E*). By this method, Vogt explained the localizations of different primordia in the blastula and drew the fate maps shown in Fig. 5. (After Vogt, 1925, 1929.)

were able to confirm the existence of these gradients by polaro-
graphic means.

The similarity of the distribution of glycogen and the gradients
of oxygen consumption has been interpreted as a case of mutual
dependence; this means that the early stages of the amphibian

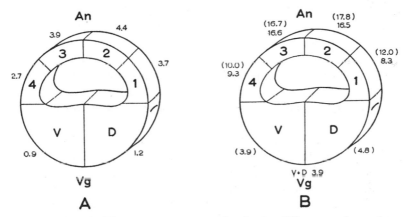

Figure 9. *A*. The oxygen consumption in the different regions of
a young amphibian gastrula. (After Sze, 1953.) *B*. Distribution
of glycogen in different parts of the amphibian blastula (within
parentheses) and of the early gastrula. (After Heatley and Lindahl,
1937.)

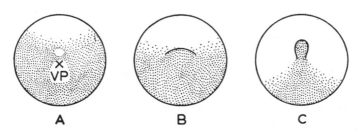

Figure 10. Dorso-ventral reduction of a vital dye (brilliant cresyl
blue) under anaerobic conditions in three subsequent stages of the
early development of amphibians. (After Piepho, 1938.)

embryo utilize carbohydrates as the main source of energy. This is
also confirmed by following changes in the respiratory quotient
(R.Q.) in amphibian embryos. It is somewhat low at cleavage
stages, increases to a value near unity at gastrulation, and thereafter

decreases smoothly (Brachet, 1934; Boell, 1955). In the main, carbohydrate metabolism seems to follow the normal glycolytic and Krebs tricarboxylic acid cycle, as demonstrated by Cohen (1954) in experiments with $C^{14}O_2$. The incorporation of labelled CO_2 increases considerably during gastrulation (Cohen, 1954; Tencer, 1958).

The increase in the oxygen consumption is accompanied by a corresponding change in the content of enzymes which mediate respiratory processes. Cytochrome oxidase, which occupies a key position in this regard, was made the subject of investigations by Boell (1948) on the embryo of the axolotl, and by Boell and Weber (1955) on Xenopus. They observed an increase in the enzyme content that was fairly parallel to that of the oxygen consumption, and to the increase in the number and size of mitochondria.

(b) *DNA, RNA and proteins in early development.* According to generally accepted views, DNA is chiefly located in the nucleus, and especially in the chromosomes of the cell (exhaustive literature on this point, Brachet, 1957, 1960), and consequently the amount of DNA might be expected to increase, though of course in correspondence with the number of cells. But as has been shown by a number of authors (Kutsky, 1950; Steinert, 1951; Gregg and Løvtrup, 1955; Hoff-Jørgensen and Zeuthen, 1952; Hoff-Jørgensen, 1954; Løvtrup, 1955; Moore, 1955; Chen, 1960) there are in the amphibian egg cytoplasm reserves of DNA which will be used in early development with no noticeable new synthesis. These authors state that the synthesis of new DNA has a marked beginning in different stages of various amphibian species: in *R. pipiens*, it starts at the beginning of cleavage, in *R. platyrrhena* and *R. fusca* at about the beginning of gastrulation, and in *T. alpestris*, *T. palmatus* and *T. cristatus* during gastrulation (figure 11). Pfautsch (1960) has recently measured the DNA content in presumptive mesoderm of early (H. 10) and late (H. 13) gastrulae, and in blastopore lip (H. 10) and archenteron roof (H. 13) of *T. alpestris* and *A. mexicanum*. She found that the DNA content in neuroepidermis is somewhat higher than in presumptive mesoderm, and that in neither of them do any appreciable changes occur *in vivo* during gastrulation. But, if the same parts of the embryo are isolated and cultured *in vitro* for 10–15 days, the content of DNA both as regards younger and older neuroectoderm shows a marked increase within five days, which means that synthesis of new DNA is occurring. In one way or another, the isolation of the ectoderm has stimulated the synthesis of DNA, obviously at the expense of the yolk. On the other hand, no marked change in this respect takes place *in vitro* in the isolated blastopore lip or archenteron roof.

As opposed to DNA, RNA is located especially in the cytoplasm and in the nucleolus of the cell (see literature in Brachet, 1944, 1950a, 1957, 1960a, 1960b), and particularly so in the Palade's

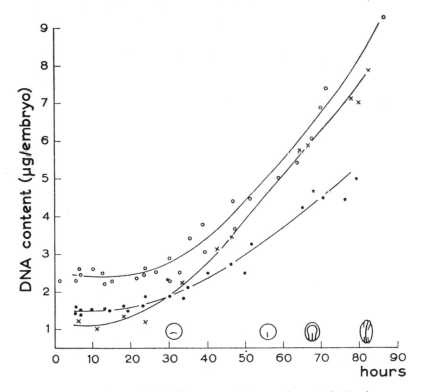

Figure 11. Changes in DNA content during early urodele development. Abscissa: hours after fertilization at 18°C. ○, *T. alpestris*; ●, *T. palmatus*; × *T. cristatus*. (After Chen, 1960.)

granules in the endoplasmic reticulum (see above, page 27). RNA was demonstrated as playing an important part in the synthesis of proteins as long ago as 1941 by Caspersson, and by Brachet (1942), and this has since been confirmed by many others making use of the cytochemical test, ultra-violet microspectrophotometry, etc.

When the increased differentiation and complexity of the endoplasmic recticulum is observed (see above, page 26), it is not unexpected that the content of RNA will also be found to increase in
amphibians during early development. This fact was first confirmed by Brachet (1941b) in *R. fusca* and *A. mexicanum* embryos.
Afterwards, this was observed by others whose findings were more
or less in conformity, but differences exist between various species.
According to Krugelis, Nicholas and Vosgian (1952), the synthesis
of new RNA begins in axolotl at the gastrula stage, according to
Steinert (1951, 1953) the RNA content remains essentially constant
until gastrulation in *R. fusca* and *R. esculenta*; Zellar (1956) found the
same increase in *T. palmatus* and *T. cristatus* at the beginning of
gastrulation, which was later confirmed by Chen (1960) who observed
the same fact in *T. palmatus* also (figure 12). Consequently, during

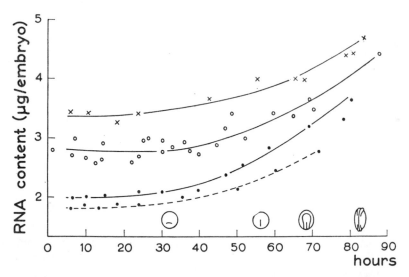

Figure 12.   Changes in RNA content during the early urodele
development. Abscissa: hours after fertilization at 18°C. ○, *T.
alpestris*; *T. cristatus.*●, *T. palmatus*; × (——— 1. bath; - - - - - 2.
batch). (After Chen, 1960.)

cleavage the amount of RNA is low, and it increases before the
beginning of the differentiation. The studies made by Kutsky (1950)
with isotopes and labelled phosphorus, and more recently those of
Grant (1958) and Rounds and Flickinger (1958), also indicate that

in the amphibian, increased RNA metabolism does not occur until gastrulation (see page 32).

Very many investigations of the spatial distribution of RNA in embryos have been carried out, as many authors are of the opinion that RNA plays an important part in induction. (See Chapter VII, page 118).

Brachet (1940) was the first to use the nitroprussic method for the detection of thiol (−SH) groups containing proteins, which has later been shown to be generally associated with RNA (Brachet, 1948): he found that the animal-vegetal gradient was extremely conspicuous (figure 13) during early stages up to gastrulation. During gastrulation, another gradient was observed, decreasing in a dorso-ventral direction. Subsequently, after gastrulation, at the neurula and larval stages, these two gradients led to the appearance on the dorsal side of the embryo of a well-defined cephalo-caudal gradient. The existence of these three successive gradients has since been corroborated histochemically by the employment of more accurate methods (pyronine-methyl green and ribonuclease, for the detection of RNA itself (Brachet, 1942, 1947; K. Takata) 1950). These findings have also been confirmed by quantitative estimations of the content and synthesis of RNA (Brachet, 1941b, 1944; Steinert, 1951, 1953; K. Takata, 1953). Recently, Pfautsch (1960) determined by biochemical means the amount of RNA in the presumptive neural plate and the blastoporal lip of the gastrula (H. 10) of *T. alpestris* and *A. mexicanum*, and correspondingly in the neuroepidermis and the archenteron roof of the neurula (H. 13). She found a marked increase in the RNA content of the presumptive neuroepidermis, and a corresponding decrease in the presumptive chordamesoderm during development from the gastrula to the neurula. As the content of RNA also rose in the neuroepidermis if it were cultivated in isolation, she concluded that this increase was not due to the diffusion of RNA from the archenteron roof into the neural plate, but was effected by the synthesis of RNA, obviously at the expense of the yolk.

After Caspersson (1941) and Brachet (1942) had arrived at the conclusion that RNA plays an important role in the biosynthesis of proteins, the problem was studied by a number of investigators using different methods and different organisms, plants and animals, both micro-organisms (yeasts, bacteria), and higher organisms (subjected to a recent exhaustive review by Brachet, 1957, 1960a,

1960b). Based upon these findings, we must consider that the essential role of RNA in the synthesis of proteins appears to be well established. It is true that less is known of the spatial distribution gradients of different proteins, except for the gradients of the proteins containing thiol-groups mentioned above (page 33). But much other evidence exists that a number of non-yolk proteins are distributed and synthesized along the same gradients as is RNA in amphibian development.

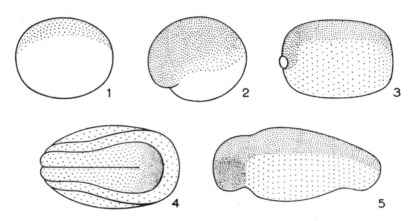

Figure 13. Distribution of -SH-containing proteins at different stages of amphibian development. The animal-vegetal and dorso-ventral gradients in the early stages (1–3) are to be seen, and later (4–5) the cephalo-caudal gradient also becomes apparent. (After Brachet, 1942.)

Studies have been made of the qualitative and also the quantitative changes of the free amino acids into different development stages of many amphibian species by the employment of paper chromatography (Eakin, Berg and Kutsky, 1950; Kutsky, Eakin, Berg and Kavanau, 1953; Chen and Rickenbacker, 1954; Deuchar, 1956). It is possible to summarize the results obtained in these experiments: in the dorsal half of the developing embryo, there are in general more free amino acids than in the ventral despite the opposite yolk-gradient. The most detailed work on this was carried out by Deuchar (1956), who measured the changes in eight amino acids during the early development of Xenopus. She found (figure 14) that at different stages of development, these amino acids are not

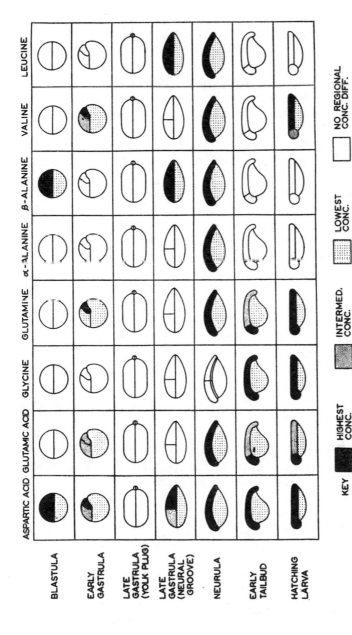

Figure 14. Significant differences in amino-acid concentration per milligramme of tissue between different embryonic regions in various developmental stages of *Xenopus* are indicated by different types of shading. The areas with no significant differences are left white. (After Deuchar, 1956.)

all represented in the same ratios. At the blastula stage, the aspartic acid and the β-alanine are the only ones to be highly concentrated in the animal half. In the gastrula stage, the highest concentration of the amino acids is in the dorsal blastopore lip, but apart from aspartic acid, glutamine and valine now reach their highest point of concentration, and especially so in the blastopore lip. At the end of gastrulation, there seems to be a latent phase when none of the amino acids measured is concentrated in any definite part of the embryo. At the beginning of neurulation, preceding differentiation, the majority of the amino acids have their highest concentration in the dorsal half, and subsequently the anterior dorsal area is richest in them.

At every stage, the amino acids seem to be concentrated at that part of the embryo in which the metabolism is most active, as shown especially by cell-division. Generally speaking, this fact has been interpreted to mean that the synthesis and breakdown of the proteins take place there. According to this point of view, some of these free amino acids might be products of proteolysis, and the remainder might equally well be the result of synthesis, and ready for incorporation into new proteins (Deuchar, 1956).

Experiments with amino acids labelled by C^{14}, P^{32} or S^{35} (Eakin, Kutsky and Berg, 1951; Ficq, 1954b; Waddington and Sirlin, 1954; Sirlin, 1955; Cèas and Naselli, 1958) have also shown that the incorporation of amino acids is particularly high in the dorsal half of the amphibian embryo, especially in the dorsal blastopore lip, during early development. As mentioned above (page 30), there is a considerable increase in the incorporation of $C^{14}O_2$ (Cohen, 1954) during gastrulation. Flickinger (1954) made a comparison of the incorporation of $C^{14}O_2$ into nucleoproteins in various parts of the gastrula, and found that the incorporation occurs according to animal-vegetal and dorsal-ventral gradients.

The moment and the locus of protein metabolism have also been studied by investigation of the appearance of proteolytic enzymes. Urbani (1955, 1957a, 1957b) found that proteases and peptidases increase in activity during late embryonic stages. D'Amelio and Cèas (1957) reported regional differences of cathepsin in the embryos of Discoglossus; they found that the dorsal blastopore lip has a higher degree of activity than the ventral parts of the embryo. More detailed knowledge of the distribution of cathepsin was provided by Deuchar (1958), who found a striking correspondence

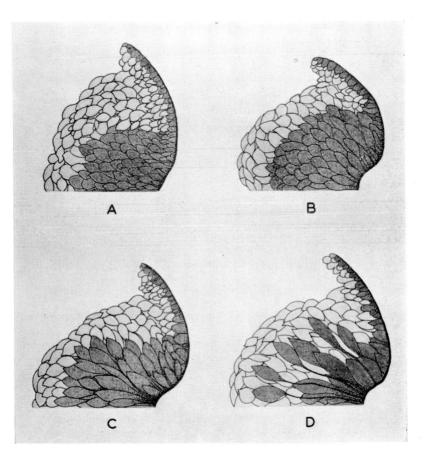

Plate 2.2. The successive changes in shape of the blastoporal cells. The invaginating cells are lengthened and take the shape of a long-necked flask with its end attached to the coated surface. (After Holtfreter, 1943b.)

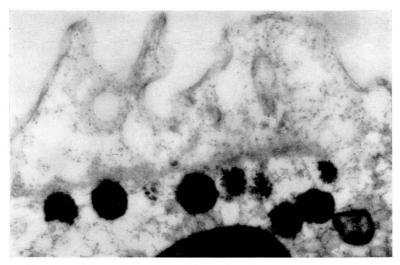

Plate 2.3. The surface coat of the cell. An electron micrograph shows irregular papillae on the surface of the presumptive neural plate, but somewhat deeper there is a dense layer which separates the cortical zone from the endoplasmic area. (Karasaki, 1959a.)

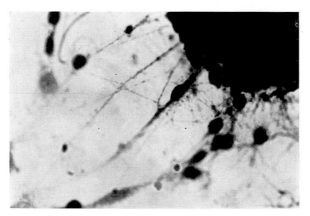

Plate 4.2. A six-day culture of dissociated ectodermal cells of *Rana pipiens* in unconditioned medium containing 0·1 per cent of globulin. Outgrowths resembling nerve fibres are to be seen in the cultures. (Barth and Barth, 1959.)

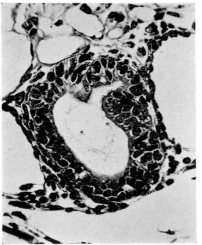

Plate 4.1. An ectodermal explant induced by bone-marrow showing endodermal differentiations, pharyngeal epithelium (right) and oesophageal epithelium (left). Age 46 days. (Takata and Yamada, 1960.)

between the appearance of free amino acids and the cathepsin activity (figure 15). In this respect, the only exception is the late gastrula in which there is no difference in free amino acids between the dorsal and ventral halves. However, she found in the dorsal part, as in the other stages from gastrula to tail-bud, that a high cathepsin activity was always present. We must conclude that the activity of the protcolytic enzymes also shows that the rate of protein metabolism is higher in this part of the amphibian embryo, where cell division is rapid and where differentiation starts.

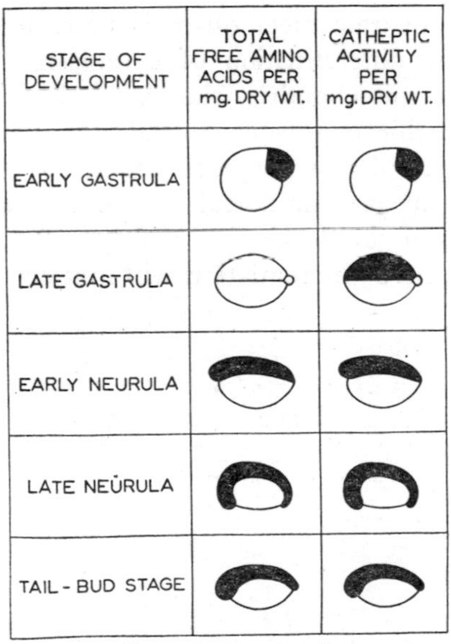

STAGE OF DEVELOPMENT	TOTAL FREE AMINO ACIDS PER mg. DRY WT.	CATHEPTIC ACTIVITY PER mg. DRY WT.
EARLY GASTRULA		
LATE GASTRULA		
EARLY NEURULA		
LATE NEURULA		
TAIL - BUD STAGE		

Figure 15. Diagrammatic comparison of amino-acid concentrations and catheptic activity per unit dry weight, in dorsal and ventral parts of different developmental stages of *Xenopus* embryos. Black areas: Significantly higher values than white areas of the same embryo. (After Deuchar, 1958.)

Further evidence for the view that proteins play an important part in the early development has been revealed by new immunological methods. Cooper (1948) and Clayton (1953) found that a synthesis of new antigenic material occurs in both frogs and newts between the blastula and the gastrula stage, before neurulation

D

and between the neurula and the tail-bud stage. Ranzi and his co-workers (1955, 1957) also demonstrated that some proteins, not present in frog eggs, are detectable at the tail-bud stage.

(c) *Concluding remarks.* By way of summary of the results reviewed above, it can be said that during the early development of amphibians there is at first, as regards DNA, RNA, carbohydrate and protein metabolism, a more or less latent phase. After the blastula stage the spatial distribution of these substances gradually forms first animal-vegetal, somewhat later dorso-ventral, and beginning at the neurula stage cranio-caudal gradients. In the early stages, carbohydrate metabolism is more important. Simultaneously with the differentiation of cytoplasm, the endoplasmic reticulum and the mitochondria, the metabolism of nucleic acids and the proteins achieves greater prominence, which is associated with the appearance of new enzymes which are particularly active in the blastopore lip and the dorsal half of the embryo, that is to say in those parts of the developing embryo where cell division is most active, and where differentiation will first occur.

III

Differentiation Capacities of the Germ Layers of the Amphibian Gastrula

1. *Introduction*

By using the vital stain method it has been possible exhaustively to ascertain how the different parts of the blastula form the three germ layers of the gastrula, and how the primary organ rudiments are formed during neurulation, as indicated by the fate maps of Vogt and others (page 11). By following the movements and the behaviour of the organ anlagen and single cells, it has also been possible to discover how the segregation of the different anlagen and spatial distribution of the cells occurs in the primary development (page 24). By biochemical methods the changes in the metabolism of the embryo have been analysed and tests made of the gradients of different chemical compounds during development (page 27). Thus by these means we have obtained rather detailed information on the descriptive side of early normogenesis. Nevertheless, these results give no account of the causality of development, nor do they show the time at which determination of the differentiations which are to be expected from each presumptive area actually occurs.

To this end, methods are necessary other than that of observing the different features of normogenesis.

As related above (page 3), Spemann and his school tended to show, from the findings of their transplantation experiment, that determination of subsequent differentiation in general occurred during the gastrula stage in amphibian development.

At the early gastrula stage, the presumptive epidermis and the presumptive neural plate seemed under experimental conditions to possess the ability to differentiate in various ways other than those implied by their normal fates. To employ the terminology of Driesch (1896), they had greater *prospective potencies* than would be expected in view of their *prospective significance* in normal development. These tissues had a *competence* (page 52) to react to different kinds of inductive

39

stimuli by differentiating not only into epidermis or central nervous system according to their origin, but also into different mesodermal and even endodermal structures. With no inductive stimuli, they were unable to differentiate at all. Thus their ability to differentiate was dependent on the actions of their surroundings. In the terminology of Roux (1894) they reveal in early development a process of *dependent differentiation* (abhängige Differenzierung).

At the late gastrula stage, on the contrary, the presumptive epidermis and the presumptive neural plate ectoderm could no longer differentiate in any other direction than that determined by their original fates. Their prospective potencies were no more than that implied by their prospective significance in normogenesis. They had also lost their competence to react towards external inductive stimuli. But now they were able to *self-differentiate* according to their origin. Their fates were now fixed, and their differentiation determinated by the inductive actions. According to Roux, they now showed *independent differentiation* (unabhängige Differenzierung).

The moment of determination of the ectoderm was studied in Spemann's laboratory (Spemann, 1918, 1919, 1921) by homoplastic (between embryos of the same species) and by heteroplastic (between embryos belonging to different species of the same genus) transplantations only. Following this, an endeavour was made in many other laboratories to determine the time of differentiation, using the same or similar methods (Goerttler, 1927; Mangold, 1928; Lehmann, 1929.) More accurate results have since been achieved by various kinds of isolation and defect experiments.

Dürken (1926) cultured fragments of the early gastrula in the orbit of an older larva after extirpation of the eye cup, and was able to follow the differentiation of the tissue *in vivo* through the transparent cornea, and, of course, also in serial sections. Holtfreter (1929) modified the method by culturing embryonic tissues in the coelom or in the lymph sacs of older larvae of the same or of different species, and also of larvae of a different amphibian genus (xenoplastically). They found that the differentiation potencies of the various primordia were in fact greater than that implied by their original fate. But this *in vivo* method was not completely satisfactory, as the differentiated tissues of the host surrounding the grafted tissue might always have their own inductive action on the transplant, and guide its differentiation in directions that would be different from those taken if it had been cultured in an indifferent environment.

After Holtfreter (1931) had formulated a synthetic culture medium, later known as Holtfreter solution, or standard-solution, it became possible to culture pieces of early embryos in neutral condition as explants, and to follow their differentiation capacities. Since then, this standard solution has been used as such, or in somewhat modified form, in all laboratories carrying out isolation experiments, and other operations on amphibian embryos. Meanwhile, Woerdeman (1930) called special attention to the necessity of aseptic precautions in experimental embryology, and this has been found to be of the greatest importance in the culture of explants and all types of operated embryos.

Holtfreter (1933e) also discovered that young amphibian gastrulae would exogastrulate totally, if cultured in hypertonic saline. This observation made possible the study of the differentiation abilities of the endo- and mesoderm without the central nervous system, and *vice versa* of the ectoderm without the other germ layers (figure 16).

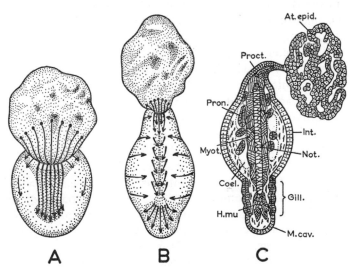

Figure 16. Exogastrulation of the amphibian embryo brought about by hypertonic saline. *A–B.* External views of two successive stages. *C.* Schematic section showing the differentiations that occur. At. epid., atypical epidermis; Coel., coelomic cavity; Gill., Gill epithelium; H.mu, head musculature; Int., intestinal epithelium; M.cav., mouth cavity; Myot., myotomes; Not., notochord; Proct., proctodaeum; Pron., pronephric tubules. (After Holtfreter, 1933e.)

Holtfreter (1933c) also applied the method of Ekman (1921, 1924a, 1924b) and Stöhr (1924, 1926), who cultured the heart primordia in an epidermis vesicle, for investigation of the inductive action of different kinds of living and killed tissues, but also in order to test the potencies of the ectoderm. This "sandwich"-method is also today one of the standard methods of experimental embryology.

By application of these new methods, Holtfreter (1938b, 1938c) carried out an enormous task in testing the differentiation capacities of all parts of the germ layers in various stages of early development in both urodeles and anurans. He drew maps of these capacities of the early gastrula, just as Vogt (page 12) has done for their prospective significance, and he compared these maps. The results of Holtfreter and many others who have made later studies of this problem are briefly reviewed below.

2. *The differentiation capacities of the ectoderm*
As mentioned above, the whole ectodermal area of an early gastrula cannot differentiate at all without external stimuli, though in terms of its competence (page 52) it is still omnipotent. This was shown by Holtfreter (1933e) in his exogastrulation experiments, but it is also always observable if pieces of ectoderm are cultured in isolation, as was first pointed out by Holtfreter (1931). Consequently, the differentiation capacities of each part of the ectoderm, that is of both the presumptive neural plate and the future epidermis, are less than their prospective significance in normal development: the ectoderm has not yet attained the state of self-differentiation; it has not yet been determined. It will form only an irregular and atypical mass of undifferentiated cells. However, it possesses some characteristic features; it has an autonomous stretching tendency (page 20), and it has as an isolate the tendency to form a vesicle. But after some two or three days, the surface of the vesicle becomes wrinkled, the inner hollow will disappear, and the cells no longer form a layer, but a spongy mass with small pores and spaces between the irregular rows of cells. The cells remain roundish, they do not assume the normal cuboidal shape of the differentiated epidermal cell.

In anurans, as shown by Holtfreter (1938c), the isolated ectoderm differs from that of the Urodeles, described above, in that in every isolate is always formed apart from an atypical epidermis, a sucker with a very rich slime secretion. The development of this sucker has not been considered to be a real self-differentiation of the ectoderm, as it is also formed in pieces of ectoderm which do not have a prospective significance to form any suckers. Holtfreter (1938c) interpreted it as an autonomous differentiation of the undetermined anuran ectoderm, which in most areas during normal development will be inhibited by the action of the adjacent tissues, but which will not be inhibited at the normal sites of the suckers.

In the late gastrula and the early neurula, the two presumptive areas of the ectoderm differ in their differentiation capacities, as Spemann (1918) first showed when he exchanged pieces of these areas. The mesoderm mantle has now invaginated, and underlies first the presumptive neural plate, and somewhat later the whole of the presumptive epidermis. The archenteron roof now acts as the primary inductor and determines the differentiation of the ectoderm. Isolation, deficiency and transplantation experiments (Lehmann, 1928, 1929; Holtfreter, 1931, 1938b, 1938c; Mangold, 1933a, 1937, 1961b; ter Horst, 1948; Mangold and von Woellwarth, 1950) showed that although the presumptive epidermis had lost most of its competence (Holtfreter, 1938a; Mangold, 1931b, Becker; 1955), it now possessed, apart from its prospective significance, potencies for the formation of secondary inductions such as the "placodes" (nasal pit, lens, ear, etc.). Its behaviour in isolates, however, was like the presumptive epidermis of an early gastrula: it would form only atypical, irregular epidermis. Nevertheless, it seemed to acquire a "labile" determination for development into epidermis, as, isolated together with some mesenchyme, it would form well-differentiated epidermis, and also, transplanted to a different part of the embryo, even into the neural plate, it would always differentiate into epidermis, and according to its new surroundings, different placodes could be formed.

At this stage the determination of the neural plate is more stable. Isolated parts of it will form well-differentiated parts of the central nervous system. These differentiations correspond approximately to the original region of the isolates. However, some regulation in their development is possible, so that an isolate from an early neurula could produce more than its prospective significance might imply (ter Horst, 1948). Further, the paired formations, such as eyes, nasal pits and forebrain, will always develop as single structures (they possess a "material" determination capacity alone). In isolation experiments, von Woellwarth (1951) divided the stabilization of the differentiation capacity of the brain into three successive phases:

(1) (at the end of gastrulation) the presumptive neural plate ectoderm develops into material of the neural crest only, or into poorly differentiated brain vesicles; (2) (the early neurula) the fore brain is not divided into two hemispheres, the nose is monorhinic and the eye cyclopic; (3) (the stage of closing neural folds) the self-differentiation capacity is complete.

The posterior fifth or seventh of the neural plate of the neurula has a special prospective significance, as mentioned above (page 16). In normal development, it will develop not only into the spinal cord, but also into the myotomes of the posterior third of the trunk, into the tail mesoderm, and into the posterior tip of the notochord. (Vogt, 1926; Bijtel and Woerdeman, 1928; Bijtel, 1931, 1958; Nakamura, 1938, 1942, 1952; Pasteels, 1939a, 1942, 1943; Suzuki, 1940; von Aufsess, 1941; Spofford, 1945, 1948; Chuang, 1947; ter Horst, 1948; Ford, 1950; Smithberg, 1954.) At an early neurula stage, these primordia are on the surface of the embryo, the presumptive tail notochord in the form of narrow longitudinal strips above the blastopore, the tissues developing into the trunk somites above and round it, with the subsequent tail mesoderm and spinal cord more cranial (figure 17). During neurulation, the presumptive trunk somites and the tail notochord invaginates to join the hind part of the archenteron roof, and when the neural folds close only the material of the tail bud round the remnant of the blastopore, and situated below it the primordia for the proctodaeum, are to be seen on the surface of the embryo.

As regards the determination stage of the posterior part of the neural plate, different authors have obtained contradictory results, and even today the question might still be regarded as somewhat confused. We are perhaps justified in concluding that at the beginning of neurulation the presumptive trunk somites and the whole of the notochord have acquired their final determination, but that the presumptive tail mesoderm and the other tail material, apart from the notochord, get their final determination by the inductive action of the posterior part of the archenteron roof (Spofford, 1948) not later than when the neural folds are closing. Prior to this, they are in a labile determination stage which allows of their differentiation as isolates, or if transplanted to foreign surroundings into structures other than their original fate would imply, such as epidermis and spinal cord (Chuang, 1947). The posterior part of the early neural plate also possesses a regulation capacity if part of it is extirpated, as demonstrated by Chuang (1947). According to the exogastrulation experiments of Holtfreter (1933e), at the gastrula stage the prospective posterior neural plate has as yet no self-differentiation capacity whatever, but forms undifferentiated epidermis only, in marked contrast to the far-reaching self-differentiation capacity of the primary mesoderm, as pointed out by Spofford (1948).

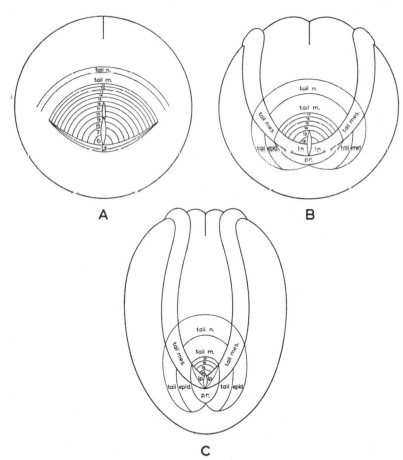

Figure 17. Schemata of the caudal region of newt neurulae, in which the different primordia are indicated at three developmental stages. l.p., lateral plate; pr., proctodaeum; tail epid., tail epidermis; tail mes., tail mesenchyme; tail n., tail spinal cord; the numbers (6–17) indicate the sequence of the somites. (After Chuang, 1947.)

3. *The differentiation capacity of the mesoderm*

The primary mesoderm, the chordamesoderm mantle, possesses before gastrulation a well developed self-differentiation capacity, as was thoroughly tested both in anurans and in urodeles in the isolation experiments of Holtfreter (1938b, 1938c). By contrast with the presumptive ectoderm, isolated pieces of the presumptive mesoderm, i.e., of the marginal zone, will always differentiate. But before invagination, the determination is not stable, and locally not finally defined, as can be seen in figure 18, in which the differentiation

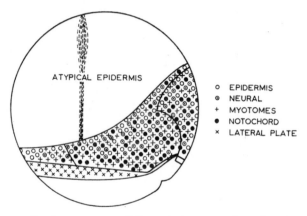

Figure 18. Autonomous differentiation capacity of various presumptive areas of early urodelan gastrula (cf. the maps of presumptive rudiments, Figure 5). (After Holtfreter, 1938b, modified.)

tendencies of every part of the marginal zone have been compared with the fate map. It can be seen that the notochord and myotomes can also be formed from isolated parts of the marginal zone other than their own presumptive areas, whereas these presumptive areas may also produce, apart from notochord and myotomes respectively, epidermis and various parts of the central nervous system.

While the presumptive epidermis and neural plate of the early gastrula possess only an autonomous stretching tendency the marginal zone has in addition a "dynamic determination" (Vogt, 1924), for invagination (page 21). While the presumptive ectodermal area has no inductive capacity, the presumptive mesoderm induces the central nervous system when underlying the presumptive neural plate, and also, as mentioned above, the tail mesoderm. The marginal zone also possesses a very marked regulation ability, as shown by experiments in which a half of the blastoporal lip has induced the whole secondary axis.

4. The differentiation capacity of the endoderm

When Holtfreter tested the differentiation capacity of the various germ layers, he found that the endoderm acquired a stable determination before the early gastrula stage, that is earlier than both of the other germ layers. A basis for this view might be that in the exogastrulated embryo, the endoderm, despite its position on the surface of the univaginated tissue, correctly attains its differentiation in every part of the digestive tract according to its prospective significance (Holtfreter, 1933e). From the results of his isolation experiments, Holtfreter (1938b, 1938c) also came to this conclusion. The results of Stableford (1948) seemed to corroborate Holtfreter's view. However, he cultured the isolated vegetal hemisphere for too short a time for the differentiations to be sufficiently clearly discernible.

However, some data seemed to conflict with this statement. Holtfreter (1939a) himself subsequently stated that a piece of isolated endoderm could differentiate only in the presence of mesenchyme. He interpreted the action of the mesenchyme as a mechanical support of the substrate that allows the intrinsic ability of the endoderm to be expressed. Balinsky (1938, 1948) found that if small endodermal pieces of a gastrula or neurula were transplanted into new surroundings, in many cases their differentiation was not dependent upon their origin, but more or less in accordance with the new environment. Moreover, when parts of the endoderm were extirpated in the gastrula or neurula stage, the remaining endoderm showed regulative development, resulting in an almost complete digestive tract with no deficiency in the endodermal differentiations (Balinsky, 1948; Okada, 1953a, 1953b, 1960). It was possible to interpret these results only by assuming that the endoderm does not acquire its final determination at the gastrula stage, and not even at the early neurula stage.

T. S. Okada (1954a, 1954b, 1955a, 1955b, 1957, 1960) and recently also Takata (1960a, 1960b) made comprehensive studies of when and how the endoderm acquires its determination. They found that an endodermal piece isolated from the gastrula or an early neurula, either with or without epidermal covering, is unable to differentiate at all. Even if cultivation in explantation was continued for more than 50 days, no differentiation could be observed. But if an endodermal piece taken from any part of the primitive gut from the gastrula until the middle neurula stage was explanted together with a piece of ectomesenchyme or the chordamesoderm mantle, it always differentiated into some endodermal tissue. The final type of the differentiated endodermal tissue depended on the prospective significance of the explanted endodermal piece, on the areas from which the mesodermal tissue originated, and on the age of the donor embryo (figure 19). It was thus observed that a certain degree of labile determination is present in the endoderm, starting from the gastrula stage, and the state of the determination will be progressively more stabilized until the end of neurulation. Until the middle neurula, every part of the endoderm was capable of differentiation even into an endodermal tissue other than its origin implied, if explanted together with ecto- or endomesodermal tissue.

Differentiation into particular types of endodermal tissues was favoured according to the origin of the mesodermal tissue added. Thus presumptive notochord added to endoderm from any region always caused the differentiation of pharynx, and inhibited the differentiation of liver. The latero-ventral mesoderm favoured differentiation into intestine, the antero-lateral mesoderm into liver, and the presumptive somites differentiation into intestine and liver. Anterior and posterior pieces of neural folds added to the piece of endoderm did not cause any great difference in the regionality of the endodermal differentiations. However, pharynx differentiation of pieces taken from a part of the endoderm other than from the presumptive pharynx area was more frequent in the series with head neural fold than in the series with trunk neural fold, especially if the endoderm piece came from a neurula.

In the light of the facts stated above, the conflicting results of Holtfreter (1938b, 1938c) might depend on the possibility of the endodermal explants having included some of the ecto- or the endomesoderm. Thus the findings reviewed above might give us the right to conclude that the endoderm acquires its determination as does the ectoderm by the inductive action of the mesoderm during gastrulation and neurulation. At the early gastrula stage, this determination is so labile that it does not permit an autonomous differentiation, but does have a weak regional influence if differentiation is caused by any part of the ecto- or endomesoderm. Determination will be progressively stabilized until the end of neurulation.

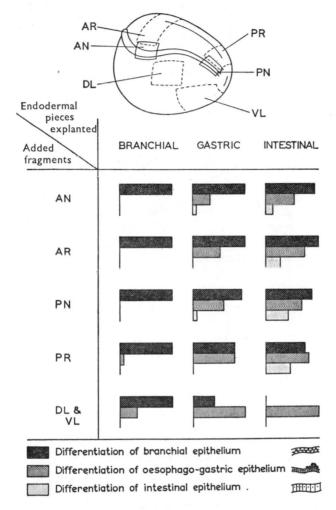

Figure 19. The relative incidence of different types of epithelium in explants in which endodermal pieces were combined with different types of mesoderm. (After Okada, 1957, 1960.)

5. *Conclusions*

The data presented above show that the determination of both the ectoderm and the endoderm is guided by the archenteron roof, i.e., by the chordamesoderm mantle. At the early gastrula stage, this will give to them both first a labile determination which will progressively become more stable towards the end of the neurulation. Simultaneously, the labile self-differentiation tendency of the mar-

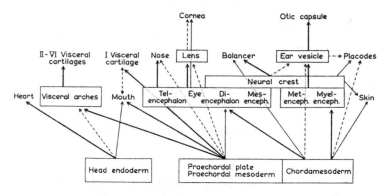

A. INDUCTION PROCESSES IN THE HEAD

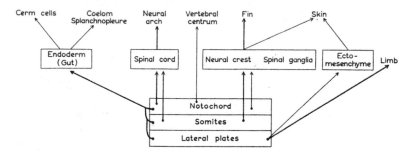

B. INDUCTION PROCESSES IN THE TRUNK

Figure 20. Schemata showing the induction process during early amphibian development in head (A) and in trunk (B) regions. The inductive action starts from the archenteron roof (inductor of the first degree), the inductors of second, third, etc. degrees effect the process by their own actions. The different strengths of the inductive action are indicated by thick, thin and broken arrows. (Mangold, 1961a.)

ginal zone of the early gastrula will be stabilized during the course of the gastrulation, and once the archenteron roof is underlying the ectoderm, the chorda-mesoderm mantle will have acquired its final autonomous determination. As will be seen in the following chapters, the primary inductive stimulus yielded by the archenteron roof is only the first differentiative action during development, and is followed by a chain of subsequent interactions. Although this book deals mainly with primary induction, some examples of these secondary interactions will be presented in Chapter X, with particular reference to those between mesoderm and neural plate. Our present knowledge of these very numerous differentiative interactions is presented below as compiled by Mangold (1961a). (Figure 20.)

IV

The Responding Tissue

1. *Introduction*

It has been seen in previous chapters that the inductive stimulus seems to be transmitted by chemical agents which are obviously incorporated in the ectodermal cells during the induction process, and thus discussion should now be centred on the significance of the reactive tissue itself in this process. There is no doubt that this has been largely neglected in the many discussions on the theories of the induction mechanism, a fact which has recently been criticized by several authors. Weiss (1958b) compared the ectoderm to a "black box which responds to an experimental input Y with a signal X without revealing the complete network of connections and the route that has led from Y to X". Most embryologists will agree with Paul Weiss in this respect, and are fully aware of the "black box". A number of attempts have thus been made to get information on the reactive nature of the ectoderm, and on the first steps of its differentiation. The data are, however, still scanty, confusing and in part controversial, and it seems that the reactive system itself is the least known factor in studies of its responses.

2. *Competence*

The term "competence" (the Reaktionsfähigkeit of Mangold, 1929b) was first suggested by Waddington (1932) and was defined by Holtfreter and Hamburger (1955) as the "physiological state of a tissue which permits it to react in a morphogenetically specific way to determinative stimuli". Expressed in a more "modern" way, Wilde (1956) states, that "competence is a term which sums the ability of the enzyme complement of the embryonic cell to adapt to a particular ratio of metabolites". Thus, before any discussion of this phenomenon, it has to be stressed that there exists no such state of cells or tissues as can simply be called competence, but that competence is always related to particular stimuli and corresponding responses. In dealing with primary induction, the first steps of tissue

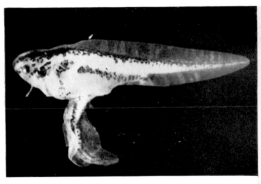

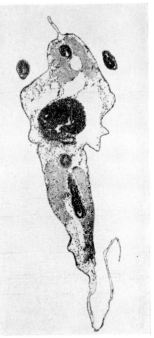

Plate 5.1. A 12-day-old Triturus larva implanted at gastrula stage with a piece of alcohol-treated guinea-pig kidney tissue. A strong spinocaudal inductive effect can be noted, and myotomes, notochord and spinal cord can be seen induced in the section. (Orig.)

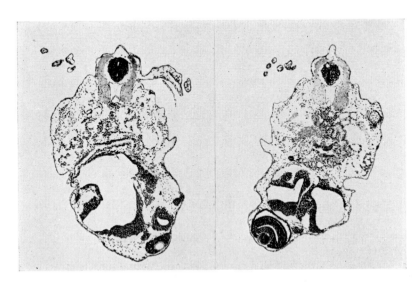

Plate 5.2. Two sections of a Triturus larva implanted with alcohol-treated guinea-pig liver tissue. An archencephalic inductive action is to be noted, resulting in the formation of secondary forebrain structures, nose and eye. (Orig.)

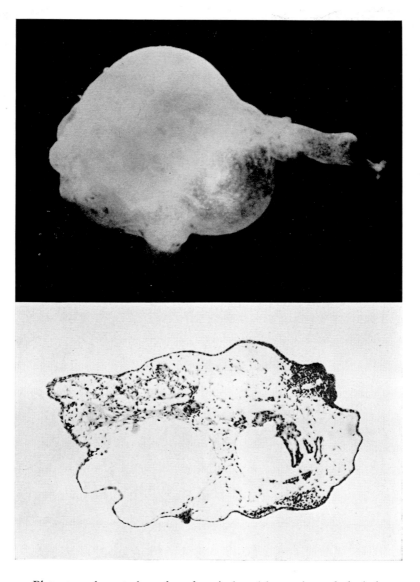

Plate 5.3. An ectodermal explant induced by a piece of alcohol-treated guinea-pig bone-marrow. On external inspection a vesicle-like formation with a tail is to be seen, and mainly mesodermal differentiations are to be noted in the sections (myotomes, notochord, pronephric tubules and mesenchyme). (Toivonen, 1954a.)

differentiation, we might be justified in speaking of the *primary competence* of the ectoderm. More exactly, this means that the ectoderm can react to certain stimuli, and that the response is similar to the normal morphogenetic events at this stage of development. Moreover, we have noted in previous chapters that there are certainly a number of different forms of induction, and obviously several factors which lead to them. In the suggestion of different neuralizing and mesodermalizing stimuli, it follows that there is a neural and a mesodermal primary competence. Furthermore, it should be pointed out that for as long as we are unaware of the exact nature of the induction process, we must speak about competence to differentiative stimuli under specified experimental conditions. We can only recognize competence by the appearance of morphological differentiations long after induction has occurred, and without knowing the different steps that have led to them. The result is thus hardly a reflexion of the tissue competence alone, but merely of a large number of external factors which control the differentiation of the tissues and the maintenance of this differentiated state.

Without entering on a discussion of the most complicated question of reversible versus irreversible differentiation of cells, we should like to stress that when talking of primary competence, we are limited to the *morphogenetic responses of the undifferentiated gastrula ectoderm* after an inductive stimulus at this stage. It will be seen later that after this induction, the differentiated tissues can still react to further differentiative stimuli, and thus change their prospective determination.

Our present problem can be put in the following form: How far in the undifferentiated ectoderm is its determination controlled by external factors as against an intrinsic stability which maintains the differentiated state. There must accordingly be a temporal and obviously a topographical change in this competence. As a third question, there is some discussion of the "species-specificity" of the primary competence.

(a) *Time patterns of competence.* Two different sets of experimental conditions have been used in testing the time patterns of primary competence. 1. Ectoderm taken from the developing embryo at different stages of development has been exposed to differentiative stimuli. 2. Ectoderm has been removed from a young gastrula, "aged" outside the embryo under artificial conditions for different periods of time, and following this tested for its

E

competence. The comparability of the results of these two types of experiment is discussed later.

Lehmann (1929) transplanted ectoderm from successive stages of development to the neural plate region, and noted a gradual loss of neural competence, i.e., of the ability to form neural tissue in the new location where it was exposed to the inductive stimulus of the chorda-mesoderm. Machemer (1932) and Schechtman (1938) used another scheme of operation. They transplanted dorsal lip tissue under the ventral epidermis at different stages of development. In confirmation of Lehmann's findings, they noted that neural competence decreased sharply at the end of gastrulation, and was completely absent in the early neurula stages. Later Lopashov (1939) used killed amphibian tissues as inductors, and noted the loss of competence, which could be decelerated by treatment in low temperature. Raunich (1942) used a *heterogenous* inductor, adult liver tissue, and also noted the loss of neural competence.

More recently, the matter was taken up by Nieuwkoop (1958), who used his clever "ectodermal fold" technique in order to test the competence of the ectoderm during development from early gastrula to neurula. In this method, the ectoderm is cut out, folded beneath a double rod, and transplanted into the presumptive rhombencephalic region of a neurula (see page 167). The results are shown in figure 21, in which are summarized the results of different experimental series. Despite the differences between the various series, we can note that the archencephalic brain structures disappear earlier (at stage $11\frac{1}{4}$) than the deuterencephalic brain formations. As mentioned later, Nieuwkoop's concepts of the inductive process differ from ours, at least in their terminology. The conclusions drawn from these findings by the author and by us thus vary somewhat. Nieuwkoop concluded that the competence of "activation" (our archencephalic or neural induction) rapidly falls off at stage $11\frac{1}{4}$ to $11\frac{1}{2}$, whereas the competence of the "activated material for transformation (our mesodermalization) probably extends up to stage 15. Without discussing the differences in our theories, one conclusion can be drawn from Nieuwkoop's experiments: during normal development of the experimental animal (*Amblystoma mexicanum*) there are obviously two separate periods of competence, one leading to archencephalic differentiation after appropriate inductive stimulus, and the other to deuterencephalic determination of the ectoderm under the *same external conditions*, that is after a similar inductive influence. According to our M/N hypothesis, the deuterencephalic differentiation is a result of a simultaneous action of neuralizing and mesodermalizing influences. Thus the change in competence observed by Nieuwkoop could be explained in our terms as a later competence to mesodermalizing stimuli.

Chuang (1955) tested neural competence by exposing the ectoderm to a toxic influence causing "autoneuralization" (figure 22). It is difficult to say how far these observations can be related to changes in competence during normal induction, but certainly they

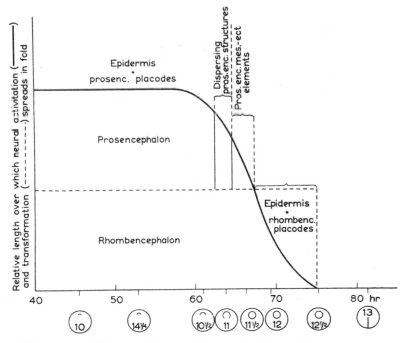

Figure 21. Diagram showing the gradual loss of competence during gastrulation when tested by the ectodermal "fold method". (After Nieuwkoop, 1959.)

do offer one more means of studying this complicated problem. His results show that the maximal neuralization occurred during early gastrulation, and that after the beginning of neurulation no neural structures were formed. The most interesting point in Chuang's results is, however, that a treatment of ectodermal pieces in Ca-free solution led to neural differentiation very early during development.

Twenty-four hours before the formation of the blastopore, at a large-cell blastula stage, the ectodermal cells were already capable of forming definite neural structures. The onset of primary competence has not yet been properly studied, and as Holtfreter and Hamburger (1955) pointed out, this might be a difficult matter, because the induced structures always appear synchronously with the corresponding structures of the host, and thus the time of inductive stimulus cannot be calculated. The only possible test would be that used, for instance, by Johnen (1956a, 1956b, 1961) and Toivonen (1958), where

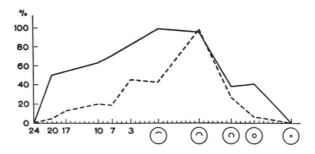

Figure 22. Changes in the neural competence of the ectoderm during development when tested with "subcytolytic" treatment. Continuous line, the frequence of neural structures in the series; dotted line, the relative weight of these structures. (After Chuang, 1955.)

the inductor was removed after a brief contact with the ectoderm. By the exposure of young gastrula extoderm to such hrief inductive stimuli, it is possible that the onset of the primary competence might be studied more adequately than in the non-physiological conditions of Chuang.

The other way of studying the time pattern of primary competence, the culturing of excised ectoderm outside the embryo, was employed by Holtfreter (1938a), Gallera (1952), and by Leikola (unpublished) in our laboratory. Some authors have pointed out (e.g., Spofford, 1953; Grobstein, 1956b; Nieuwkoop, 1958) that results obtained by this method might not be comparable to the *in vivo* experiments mentioned above, because the ectoderm is separated from the normal differentiating and stabilizing influence of the surrounding tissues.

Holtfreter (1938a) excised pieces of the competent ectoderm from young Triturus gastrulae, and cultivated them for varying lengths of time in standard solution. The pieces were then transplanted into young neurulae, where they were exposed to the inductive stimuli of the chordamesoderm. As in the experiments mentioned above, a gradual loss of competence for neural formations was observed. This was shown both by the decreasing size of the secondary neural formations and by the quality of these formations. After about thirty hours rearing *in vitro*, no brain structures were seen, but derivatives of ectodermal placodes and neural crest were still induced. After 50 hours, the loss of ability to react to the normal inductor was complete. The author thus concluded that the loss of competence in the ectoderm is an autonomous process of ageing. The results also indicate that the loss of competence *in vitro* corresponds to the loss of reactivity *in vivo*; in other words, the ectoderm reared *in vitro* is able to react only to the inductive stimuli corresponding to its actual age. Thus after 30 hours' cultivation the ectoderm forms only derivatives of epidermal placodes, i.e., formations which are determined at the corresponding time in young neurulae. In this respect, the results are similar to those of Waddington (1936) who studied the competence for lens-induction.

Gallera (1952) removed the competent ectoderm of two young gastrulae, and in order to protect the sensitive inner surface, made a "sandwich" from the pieces, with the inner surfaces adjacent. This was again aged *in vitro*, and after different lapses of time, transplanted into young neurulae in place of the cephalic ectoderm. Intact gastrulae of the same age as the donors were cultured as controls. During a period which corresponded to the gastrulation of these controls, the transplanted ectoderm took part in the development of the host tissues (brains), but at the time when the control embryos began their neurulation, the aged ectoderm lost its competence to form neural structures, but was still able to differentiate into certain derivatives of ectodermal placodes (ear vesicle). The results thus fully confirm the observations of Holtfreter (1938a) and are in agreement with the *in vivo* observations of Nieuwkoop (1958).

As regards the primary competence of gastrula ectoderm, we have discussed only neural competence, i.e., the capacity to differentiate into neural structures after an inductive stimulus. However, we know that under experimental conditions mesoderm can be induced from the presumptive ectoderm (Toivonen, 1953a, 1953b). Several authors have shown that during normal development the tail mesoderm develops from the posterior portion of the medullary plate (Bijtel, 1936, 1958; Chuang, 1947; Smithberg, 1954). It is thus logical to think that during normal development this part of the ectoderm is determined by a mesodermal inductive stimulus (see Spofford, 1948; Eyal-Giladi, 1954) and from this it follows that in addition to neural competence, a mesodermal competence must be present in the presumptive epidermis. Experimental data on this competence and its time-pattern are scanty. Borghese (1943) studied the inductive effect of the chorda excised from neurulae. Using gastrulae of different ages, as hosts, he observed that the neural structures induced decreased with the increasing age of the hosts. Simultaneously, mesodermal structures became more frequent and their size increased. In some late gastrulae, large masses of muscle tissue were the only forms of induced tissue, despite the known neuralizing effect of the inductor when used in younger hosts. In Nieuwkoop's (1958) experiments, we noted that after the disappearance of inductions of cranial brain structures at stage $11\frac{1}{4}-11\frac{1}{2}$, some hindbrain differentiations were still to be observed. As stated above, Nieuwkoop explained this as a later competence to a "transforming" influence which in several respects seems very close to our "mesodermalizing" effect. However, direct evidence for this more enduring mesodermalizing competence has not been presented. In the light of the time-sequence of normal development, and the late invagination of the mesoderm forming posterior part of the medullary plate, this might be expected.

Recently Leikola (unpublished) has studied in our laboratory the mesodermal competence of gastrula ectoderm. After removal of the presumptive epidermis of two young gastrulae, he made an explant without inductor, and after cultivating this for various periods of time in Holtfreter-solution, he explanted pieces of alcohol-treated bone-marrow (Toivonen, 1954) into the vesicle-like explant. In contrast to the scanty information obtained from *in vivo* experiments, and the conclusions based on normal development, the capacity of the ectoderm to react to the known mesodermalizing action of the bone-marrow dropped rapidly, and after 4–6 hours mesodermal structures were observed only occasionally. These results indicate two interesting facts. First of all, they demonstrate that there are quite definitely at least two different competences, as suggested by Nieuwkoop (1958); because after the last mesodermal structures had disappeared, there were still to be noted neural and epidermal differentiations. Secondly, the observations indicate that the *in vivo* and *in vitro* changes in competence may not be the same, and, as Spofford (1953) mentioned, when it is exposed to the influence of the underlying and surrounding tissues *in vivo*, the behaviour of the ectoderm differs from that obtained after culture and isolation *in vitro*. Furthermore, the observations of Leikola may explain what has been noted by several authors; the differences in amount of mesodermal structures formed in implantation and in explanation experiments. As is generally known, mesodermal structures are more common in implantation than in explanatation experiments with the same inductor. In the light of these findings, this could be explained as a result of the more rapid loss of mesodermal competence *in vitro*.

(b) *Regional patterns of competence.* In Chapter II the gastrula fate map was presented, and the borders of the competent ectoderm given. Within these borders, there seems to be no variation in the behaviour of the different areas (see Holtfreter, 1947c). Subsequently, during the course of development, this presumptive epidermis becomes segregated into different areas with different competences but now for *secondary or late inductions*, e.g., for the capacity to form lens, balancer, ear vesicle, etc. These areas of different competence partly overlap each other, and cannot be due to changes in the primary competence, but are the first steps of determination. During the development that follows, this prospective determination continues, and the competence of different parts becomes restricted to more and more limited differentiations, ending in what has been called the irreversible differentiation of cells. This will be briefly discussed later.

(c) *Differences between species.* A number of different amphibian species have been used in experiments concerning primary induction, and there is no doubt that some at least of the controversial results obtained are due to species differences in the competence of the ectoderm. Little is known of these differences, but every embryologist who has worked with different species has established definite differences in their reactivity (Lopashov, 1939). Some well-studied examples are given below. The results of Smith and Schechtmann (1954) are often cited as a demonstration of a definite difference between anuran and urodele ectoderm in their competence to respond to killed inductors. In these experiments, Smith and Schechtmann (1954) used two anuran species, *Hyla regilla* and *Rana pipiens*, and gastrulae of axolotl as control material. The authors killed the normal inductor tissue by various methods (alcohol treatment, treatment at low and at high temperature, and formol-treatment) and used it as an inductor in homoplastic explantations. Axolotl dorsal lip treated similarily was a potent neural inductor in homoplastic experiments, whereas with the anuran material, the only positive cases were the explants in which the alcohol-treated tissue had been only briefly washed. The authors concluded that in this series the neuralization was due to the toxic effect of the residual alcohol, but that if no such toxic effect is produced by the inductor tissue, the *anuran ectoderm is not competent to react to the inductive stimuli of dead organizer tissue*, differing in this respect from the urodele tissues generally used in similar experiments. From some earlier experiments with different anuran tissues, the authors concluded that they contain inductive agents and that their negative results are due to the lack of competence of the anuran ectoderm. This might be the correct conclusion, but the authors mention no results of the only adequate control, which would be a chimeric explantation of dead anuran dorsal lip into axolotl-sandwiches. As long as this is not done, we have to consider as another explanation, the inactivation of the inductive agents in anuran tissues after alcohol, heat and formaldehyde treatment. The fact that corresponding urodele tissues do not lose their inductive capacity is not enough to exclude this possibility in anuran tissues.

As another example of definite differences in primary competence between different species, the experiments of Johnen (1956a, 1956b) deserve mention. She examined the temporal relationships in primary induction by removal of the inductor after different periods of contact with the ectoderm. When using Ambystoma ectoderm, she observed neural inductions after a very short exposure to the living inductor (10–15 min.), but when Triturus ectoderm was used as the reacting material, a contact or 4–5 hrs was necessary for neuralization. Thus, the most probable explanation is a difference in the neural competence of the two species used.

A definite difference in the reactivity of the ectoderm between different species was obtained in the experiments of Holtfreter (1944b, 1947c), in which ectoderm was exposed to certain unphysiological conditions leading to autoneuralization. The ectoderm of *Amblystoma punctatum* was much more sensitive to certain toxic factors than the ectoderm of *Triturus torosus*—an observation which is today known by many embryologists working with axolotl and newt embryos.

(d) *Factors behind primary competence.* Little is known of the intrinsic factors and environmental conditions which control the competence of the ectoderm. Here again, we can state that while a large number of authors have made experimental studies of the factors (inductors) affecting the inducing tissue, the responding system has received much less attention. The few attempts to change the primary competence experimentally should be mentioned, but no far-reaching conclusions can yet be arrived at.

Moore (1947) analyzed the mechanism of the development of *Rana pipiens* × *Rana sylvatica* hybrids, and tested the competence of the hybrid ectoderm by transplanting it to the dorso-lateral region of the host gastrula (normal neurula). On comparison with the reactions of the control ectoderm (*R. pipiens*), he observed definitely weaker reactions, and concluded that one effect of hydridization is the prevention of the attainment of full competence.

Smith and Schechtmann (1954) used anuran ectoderm which had been in contact with an inductor tissue previously treated with formaldehyde. If the tissue was washed after this treatment at pH 7, neural competence was inhibited after a certain time of contact, but if the formaldehyde-treated tissue was washed at pH 3, the "anti-competence" effect was not obtained. The authors pointed out that this "anti-competence" effect of the formaldehyde-treated tissues did not affect the general vitality of the ectoderm, and that definite secondary ectodermal structures were differentiated after contact with the treated tissues. The effect accordingly seems to be purely an "anti-neural competence" effect. The mechanism of this phenomenon is unknown.

Extremely interesting and puzzling results have recently been reported by Masui (1956, 1959, 1960a, 1960c), in studies on the effect of Li-treatment on primary competence. After treatment with LiCl, ectoderm was brought into contact with a potent inductor (dorsal lip or chordamesoderm), and the inductions compared with those obtained after similar operations using non-treated, competent ectoderm. Throughout the whole of his series an inhibition of the formation of archencephalic structures was observed; neural structures formed in Li-treated ectoderm were always deuterencephalic or spinal cord like, in contrast to the large archencephalic brain parts of the control series. At the same time, the mesodermal structures induced in the Li-treated ectoderm were more frequent and voluminous than in the control experiments. In one of his most recent papers, Masui (1960b) reported that even after using boiled dorsal lip as an inductor in contact with Li-treated ectoderm, mesodermal inductions were noted. As had been shown in his control experiments with non-treated ectoderm, as well as in a variety of earlier experiments, heating the dorsal lip will inactivate its mesodermalizing principle. These unexpected results will be dealt with later, on page 70.

Finally a brief discussion of the species-specific reaction of competent ectoderm is called for. Xenoplastic transplantations offer a suitable means of studying the reactions of competent ectoderm when exposed to the inductive effects of tissues from another species. Previous chapters contain a variety of examples which demonstrate the inductive activity of both adult and embryonic foreign tissues. In all these experiments, the secondary formations induced from the ectoderm were typical of the host species, and never resembled the donor tissues. This phenomenon was conclusively proved in a series of experiments in which transplantations between different urodelan and anuran species were performed (see Spemann, 1936). Only one example of these experiments will be presented:

Newt embryos are equipped with a pair of balancers on the lateral side of the head—an ectodermal organ which is frequently seen as an induction product in various types of experiment. The axolotl lacks these structures, and in anuran larvae a pair of adhesive glands is seen instead of the balancers. If now a piece of competent axolotl ectoderm is transplanted into the head region of a Triturus gastrula, no balancer is formed; but if a similar transplanataion from Triturus ectoderm is made into axolotl head, a balancer is always induced (Mangold, 1931b). If, on the other hand, similar xenoplastic transplantation is made between newt and certain anuran species, the newt ectoderm will again form balancers in the anuran head region. In the reciprocal experiment, the anuran ectoderm transplanted into the head region of a salamander forms typical anuran adhesive glands (Spemann and Schotté, 1932; Holtfreter, 1935; Rotmann, 1935) (figure 23). From these experiments, certain important conclusions can be drawn: balancer-inducing capacity can be found in the head region of not only the newt, but also in axolotl and anuran species which lack this organ. On the other hand, the axolotl ectoderm is not competent to form this organ, and in the anuran ectoderm a structure typical of anurans will be induced, even after transplantation into species lacking this organ. This means that induction operates across the borders of species, but that the type of the induced structures is controlled by the genetical constitution of the reacting material.

From this scanty information, we know that both genetical and environmental factors control primary competence. The nature of the factors which control competence during normal development remains an open question. There is no doubt that this is done at least in part by external, inducing factors, and that the loss of competence may be considered the first step of determination. However,

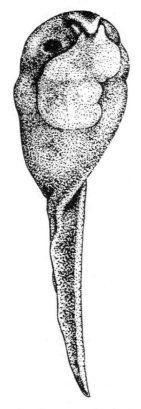

Figure 23. The result of a xenoplastic transplantation of the competent gastrular ectoderm of Triturus taeniatus into the prospective head region of a Bombinator pachypus gastrula. The urodele ectoderm has been induced by the anuran head tissues and forms a balancer (right), instead of a sucker typical of the host (left). (After Rotmann, 1935.)

the loss of competence of the ectoderm cultivated *in vitro* in the absence of normal determinating or stabilizing factors, shows that changes in the cells leading to the decrease in competence do occur with no further differentiation. Whether this is caused by changes in permeability (Gallera, 1952) or by some "intrinsic factors" (Chuang, 1955; Nieuwkoop, 1958) cannot yet be concluded, mainly because we do not know the conditions necessary for induction.

(e) *Totipotency of the ectoderm.* The competent gastrula ectoderm is often referred to as "totipotent" or "omnipotent". A large number of experiments have already demonstrated the capacity of the ectodermal cells to form almost all kinds of neural, ectomesenchymal and mesodermal structures. Of course, this does not mean that all these formations are directly stimulated by the primary inductive effect, but it demonstrates the "totipotency" of the gastrula ectoderm.

Information is scanty on the competence of the ectoderm to become transformed into endodermal derivatives. Both Mangold (1923) and Holtfreter (1933d) reported cases where presumptive ectoderm grafted into a gastrula may have participated in the formation of the host endoderm, but in consequence of the early age of these embryos when fixed, the differentiation was poor and the data not quite conclusive. Raven (1935b, 1938) transplanted presumptive ectoderm into neurulae of the same species, and obtained, in addition to neural and mesodermal structures, gut-like formations. In his embryos, the differentiations were in a more advanced stage, and the data thus more convincing. Not until very recently was the explantation method used for the demonstration of the endodermal competence of the ectoderm (Yamada, 1958b; Takata and Yamada, 1960). As inductor these authors employed guinea-pig bone-marrow tissue after alcohol treatment, known from earlier experience as a potent inductor of mesodermal structures (Toivonen, 1953a, 1953b, 1954a). In a long term culture of the explants, a number of definite endodermal differentiations were noted (pharynx, oesophagus, lung, stomach, intestine) (Plate 4.1). One curious fact which demonstrated the competence of the ectoderm was that in one explant of Takata and Yamada (1960) a pulsating heart was induced. The observation of Niu (1958b) supplement these results. In his ectodermal cell structures, treated with RNA-fraction of thymus gland, and subsequently transplanted into the body cavity of older larvae, he noted small, roundish bodies with two cell types and resembling the thymus rudiment of the host.

We can thus conclude, following the extensive study of Takata and Yamada (1960), that almost all embryonic structures have been noted as products of induction of the ectoderm. In addition to its normal derivatives, both trunk and tail mesodermal structures have been observed, as well as endodermal derivatives. It thus seems that the term "totipotent" has become justified.

(f) *Other inductive systems*. In contrast to primary competence, the "secondary" or "late" competence refers to the capacity of *already determined* tissues to react to inductive stimuli. In the induction of lens, the reactive tissue is already determined as epidermis, in the induction of nephric tubules the responding tissue is determined as mesenchyme, and so on. In addition to these, and many other normal events during development, there are experiments demonstrating an abnormal change in the prospective determination of cells and tissues. In other words, when discussing "late" competence, we are in fact concerned with one of the basic questions of embryology today, that is the stability of differentiation. This problem has often been given thorough discussion (see Harrison, 1933; Weiss, 1949, 1953; Trinkaus, 1956) and in this book, we will content ourselves with presenting but a few examples which demonstrate the problem of late competence.

A number of experiments dealing with the development of the lens and the optic cup are summarized in figure 24. It has been shown repeatedly that after the totipotent or competent ectoderm has lost its capacity to form neural tissue, some areas are still capable of reacting to the inductive stimulus of the optic cup to form the lens (see Spemann, 1912; Twitty, 1955). Although there are considerable variations between different species in this "lens-competent" epidermal area, we can conclude that normally the lens is formed from tissue already determined as epidermis by the primary inductive stimulus (figure 24.1). The occurrence of "free lenses" in some experimental series (Holtfreter, 1943b; Toivonen, 1940; Becker, 1959a; Mangold, 1961b) suggests that under certain circumstances the lens can be formed directly from the presumptive epidermis, and without the normal inductive stimulus of the optic cup (2). In addition to these two pathways, lens can be formed from tissues which are older than the epidermis, and already determined in another direction. In the well-known phenomenon of Wolffian regeneration, a new lens is formed from the pigmented retina (3) (Reyer, 1948; Twitty, 1955). However, not only the outer layer of the optic cup possesses the capacity to form lentoid tissue. Moscona (1957b, 1960) demonstrated that dissociated cells of the embryonic chick neural retina can *in vitro* form lentoidbodies, and thus change their prospective determination (4). And, to complete our scheme, there are a number of experimental series which demonstrate the changes from neural retina into pigmented epithelium and *vice versa* (Dragomirow, 1936; Ikeda, 1937; Dorris, 1938; Detwiler and Van Dyke, 1953, 1954; Stone, 1950; Bertolini, 1958; Lopashov, 1959, 1961; Lopashov and Stroeva, 1961) (5, 6).

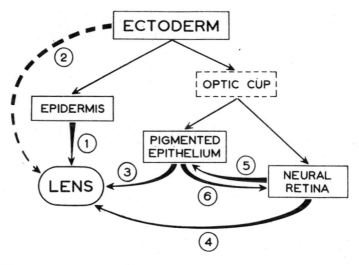

Figure 24. A schematic presentation of the "competencies" of optic tissues during early development. The numbers refer to different experimental series described in the text. (Orig.)

As another example can be taken epidermal differentiations. *In vitro* cultivations of embryonic chick skin have demonstrated the multipotency of the already determined epidermis. In the presence of a high level of vitamin A, the epidermis undergoes changes which result in cuboidal epithelium with mucus secretion, and often ciliated cells (Fell and Mellanby, 1953; Fell, 1957). When combined *in vitro* with different types of mesenchyme, the embryonic epidermis can be changed into similar cuboidal epithelium, into one-layered, epithelial-like tissue, and into keratinizing squamous epithelium (MacLoughlin, 1961). In connection with these very interesting findings one must bear in mind the observation of pathological changes in adult epithelium. A change well known to all pathologists is the squamous metaplasia of different cuboidal epithelia, both under experimental and under pathological conditions (see Willis, 1958). One of the best known cases is the squamous metaplasia of the bronchial epithelium. These epithelial changes might be "true differentiations" or alternatively "modulations" (Weiss, 1939) but they show that certain determined and even adult tissues are still capable of changing their morphology.

The examples of the change in the prospective determination of certain tissues just presented, together with a large number of other similar results, allow certain conclusions to be drawn. (1) In differentiated tissues, there remains a certain competence to react to inducing stimuli, followed by a change in their prospective determination. (2) Competence seems to be still "unspecific" to a certain extent, and different stimuli can change the determination in different directions. (3) The same differentiated structure (lens, keratinized epithelium) can develop from different sources, and from tissues which are younger or older than those normally involved in the formation of the structure. It should nevertheless be pointed out that no generalizations can yet be made, and that there might be cells and tissue which have completely lost their competence and are irreversibly differentiated (e.g., nerve cells). Thus we have to agree with Trinkaus (1956): "Because of the incomplete nature of the evidence I take a frankly phenomenological position and define differentiation on the cellular level simply as an increase in the structural and functional specialization of cells. We cannot at present take a general position on the matter of cell stability."

(g) *Conclusions.* At an early gastrula stage, a definite part of the ectoderm has the capacity of reacting to normal and abnormal stimuli by differentiating. The differentiations correspond to the normal tissue-types formed during primary induction, and under experimental conditions the secondary structures appear synchronously with the tissue differentiation of the host. This spatially limited competence decreases during gastrulation, and at the early neurula stage the ectoderm has lost its "primary" competence. Apparently, during normal development the competence to react to neuralizing stimuli disappears first and the capacity to form mesodermal tissues, later. If the ectoderm is cultivated *in vitro*, the loss of competence is also observed.

The loss of competence during normal gastrulation has been

referred to as the first step of determination, obviously dependent upon the differentiative and stabilizing influences of the underlying tissues. In the *in vitro* experiments, the mechanism is not the same, and obviously both intercellular and extracellular factors play a role in the loss of the primary competence. A thorough understanding of the mechanism of this process and the factors controlling tissue competence cannot be expected before more knowledge of the mechanism in the induction process has been gained.

During progressive differentiation of the tissues, the primary competence, the "totipotency" of the ectoderm, changes into a more limited competence to form structures which are typical of later embryogenesis, and to react to inducing stimuli. This competence to change the prospective determination seems to remain in certain tissues throughout larval life, and even in adult tissues, but no generalizations can be made and the question of the stability of cellular differentiation remains open.

Finally, it has once again to be pointed out that when primary induction is being investigated the reactivity of the ectoderm has always to be borne in mind. Local differences in this competence, the gradual loss of competence during development, and the differences between different species, may explain a large number of contradictory findings. As long as we do not know the exact mechanism of the induction process, the experimental errors brought about by such differences in primary competence can be excluded only by using ectoderm of the same age, from the same species and from the same place on the embryo. This seems self-evident, but has been forgotten in a number of experiments.

3. *Autoneuralization*

(a) *Differentiation without inductor.* The classical concepts of embryonic induction and of specific factors which mediate it, were first confused at the end of the thirties by detection of a variety of inductively active agents (see Chapter VII). In 1941, Barth published his observations which seemed to explain some of these earlier results, but which at the same time seemed to be contradictory to the concepts of Spemann and his school.

Barth's (1941) experiments were originally stimulated by some occasional cases in which neuralization had been observed in ectodermal explants with no inductor tissue or inductively active chemical present. He suggested that the important point in this neuralization might be the preservation of the normal polarity of the cells during the curling of the explanted ectoderm. He therefore arranged experiments in which this polarity was preserved by fusion of two ectodermal pieces. When these explants were reared in standard solution, a high percentage of neural tube formation was obtained. Barth's observation has later been confirmed by several authors, but simultaneously the question has become more complicated, and the original idea of the importance of cellular polarity no longer seems valid.

Barth's (1941) experiments were carried out with *Amblystoma punctatum*, and his findings were first confirmed by Holtfreter (1944b) with the same species. However, he did not correlate this with the orientation of the curling of the ectoderm, as had Barth, but pointed out that a prolonged exposure to saline solution led to disintegration and cytolysis of some of the uncoated ectodermal cells. The extent of these changes appeared to be proportional to the degree of subsequent neural differentiation. Holtfreter thus concluded that the inductive stimuli might have been emerging from the dying cells and affecting the living cells, causing them to become neuralized. Later he modified this concept, but we will return to these questions in connection with the mechanism of autoneuralization.

So far, all the results had been obtained with Amblystoma, but certain observations seem to indicate that the ectoderm of this species reacts in an exceptional way and not like most of the urodeles. Holtfreter (1945, 1947c) cultured explants of *Triturus torosus* under conditions leading to autoneuralization of Amblystoma explants, but could see no differentiation. When, on the other hand, the Triturus material was reared under more unphysiological conditions (high pH, Ca-free solution, hypotonic medium), an autoneuralization could again be demonstrated. There thus seems to exist a definite difference in the "sensibility" of these two species. Later, Karasaki (1957b) used *Triturus pyrrhogaster* in similar experiments, and noted that its ectoderm was even less susceptible to the injurious effects of different toxic or non-physiological conditions.

Following Holtfreter's experiments, very many different toxic factors have been tested—either by continuous cultivation in unphysiological conditions, or by a short "shock" treatment, and in many instances the result has been neural differentiation of the ectodermal cells. The following toxic or injurious factors of this type can be mentioned: high or low pH, alcohol, Ca-free culture medium, ammonia, urea, NaSCN, CO_2-shock and mechanical damage of the

F

cells (Holtfreter, 1944b, 1945, 1947c; Yamada, 1950a; Chuang 1955; Karasaki, 1957b, 1957c; Flickinger, 1958b). Today, one feels justified in adding to these findings most of the toxic and injurious agents used in earlier work in the search for a specific inducing chemical (see Fischer, Wehmeyer, H. Lehmann, Jühling and Hultzsch, 1935; Waddington, Needham and Brachet, 1936; Barth and Graff, 1938; Beatty, de Jong and Zielinski, 1939; Shen, 1939; Brachet, 1944; Lehmann, 1945). Treatment with these chemicals, or rearing in these non-physiological conditions, caused differentiation of the ectodermal cells into neural structures (brain-like formations and sense organs), pigment cells, and in some cases into mesenchyme. There were thus noted tissues normally derived from ectoderm or ectomesenchyme, but none of the reports mention any definite mesodermal differentiations following injurious treatment. The only exception in this respect is the recent paper by Masui (1960b) dealing with the effect of lithium treatment upon gastrula ectoderm (cf. page 62). In these experiments, the competent gastrula ectoderm was used in explantation experiments after a 4-hr treatment in Ca-free Li-solution, and either the dorsal lip tissue or the pre-chordal plate used as inductor. Control experiments were made with boiled dorsal lip as inductor, or without an inductively active implant. As already mentioned, the Li-effect noted might be referred to as an inhibition of the formation of cranial neural structures, but what interests us in this connection is the observation of *mesodermalization in the control series*. Both in series with boiled dorsal lip as inductor, and in series without inductor, Li-treated ectoderm showed muscle, pronephros and blood cell differentiations, and even notochord in two instances. This "automesodermalization" was even more frequent in those series in which the Li-treatment was combined with dissociating treatment.*

These results of Masui (1960b) seem of great importance, and might change our earlier conceptions of the differentiation potentialities of the ectoderm. It might be possible that in the ectoderm there always exists a weak tendency to become mesodermalized, but only after a suppression of the neuralizing tendencies by Li-ion does this become manifest. On the other hand, certain points in the findings of Masui (1960b) should be discussed and perhaps repeated before far-reaching conclusions are drawn. As Masui (1960b) stated,

---

* Very similar results were quite recently reported by Ogi (1961).

the muscle differentiation was poor despite the 2–3 weeks of cultivation (which in the light of our experience is sufficiently long to bring about definite differentiation of somites). Only in a few cases was striation noted, and in most cases only spindle-shaped cells with "fibrilar structures" were seen. The other quite unexpected observation of Masui (1960b) was that in series in which "the perchordal plate of the archenteron roof of advanced gastrulae" was used as inductor, mesodermal structures were noted not only in Li-treated explants but also in untreated controls. The mesodermalizing inductive action of the invaginated praechordal plate does not seem to be in accordance with the observations of other investigators (e.g. Okada and Hama, 1945a, 1945b; ter Horst, 1948; Gallera, 1949; Eyal-Giladi, 1954; Sala, 1955b).

A short while ago, a paper of great interest was published by Barth and Barth (1959). They cultured dissociated cells of *Rana pipiens* gastrula ectoderm in a saline medium. Under these conditions, the small ectodermal explants showed cytolysis, but no differentiation. If 0·1 per cent of globulin, which appeared to have a protective effect, was added to the culture medium, nerve fibres and cells were obtained in the cell culture. (Plate 4.2.) This seems to be a new demonstration of neural differentiation of the presumptive ectoderm in the absence of either inductively active or toxic substances. The only comment possible is that certain morphological changes obtained in cell cultures cannot always be considered as differentiations if no organ rudiment formation or specific histochemical properties can be demonstrated. Very similar and often reversible changes can be obtained in different cultures, and they might be more adequately attributed as "modulations" (see also Benitez, Murray and Chargaff, 1959). More recently the authors reported certain new observations obtained in similar cell cultures (Barth, Barth and Nelson, 1960). A number of different compounds were observed to stimulate the neuralization of the ectodermal cells: sodium thioglycolate, sodium thiosulphate, magnesium chloride, calcium chloride, carbon dioxide and high pH. It thus looks to us as if there is again in fact an effect of toxic materials which at an early stage damage the dissociated, uncoated cells.

Before beginning a discussion of the mechanism of autoneuralization, mention is necessary of certain observations of an experimental suppression of this phenomenon. Holtfreter (1947c) added glucose or sucrose to his culture medium, and obtained a weak epidermalization

instead of the neuralization of the explants noted if no additional
factors were added. This was confirmed by Karasaki (1957c). The
same suppressing effect has been noted on numerous occasions with
the lithium ion (Okano, 1957; Karasaki, 1957c; Okano and Kawakami,
1959); both pretreatment with lithium, or the addition of Li-chloride
to the culture medium suppress the tendency of toxic factors to cause
neuralization. The same observation was made in the above work of
Barth and Barth (1959), and more recently by Barth, Barth and
Goldhor (1960) in which lithium was added to the globulin-saline
medium; no nerve cells differentiated, but instead pigmented cells
and mesenchyme-like cells were obtained. The "antineuralizing"
effect of lithium has also been demonstrated in normal induction,
where a Li-pretreatment of the ectoderm leads to a definite caudalization of the induced structures (Masui, 1956, 1959, 1960a, 1960b,
1960c).

As can be seen from these numerous examples, both neural
induction and the formation of neural structures without an inductor
are suppressed by lithium. It might be too early to conclude that the
mechanism is the same in both cases, but there seem no grounds to
invalidate this assumption. Moreover, this can be considered as
definite evidence in favour of similar factors in autoneuralization and
normal neural induction.

(b) *The mechanism of autoneuralization.* We cannot yet determine
the actual mechanism of autoneuralization. The original concept of
a gradient for neural differentiation and its manifestation in experiments when the polarity is preserved (Barth, 1941) does not seem to
explain later findings. As mentioned above, Holtfreter's original
idea was that inductively active agents were released from cytolysed
cells, and that they induced the surviving cells. (In this connection,
the old observation of Bautzmann (1932) has to be recalled: presumptive epidermis, always inactive in living condition, will act as a neural
inductor after killing.) To test this suggestion Holtfreter (1945)
arranged experiments in which the killed or severely damaged cells
were mechanically removed from the culture. Subsequently, the
ectoderm largely failed to become neural, and the results thus corroborated the idea of a "relay mechanism". However, when these
experiments were repeated under somewhat divergent conditions, the
results were quite different and the explants became neuralized in
the total absence of discharged or non-viable cells (Holtfreter, 1947c).
"Obviously the external stimulus liberated the inductive agent within

the reacting cells themselves by causing initial and reversible steps of cytolysis" (Holtfreter and Hamburger, 1955). According to Holtfreter (1948a), the neuralization obtained was proportional to the degree of "sublethal cytolysis", and the closer the cells were brought to a state of irreversible cytolysis the greater was their tendency to become neuralized. He suggested that the morphogenetic agents, the neuralizing agent X and the neurogene, N, are present in the competent ectoderm in an inactive form "XN". After a cytolysing treatment, this compound will be dissociated, the active X-factor is liberated and attacks the other "XN" compounds. In this chain reaction, the neurogene N is liberated and activated, and produces neuralization (figure 25). In reality, this theory is not far removed from the ideas presented by Waddington, Needham and Brachet (1936) before autoneuralization had been experimentally demonstrated. Their findings and hypotheses are discussed in more detail in Chapter VII. These ideas were later accepted not only by Holtfreter, but also by Eakin (1949).

The hypothesis of Holtfreter (1948a) is doubtless very tempting, and in the same paper the author correlated it with normal induction. The suppressive action of lithium might quite well corroborate this hypothesis—the specific action of this ion is not known exactly, but it is generally considered to have a "stabilizing" effect (Ranzi, 1952; Ranzi, Citterio, Copes and Samuelli, 1955; Tamanoi and Kawakami, 1959; Okano and Kawakami, 1959). However, certain observations speak against this suggestion, which must in fact be considered as a working hypothesis. In some investigations, cytolysis was noted without a subsequent neuralization (Barth and Barth, 1959 in their control series). Furthermore, Karasaki (1957b) indicated that the degree of cytolysis is not always proportional to neuralization. As his main evidence for this hypothesis, Holtfreter presented his experiments in which the cytolysed, killed cells were removed, and where factors released by them could accordingly be excluded. However, we do not think that this experiment can exclude the possibility that the morphologically normal and viable cells remaining in the culture had changed during the treatment, and had been able to release certain factors which stimulated their neighbouring cells (as in cases where physically treated ectoderm becomes inductively active). The fact that morphological changes are not necessary for a release of relatively large molecules from cells has recently been demonstrated by Goldberg and Green (1960). After an anticomplement treatment of cells, RNA-particles were lost to the medium through the "visibly intact" cell membrane, which still prevented larger organelles from leaving the cell. Thus, we are of opinion that all the experimental data on autodifferentiation can be explained as a release of active

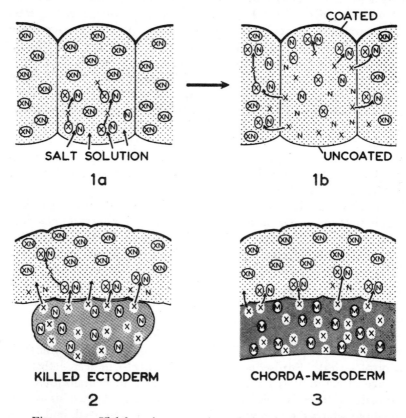

Figure 25. Holtfreter's conception of the mechanism of auto-neuralization and its relation to inductive action of killed and normal inductor tissues. The concept is discussed in the text. (After Holtfreter, 1948a.)

factors from damaged cells, and their induction of the viable cells. The suppressive effect of lithium could quite hypothetically be explained as a decrease in the sensitivity of the reacting cells (e.g., as an increase of their permeability), a suggestion which might explain the same suppressive action in normal induction (Masui, *op. cit.*).

As another correlation to normal induction, species specificity can be mentioned. Holtfreter (1945, 1947c) demonstrated that the ectoderm of Amblystoma became much more easily neuralized under non-physiological conditions than that of *Triturus torosus*. A similar difference in the sensitivity to normal inductors was observed between Amblystoma and *Triturus vulgaris* by Johnen (1956a, 1956b).

(c) *Cytological changes following toxic treatment.* As can be expected from the irreversible cytolysis observed in experiments with toxic agents, certain less conspicuous cytological changes have been noted in the viable cells (Holtfreter, 1946). These changes have recently been described in detail by Karasaki (1957c). He noted the following changes: "swelling by hydration, increase of the intracellular Brownian movement, active protoplasmic movements accompanied by the various types of pseudopodia, solation of the endoplasmic layer, structural changes or breakdown of cytoplasmic inclusions". Karasaki (1957b) suggested that the activation of these protoplasmic movements may be connected with the neuralization that follows this treatment. This possibility cannot of course be excluded, but we should like to point out that these changes are typical of a variety of cells under unfavourable conditions. As a matter of fact, we have quite recently seen exactly the same changes in a time-lapse film showing the responses of HeLa cells to different, obviously toxic factors in human serum (E. Saxén and Penttinen, 1961). We are thus inclined to consider the cytological changes and the subsequent neuralization as parallel phenomena following toxic treatment and not necessarily the result of any causal relationship.

(d) *Conclusions.* Following this discussion, it has to be stated that the neuralization of ectoderm in the absence of specific inductive agents has definitely been proved. The mechanism of this process is, however, still unknown and the object of speculation. There is one passing observation made by Karasaki (1957c) which should be mentioned—although no conclusions are drawn from it. This author noted a release of mucous material in the ectodermal cells after a neuralizing treatment. Although the amount of this material was not in different series proportional to the neuralizing effect it must be remembered that American embryologists have repeatedly stressed the importance of certain extracellular materials (Grobstein, 1955a, 1955b; Auerbach and Grobstein, 1958; Edds, 1958b; Moscona, 1960, 1961; Wilde, 1961a).

Finally, the question must be raised, as to the extent to which similar unspecific factors play a role in normal neural induction, and especially in experimentally produced "real" inductions. As pointed out by Holtfreter and Hamburger (1955), it is not likely that similar mechanisms are involved in normal development. Nevertheless, the findings presented in this chapter demonstrate that all the factors necessary for neuralization are already present in the ectoderm (at least in the form of their precursors). Whether during the course of normal induction only an "unmasking" or release of these factors occurs, or whether there is an actual transfer of similar active factors from the inductor to the ectoderm, still remains unsolved.

In practice, the definite demonstration of an induction without specific external stimuli has always to be considered as a source of experimental errors. Most of the "inductions" observed earlier with different chemicals (see Chapter VII) have to be taken as toxic effects leading to autoneuralization. Even the inductions produced by heterogenous or killed inductors have been referred to as possibly belonging to this category (Holtfreter and Hamburger, 1955). However, the tissue specificity and the stability of these inductive effects in foreign tissue speak strongly against this suggestion. Furthermore, it must once again be pointed out, that the differentiations observed in the very numerous experiments employing toxic or damaging agents belong to the neural or ectomesenchymal derivatives, whereas true mesodermal differentiations have not been observed without an external inductive stimulus (except for the recent reports of Masui, 1960b; and Ogi, 1961).

V

Heterogenous Inductors

1. *Introduction*

As early as in the twenties, several authors demonstrated that the capacity to stimulate neuralization in competent gastrular ectoderm was not restricted to normal inducing tissue, i.e. the archenteron roof. Mangold (1928) obtained neural induction with brain tissue of Triturus-larvae, and somewhat later than this, inductions were produced by tissue from regenerating Triturus limbs (Umanski, 1932), and by the notochord and somite tissues of Triturus larvae (Holtfreter, 1933a). At the same time, a number of reports showed that inductive action was not "species specific", and consequently inductor tissue could be exchanged between anuran and urodelan species (Geinitz, 1925; Bytinski-Salz, 1929; Mangold, 1931b; Spemann and Schotte, 1932). The first extensive investigations to map out the distribution of inductively active agents in the animal kingdom were carried out by Holtfreter (1933a, 1934).

Before presentation is made of observations on heterogenous inductors, some points have to be stressed. The significance of these investigations seems to be two-fold: heterogenous tissues, often available in large quantities, have been used as material for chemical fractionation of the active agents, for experiments concerned with the mechanism of the induction process, the diffusibility of inductive agents, the stability of these factors, and so on. This form of use of heterogenous inductors is presented in different chapters of this book, along with some justified criticism directed against the conclusions based on the results achieved by means of these "artificial" stimuli. Despite this criticism, we can state that investigations employing heterogenous inductor material have yielded a very great deal of important information.

The other line of research work on heterogenous inductors has not met with so much success. We refer here to those investigations concerned with a possible elucidation of the significance of these active agents in the *adult organism* after known inductive interactions

77

have already ceased. In other words, what is the significance of the agents present in almost all embryonic and adult tissues, and which possess an activity demonstrable as a capacity to control differentiation of competent ectoderm? Some of these approaches are presented below, but it may already be stated here that this problem seems to be completely unsolved and obscure. It is quite possible that the whole "problem" has been incorrectly posed, and that no justification exists for investigations following this line.

2. *The distribution of inductive activity in different tissues*

As was mentioned in the introduction, the first extensive investigation of the distribution of inductive agents in animal tissues was made by Holtfreter (1933a, 1934) In this work he tested tissues from a large number of animals ranging from lower invertebrates to Man; he arrived at the somewhat unexpected result that neuralization of gastrula ectoderm could be produced by practically all the tissues tested. To mention a few of them, they included: Limnea-foot, imaginal plate of insects, fish-liver, limb rudiment and retina of the newt, striated muscle of anurans and mouse heart muscle, liver, suprarenal gland, brain and adipose tissue. (In these experiments, the fresh heterogenous tissues were implanted into the blastocoele, and the induction product was usually a secondary neural plate.)

These investigations were followed by a variety of similar experiments; some of the results of these are presented in Table 1 and in Plates 5.1 to 5.5. Before discussing these observations, it is necessary to emphasize that results from different laboratories and different experimental series can be compared only if certain reservations are made. It may be useful to mention here some of the multitude of factors responsible for differences in such results:

Reactive tissue: Different reactivity in different species.
           Differences in the age of the ectoderm (Competence).
           Differences in its sensitivity to injurious factors.

Inductor tissue: Differences in the pretreatment of the tissue.
           Variations in the condition of the donor animal.
           Size and site of the implanted tissue piece.

Experimental methods: Different methods of operation (implantation-explantation).
Differences in the methods of culture (age, etc.)
Differences in the classification of inductions etc.

These, and many other methodological variations, lead to certain differences and controversies in respect of the findings of different authors using the same heterogenous tissues, but in general the observations are in reasonable correspondence. The examples presented in Table 1 are mostly of results obtained by authors employing similar methods, and are accordingly comparable. It can first be noted that there appear to be no relationships between the type of inductive action of these tissues and their origin. For example, the ectodermal skin of the frog shows an inductive activity which is very similar to that of the mesodermal bone marrow of certain other animals. Furthermore, heart muscle and liver tissue of the guinea pig are very similar in their morphogenetic capacity, etc. In different animals, similar organs seem to have certain resemblance in their inductive actions but, for instance, the retina is a definite exception to this rule. Moreover, some investigations have shown that even the different components or parts of the same organ can exert different inductive actions, such as the white and red pulp of the spleen and different parts of the kidney tissue (Kawakami and Mifune, 1955; Mifune, 1955; Kuusi, 1957b). Thus, without further analytical examination of the results, it may be stated that the distribution of inductively active agents in different tissues and species provides no information on their possible significance in these tissues.

Some examples additional to the data presented in Table 1 may be mentioned. Not only animal tissues, but also certain plant tissues yielded a weak inductive action in the experiments of Ragosina (1936, 1937) and of Toivonen (1938a). Furthermore, the inductive capacity of heterogenous tissues does not seem to be associated only with their cellular elements; both blood plasma and serum have shown a weak neuralizing and mesodermalizing action (Vainio, Toivonen and Saxén, 1958), and chicken embryo extract is a potent inductor (Holtfreter, 1934; von Woellwarth, 1956b; Sasaki, Kawakami and Okano, 1957; Sasaki, 1960). Tissues and cells with no inductive activity seem to be extremely rare, and as an example of this may be mentioned leucaemic bone marrow of the rat (Saxén and Toivonen, 1956; Toivonen and Saxén, 1957).

A claim has been made that the inductive action of heterogenous inductors might be due to quite unphysiological, toxic effects, thus being comparable to the autoneuralization produced by certain

A = Archencephalic. D = Deuterencephalic. SC = Spinocaudal.

Tissue	A	D	SC	
Cavia thymus	+	−	−	Toivonen, 1940
Rana retina	+	−	−	Toivonen-Saxén unpublished
Gram + bacteria	+ +	−	−	Vahs, 1957b
Triturus oocyte nuclei	+ +	−	−	Kriegel, 1956
Percha liver	+ +	(+)	−	Toivonen, 1940
Vipera liver	+ +	(+)	−	Toivonen, 1940
Rat liver	+ +	(+)	−	Saxén-Toivonen, 1957
Cavia liver	+ +	+	−	Toivonen, 1940
Mouse liver	+ + +	+ +	+	Vahs, 1957a
Cavia heart muscle	+ +	+ +	+	Engländer-Johnen, 1957
Lepus bone marrow	+ +	+ +	+	Mifune, 1959
Perca kidney	+	+ +	+ +	Toivonen, 1940
Cavia parotic gland	+	+ +	+ + +	Engländer-Johnen, 1957
HeLa-cells in vitro	+	+ +	+ + +	Saxén-Toivonen, 1958a,
Cavia kidney	(+)	+ +	+ + +	Toivonen, 1940
Rat retina	−	+	+ +	Kawakami, 1959
Rat bone marrow	−	(+)	+ + +	Toivonen-Saxén, 1957
Cavia bone marrow	−	−	+ + +*	Toivonen, 1953a
Frog ventral skin	−	−	+ + +*	Okada, 1948

TABLE 1. The inductive action of certain heterogenous tissues tested in implantation experiments. (* Inductive action was an almost pure mesodermalizing action showing in the main trunk-mesodermal differentiative properties.)

chemicals and physical treatments leading to cytolytic processes in ectodermal cells (see Chapter IV). However, this does not seem to be a proper explanation. First of all, we should like to stress that the inductive actions of different tissues are reproducible; for instance, certain tissues have been used in our laboratory for twenty years, and subsequently in various other laboratories. The same action, typical of these particular tissues (e.g. liver and kidney tissues of the guinea pig) has always been obtained. With certain reservations regarding the condition of the donor animal, this seems to be true of all the heterogenous tissues. Furthermore, the conception of an unphysiological, toxic or injurious effect of these tissues can hardly explain the tissue-specificity of this action particularly stressed by Chuang (1939), Toivonen (1940) and Engländer, Johnen and Vahs (1953). The most probable explanation is thus that in practically all tissues there are certain active factors present, and that these are found in certain constant amounts and ratios typical of each tissue. Certain exceptions to this rule, that is to say in respect of changes in the tissue-specific inductive action of heterogenous tissues, will be dealt with below.

3. *Changes in the inductive action of heterogenous tissues*

In what follows, discussion is limited to the "physiological" changes in the inductive action of heterogenous inductors (and not the changes produced by physical or chemical treatments of the tissue samples). Once again, our information is quite fragmentary, and certainly represents only a few examples of the very many factors which can affect the inductive action of cells and tissues *in vitro* and *in vivo*.

(a) *The influence of age on inductive capacity.* In the light of knowledge that inductive agents are particularly active during early development and initial differentiation of the tissues, it is easy to understand that a number of authors have been interested in possible changes in the inductive capacity of tissues during embryonic and postnatal life. Kawakami (1958) suggested that the onset of inductive activity of a certain tissue occurs at the time when its anlage initiates its morphogenetic activity, and thereafter its development is controlled by these factors. This hypothesis was experimentally investigated by I. K. Kawakami (1959, 1960) using chick and rooster retinal tissue as inductor material. The youngest retinas originated from 44-hr embryos, in which the retinal tissues were already "morphogenetically active" (I. K. Kawakami, 1960), and in addition, five older stages and adult animals were used as donors. However, the youngest retinas, implanted fresh, showed no inductive action; this could not be demonstrated in retinae from embryos less than 14 days old. On the other hand, after a short alcohol treatment, even the youngest retinas were inductively active and in the main produced archencephalic inductions. Despite this difference, the same principal change in inductive activity was demonstrated in both series: during the foetal period, the retinal tissues yielded mainly archencephalic inductive action, which changed to a deuter-encephal-spinocaudal activity of newly hatched and adult animals (in the alcohol-treated series, however, a weak mesodermal activity was noted throughout foetal life). Thus the suggestion of Kawakami (1958) could not be proved, but certain definite alterations of the inductive action during embryonic life were demonstrated.

A similar change from a form of activity which was mainly archencephalic towards a spino-caudal type of inductive action was reported by Vahs (1957a), who studied the inductive effect of embryonic mouse kidney and liver tissues. The tissues were taken from mouse embryos of 22 mm. C.R. length, and compared with the inductive action of adult organs. The results depicted in figure 26 demonstrate the alterations in the inductive capacity, which might be regarded as an increase in mesodermal inductive action (see Chapter IX).

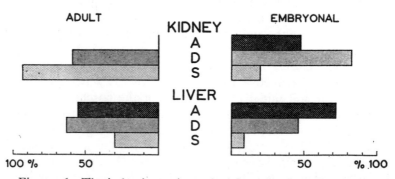

Figure 26. The inductive actions of adult and embryonic mouse tissues (kidney and liver). (A, archencephalic inductions; D, deuter-encephalic inductions, and S, spinocaudal inductions.) (After Vahs, 1957a.)

Certain postnatal alterations in inductive capacity have also been demonstrated in some other heterogenous inductors. Rotmann (1942a) and Toivonen (1945) obtained quite different results when guinea pig thymus tissue was used as inductor in implantation experiments. These differences were quite obviously due to the different ages of the donor animals, and Rotmann (1942a) made a systematic study of the effect of age (figure 27). In this case, a change opposite to that noted during foetal life was shown, and simultaneously with a decrease in the spinocaudal activity, archencephalic formations were induced more frequently (Toivonen, 1945). A somewhat similar comparison was made between the bone-marrow from 5-day and 5-month old rabbits by Mifune (1959). The change in the inductive capacity might best be described as a general weakening, but no definite qualitative changes were noted.

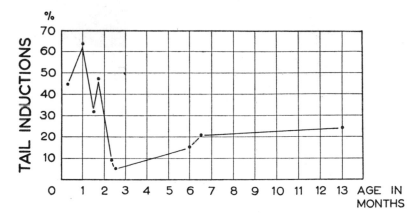

Figure 27. The tail-inducing capacity of guinea-pig thymus tissue taken from animals of different ages. (After Rotmann, 1942a.)

The results presented above accordingly show that the inductive activity of certain organs and tissues does change during embryonic life as well as during the postnatal period. Nevertheless, no generalization can be made from the few examples available.

(b) *The effect of starvation on the inductive action.* Taking as a starting-point certain reports of the changes in the RNA-content of liver during short-term starvation of the animal, Toivonen (1951, 1952) tested the inductive action of the liver from such animals, and compared it with the action of liver from well-fed guinea-pigs. (As a matter of fact, his analysis of the changes in the RNA content did not display any alteration in the relative amount of RNA per dry weight, and the role played by RNA in induction is discussed elsewhere.) What interests us in this connection is that the results (figure 28) demonstrate a definite change in the tissue specific inductive action of the liver after a 3-day starvation of the donor animal. The change was a decrease in the spinocaudal-deuterence-phalic inductive action, accompanied by a strengthening of the archencephalic inductive action.

The experiments were continued by Vahs (1957a) and by Engländer and Johnen (1957), who studied the effect of starvation upon the inductive activity of guinea-pig and mouse tissues (liver, kidney

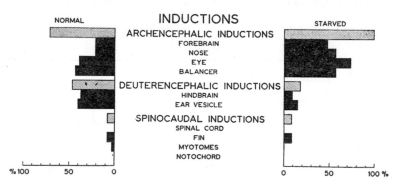

Figure 28. The inductive action of liver tissue taken from nor-mally-fed guinea pigs and from animals after short-term starvation. (After Toivonen, 1952.)

and salivary gland). As regards the tissues of kidney and salivary gland, the main change noted was the same as in Toivonen's (1951, 1952) experiments, but even more definitely: both spinocaudal and deuterencephalic activities became weaker during starvation, whereas archencephalic inductions occurred more frequently. These changes as a function of the duration of starvation are shown in figure 29.

Some observations on the alterations of the inductive action of liver tissue in these experiments seem to be of great interest, and the information gained from these indirect experiments might give us some idea of what actually does occur during starvation. Both in the experiments of Toivonen (1951, 1952) and those of Vahs (1957a) the normal liver tissue used showed an archencephalic-deuterence-phalic effect, and in the mouse liver of Vahs (1957a) even a spino-caudal one. After starvation, this was altered to an almost pure archencephalic inductive action, and simultaneously the *percentage of archencephalic induction increased*. On the other hand, when

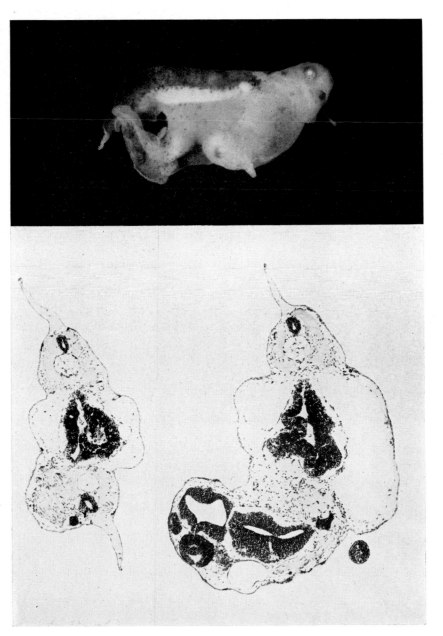

Plate 5.4. A very complete induction of a secondary embryo obtained by the implantation of a crude protein extract from chick embryos. A secondary head with an eye, and brain vesicles, is to be seen, together with a tail with notochord, spinal cord and myotomes. (Orig.)

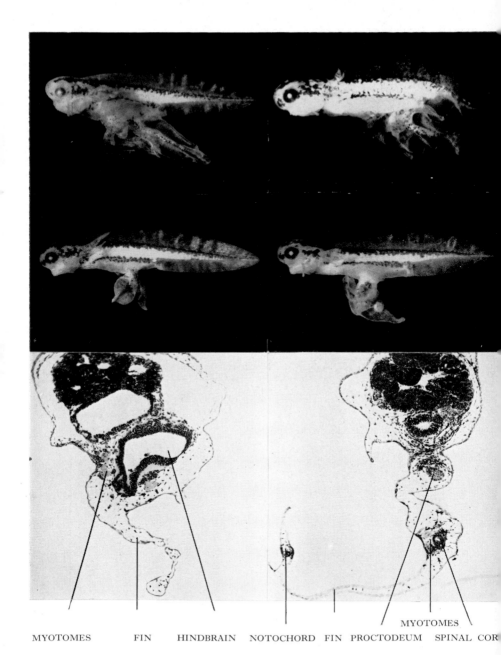

MYOTOMES   FIN   HINDBRAIN   NOTOCHORD FIN PROCTODEUM   SPINAL COR

MYOTOMES

Plate 5.5. Four examples of the inductive action of HeLa-cells grown in a media containing fresh human serum. A strong spino-caudal inductive action can be noted. (Saxén and Toivonen, 1958b.) The micrographs show typical sections from the larvae in the upper row.

Engländer and Johnen (1957) used guinea-pig liver originally lacking all deuterencephalic and spinocaudal tendencies, *no changes were noted*. We will return to the possible significance of this observation in the discussion of this chapter.

(c) *The inductive action of malignant tissues.* If, as may be suggested quite tentatively, the inductively active factors play a role in adult organisms and in the continuous growth and regeneration processes in these, there might exist certain differences in inductive capacity between malignant, rapid-growing and less differentiated tissues on the one hand and their normal sources on the other. Before presenting some results in this connection, we wish to repeat our earlier comment: "Information regarding both the process of embryonic induction and carcinogenesis is so scanty that correlation of the relevant data is impossible". (Toivonen and Saxén, 1957.)

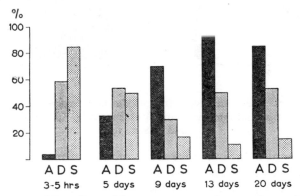

Figure 29. The effect of long-term starvation on the archence-phalic (*A*) deuterencephalic, (*D*) and spinocaudal (*S*) inductive actions of the kidney tissue of the guinea pig. (After Engländer and Johnen, 1957.)

When examining the inductive activity of malignant tissues there must be an adequate normal control, but it is quite a difficult matter to discover normal and malignant tissues such that everything but the malignant cells and their normal controls can be excluded. For instance, in almost all epithelial tumours the stroma might be inductively active, and consequently the changes or similarities between malignant and normal tissues cannot be referred to as being due to the neoplastic components of the implanted tissue. In order to avoid this as much as possible, we initiated experiments with

G

leucaemic bone-marrow (Saxén and Toivonen, 1956, Toivonen and Saxén, 1957). Young rats were injected with a suspension from a transplantable myeloid leucaemia tumour tissue (Shay *et al.* 1951), and after a generalized leucaemia had developed (as shown by the peripheral blood), the bone-marrow was used for implantation experiments. Normal, healthy rats of the same age and strain served as control. The results demonstrated in figure 30 show a

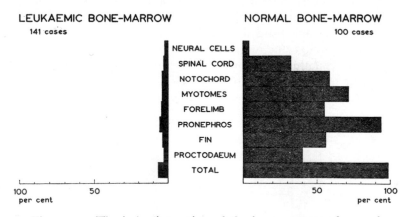

Figure 30. The inductive action of the bone marrow of normal rats (right) and of rats with a myeloid leucaemia. (After Toivonen and Saxén, 1957.)

definite change in the inductive action of the malignant bone marrow in comparison with the controls. Only nine cases with weak, atypical induction were recorded among the 141 operations employing the malignant tissue. To exclude the possibility of an inhibitory action of the leucaemic marrow, simultaneous implantations were made with normal and malignant tissues, but the results of these series were identical with those in which normal bone marrow was employed.

More recently our findings were partly confirmed by Becker, Dostal, Tiedemann and Tiedemann (1959). Instead of leucaemic rats these authors used mice with leucaemia, but no information is available of its nature. The bone marrow of these animals showed some inductive action in contrast to ours, but this was definitely weaker than the activity of the controls (47 per cent inductions in the leucaemic series, and 88 per cent in the control series). Thus there might be some justification for concluding that at least in these cases of malignancy, definite changes had occurred in the inductive capacity of the tissues, but that, as pointed out by us and by the German group, no generalizations could be made. In fact, several malignant tissues have displayed definite inductive activity, although control series in these cases are either lacking or are not quite adequate. Such tissues with positive inductive action include Walker Rat Carcinoma 256 and Peyton-Rous sarcoma (Woerdeman, 1933e), rat ascites hepatoma AH 7974 and AH 130 (Kawakami, 1958), rat hepatoma (Saxén, Toivonen and Vainio unpublished), mouse Ehrlich ascites tumour in solid and cellular form (Becker, Dostal, Tiedemann and Tiedemann, 1959; Saxén, Toivonen and Vainio, unpublished), mouse malignant thymoma (Saxén, Toivonen and Vainio, unpublished) human hypernephroma (Becker, Dostal, Tiedemann and Tiedemann, 1959), and carcinoma of the pancreas (Saxén, Toivonen and Vainio, unpublished). Only as regards the rat ascites hepatoma and the human hypernephroma were adequate control series made (Kawakami, 1958; Becker, Dostal, Tiedemann and Tiedemann, 1959). In both cases, certain differences were noted. The rat ascites hepatoma was a definitely weaker inductor than the healthy liver tissue, and the hypernephroma as inductor produced less spinocaudal formations than the non-infiltrated kidney parenchyme of the same patient. It may thus again be concluded that certain differences do exist between malignant and normal tissues as regards their inductive action. The nature and significance of this phenomenon is completely unknown, and no generalizations can yet be made.

(d) *Other changes in the inductive action.* Brief reports may also be given of two more experimental series on changes in the inductive action of heterogenous tissues. The Japanese authors Kawakami and Mifune studied the effects of total-body X-irradiation and of nitrogen mustard on the inductive capacity of different mouse tissues (Kawakami and Mifune, 1957, Mifune, 1957). The mice were exposed to a very high dose of whole-body irradiation (600 r), and the tissues were tested 7–9 days later. In all the tissues examined, (liver, kidney, spleen, bone-marrow) there was noted an increase in the archencephalic inductive capacity, accompanied by a weakening in the mesodermalizing capacity. A similar change was noted after injection of 0·5 ccm of a 0·1 per cent solution of nitrogen mustard-N-oxide, although the series were relatively small.

The authors concluded that the changes were due to the destruction of the mesodermalizing agent, resulting in a relative increase in the neuralizing agent.

(e) *The inductive action of cells cultivated in vitro*. As experiments like those presented above strongly suggested that certain changes in the tissue-specific inductive action of heterogenous inductors were due to external factors (e.g. nutritional), we began some experiments in which cells cultivated *in vitro* were used as inductors. These experiments were concerned with study of how the inductive action was in fact dependent on the external conditions of the inductively active tissue. Different cell lines were analysed (HeLa-cells, continuous amniotic line cells, Detroit-6 cells, fibroblasts, fresh explants of human amniotic cells, etc. (Saxén and Toivonen, 1958a, 1958b, 1961; Saxén, Toivonen and Vainio, 1961; Toivonen, Saxén and Vainio, 1960 and unpublished). Before the implantation or the explantation of these cells, they were cultured either in "active" (fresh, untreated) human serum or in a culture medium containing "inactivated" (heat-treated) serum or in a protien-free culture medium respectively. The heat-treatment (30 min. at 65 °C) was performed in order to destroy the mesodermalizing principle from the culture medium, and to determine whether cells were still able to induce mesodermal structures in the absence of this principle in their medium.

HeLa-cells and cells of continuous amniotic line (CAL), when cultured in medium containing non-treated, "active" serum, induced structures which were mainly spinocaudal and mesodermal. After transferring them to a protein-free culture medium, or to a medium containing heat-inactivated serum, a definite weakening of the mesoderm-inducing capacity was noted (figure 31), but when the cells were retransferred to the "active" serum, their original inductive capacity was restored. In a great number of subsequent, unpublished experiments, it became evident that the spinocaudal inductive activity could always be affected by environmental factors, but that a total inactivation of this principle was possible only through a direct treatment of the cells. Furthermore, it was noted that this principle was weakened not only during cultivation in heat-treated serum but also during prolonged cultivation in an originally active serum. Thus a maximal spinocaudal effect was observed only if the culture medium of the cells was changed daily. This last mentioned fact might explain certain discrepancies in our own results, as well as some contradictory findings of the German group (Becker, Dostal, Tiedemann and Tiedemann, 1959; Becker, 1959).

Later, some new observations resulted from experiments with fresh explants of human amniotic cells. It was shown that in contrast to the continuous cell lines, these cells were almost independent of the culture medium, and their relatively weak inductive action was similar in cultures in medium containing either "active" or heat-treated serum. Furthermore, their inductive effect was definitely weaker and dissimilar to the continuous line of the same cells (CAL) (Saxén, Toivonen and Vainio, 1961).

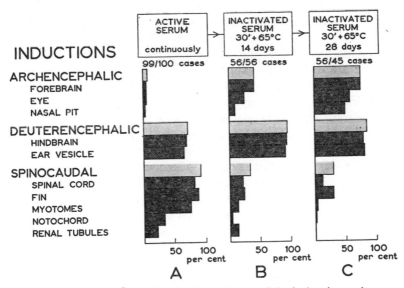

Figure 31. Results showing the dependence of the inductive action of HeLa-cells cultivated *in vitro* on their growth medium. When cells are grown in a medium containing fresh human serum, they are inductors of mainly spinocaudal structures (Plate 5.5), but when transferred to a medium containing heated serum, the inductive action is gradually changed into an archencephalic-deuterencephalic type. (After Saxén and Toivonen, 1958b.)

(f) *Discussion.* Some concluding remarks are perhaps called for after the presentation of these data. Firstly, there still seems to be every reason to agree with the old concept of Chuang (1938, 1939, 1940) and Toivonen (1938b, 1940), that almost all heterogenous tissues exert an inductive action, which is relatively stable, reproducible and typical of each tissue. Moreover, the most probable explanation is that this action is due to certain active compounds which are present in these tissues in constant ratios. This point will be discussed later in several connections, but we wish to stress here that the *changes in the tissue specific inductive action* after starvation, irradiation etc., can well be explained on the basis of such agents. In all the changes such as those presented above, the same type of alteration seemed to take place: a weakening of the spinocaudal and deuterencephalic tendencies, and a strengthening of the capacity to induce archencephalic formations. The only change in an opposite sense was noted during normal development, in which an activity originally archencephalic was gradually changed into a deuterence-phalic-spinocaudal inductive one. It might be too early here to discuss the mechanism of these changes, but it should be mentioned that we are inclined to explain these alterations as changes in the *mesodermalizing* inductive agent(s), which seem to be more labile as regards different treatments than are the neuralizing agent(s). The neuralizing agents of the cells and tissues may not easily be affected by environmental conditions, and consequently changes in the regional character of the neuralizing capacity are explained as an alteration in the neuralizing/mesodermalizing ratio (Saxén and Toivonen, 1958b, 1961). This point is discussed in conjunction with the chemical data on the inductive agents, as well as in con-nection with the different conceptions of primary induction.

As was mentioned in the introduction, the problem of the significance of inductively active agents in adult tissue, their relation to tissue regeneration and growth as well as to malignancy, has to be considered as completely unsolved. Whether this is a "side-effect" of certain compounds with a quite different function in adult organism, or whether they are involved in the continuous growth processes, cannot be determined. As a tentative working hypothesis for future research, the last mentioned possibly might be useful, but to date any evidence of such functions is lacking.

VI

Diffusibility of Inductive Agents

1. *Diffusion versus surface reaction*

The demonstration of the inductive capacity of killed tissue by Bautzman *et al.* (1932) led naturally to two working hypotheses of the mechanism of embryonic induction: that the inductive stimulus might be effected by chemical substances, and that the primary stimulus might be due to the diffusion of these agents from the inductor tissue to the reacting ectodermal cells. As will be seen in Chapter VII, the first hypothesis has been at least partially proved correct, since an inducing stimulus can be provided by certain chemical factors. The second concept, that of the diffusibility of these agents, was originally presented by Mangold (1932) and has since been the object of controversial opinions. This concept was further developed by Dalcq (1941), and by Needham (1942), who compared induction to a virus infection of the cells. Jean Brachet has used a modification of the concept as a working hypothesis since 1940. He and his co-workers have suggested that the inductive stimulus is transmitted by transfer of microscome-like particles from the inductor to the ectoderm, and that the active factor may be a nucleoprotein (Brachet, 1950a, 1950b, 1959, 1960a, 1960b). An opposing theory of the induction mechanism has been presented by Paul Weiss (1947, 1949, 1950, 1958a); this postulates that a close contact between the active and the reactive cells is essential for induction which is a reaction on the cell surfaces, "an attraction of key molecules to the new contact area followed by oriented absorption, the building on of oriented chains of molecules and consequent redisposition of the chemical system of the cell" (Weiss, 1949).

Since 1950 the problem of an actual diffusion of chemical factors as against a surface reaction has been subjected to much discussion and experiment, and the solution is not yet clear. We consider this lack of knowledge to be one of the major problems of the inductive mechanism, and it will accordingly be discussed in detail.

In examining the problem of the diffusibility of inductive agents, three main types of experiment can be made: 1. Separating the react-ing and active tissues by means of material which allows of no contact of the cell surfaces. 2. Testing the inductive capacity of cellfree extracts of tissues, either by using the classical implantation and explanation methods, or by the culture of competent ectoderm in solutions containing "inductive agents". 3. Using labelled inductors or immunological methods to follow any transfer of substances from the inductor to the ectoderm.

2. *Early experiments in tissue separation*

Let us first describe the experiment of Mangold (1932), which originally led him to present the idea of a diffusion of active factors. Instead of using tissues, Mangold implanted pieces of agar which had previously been in contact with the medullary plate of an older gastrula, a tissue known to be inductively active. Following these implantations, an induced neural tube was observed in some cases. To date, however, this convincing experiment has not been repeated, and our knowledge of the "incorporation" of inductively active factors in foreign material is still based on the preliminary findings of Mangold.

The first, somewhat controversial, results were reported as early as the following year. Holtfreter (1933b) placed a sheet of vitelline membrane between the inductor tissue and the ectoderm, and could by this operation prevent induction. Brahma (1957) studied induc-tion through the surface coat of the ectoderm by implanting pieces of competent ectoderm between the invaginating dorsal lip and the host ectoderm. In these experiments, the outer surface of the ecto-derm (with its surface coat) was against the inductor, and he observed a differentiation of the implant into neural tissue. Thus the author concluded that the inductive stimulus is effective through the surface coat of the ectoderm.

In 1955, Holtfreter re-examined his old and partly unpublished results in which pieces of competent ectoderm grafted in the coelomic cavity of amphibian larvae had become neuralized. Similar trans-plantation experiments of embryonic tissues into the abdominal cavity were carried out by Tseng (1956) and Waechter (1951). In the first-mentioned experiments, embryonic mesoderm was transformed in different directions, in the latter investigation the presumptive epidermis was induced to form different tissues. However, we do not hold the opinion that experimental findings of this kind can be used as evidence for inductions without contact, as this can never be excluded when the site of the explants is examined 1 to 4 weeks after transplantation. When Holtfreter (1955) re-investigated the question of induction without cellular contact, he used two different techniques: the inductors (pieces of heterogenous inductor) were coated with agar jelly and implanted into the blastocoele, or the heterogenous inductors were minced up, placed in a hole in paraffin at the bottom of the culture dish, and covered with a cellophane membrane. Following this, pieces of gastrula ectoderm were transferred in a small drop on to the top of the cellophane membrane. Neuralization of the ectoderm was observed in both of these experimental series, but their conclusiveness is questionable. Firstly, as Holtfreter himself points out, and at least as regards the latter experiments, certain toxic materials were released by dead tissues, causing cytolysis of the ectodermal explants, which is known to cause non-specific neural "induction" or autoneuralization (see Chapter IV). In addition, we know nothing of the nature of the agar coat or the cellophane membranes separating the two tissues in these experiments. As for the agar jelly coating the implant, one can hardly exclude the possibility of incomplete coating, or of larger defects in the coat. In the experiments with cellophane membrane, the author mentions that in order to increase the porosity of the membrane, it was "either briefly dipped into boiling water or pretreated with strong alkali". Despite this rather severe treatment, no information of the porosity is given, and one must bear in mind the possibility of serious defects in the membrane permitting true contact through it. In discussing these results, Holtfreter felt it unlikely that the neuralizing effect of his inductors could be explained as a surface reaction of the kind suggested by Weiss (1949). Nevertheless, as mentioned above, more accurate information of the nature and the porosity of the material used for separation of the tissues is needed before the possibility of a surface reaction can be excluded.

3. *Trans-filter experiments*

In addition to the vitelline membrane, surface coat, agar jelly and cellophane membrane mentioned above, filter membranes of a known size of pore have been used in testing for the necessity of cellular contact during primary induction. After achieving complete interruption of induction by placing a cellophane membrane between the inductor and the ectoderm, Brachet and Hugon de Scoeux (1949) tested the effect of certain filter membranes. Living normal inductor and competent ectoderm were separated by two different kinds of membrane, one with a pore size of 230 mμ, and the other with an average pore size of 3.4 μ. A weak neural reaction of the epidermal cells was observed, mainly consisting of neural "palisades", in both series. With the more porous filter, this reaction was noted in 17 of the 24 cases; in the series with the less porous filter the reaction was even weaker. Subsequently, however, Brachet (1950b, 1959, 1960a) was inclined to interpret these results as due to non-specific irritation by the filter, as he had noted similar palisades in control experiments without an inductor. After the stimulating results of Niu (see below), Brahma (1958) re-opened the question of trans-filter induction during primary neuralization. The living dorsal lip inductor and the competent ectoderm were separated by membranes, either in explantation experiments or by interposing the filter between the tissues in whole gastrulae. Two types of filter were used: one with an average pore size of 4 mμ and a thickness of 31 μ, and the other with an average pore size of 1·45 μ and thickness of 164 μ. The results were invariably negative, i.e., induction was prevented by the interposition of these membranes (Plate 6.1). On consideration of these results in the light of more recent, positive results, two explanations seem feasible. As Grobstein (1961a) has pointed out, the filters used by Brahma might be either too thick, or their pore size too small, for neither of them would permit an induction in Grobstein's experiments in another inductive system (see on). The other possibility is that induction is not prevented, but is delayed by the filter. Thus the ectoderm opposite the filter membrane has either lost its competence, or is already determined by the agents on either side of it at the time when the inductive agents reach it.

Recently, the problem of trans-filter induction has been re-examined by Saxén (1961). The method used was a modification of that developed by Grobstein (1955a), and subsequently employed in several experiments on tissue interaction during later development (figure 32). When heterogenous inductor tissue or dorsal lip of *Triturus vulgaris* was separated from the competent ectoderm by this technique, neural or epidermal differentiations were observed in about 50 per cent of cases (Plate 6.3). However, no definite mesodermal structures were seen in these explants. Non-specific irritation by the filter membrane (Brachet, 1959) was excluded by grafting of control ectoderm on the same filter material and under similar pressure. No differentiation was seen in these cases.

Some filter assemblies were fixed after 24 hours (the time after which the weight was normally removed) but no visible material penetrating the filter membrane was observed under the light microscope (Plate 6.2). No electron-microscopic examination was carried out, and the penetration of submicroscopic material into the filter cannot be excluded; the pore size of the filter used was 0.8 μ. Working with mouse tissues, Grobstein and Dalton (1957) observed an abundant penetration of material which was visible by both light and electron microscope. Thus the only conclusion that can be drawn is that the neuralizing stimulus during primary induction can operate over a distance of 20 μ, and through pores of 0.8 μ. No information is available from these experiments on the material passing this membrane.

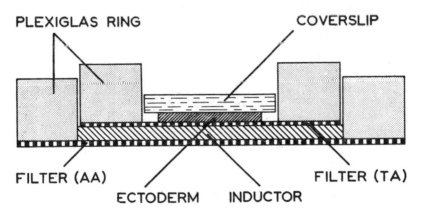

Figure 32. A method for separating the active and the reactive tissues by membrane filters. The filter is cemented on to a plexiglas ring, the reactive ectoderm stretched on it and covered by a slip, which is removed after some hours. The inductor tissue is placed in a large filter-cup and covered by the ectoderm-bearing filter. (Saxén, 1961.)

4. *Differentiation in conditioned medium*

If the inductive agents are soluble and diffusible, one might expect that they could be concentrated in solution, and that competent ectoderm placed in "conditioned" medium might undergo changes typical of post-inductive differentiation. The main practical difficulty in such experiments has been that ectodermal explants very rapidly curl up on removal from the gastrula, and form vesicles with an obviously less-sensitively coated outer surface. This has been avoided in two experimental series, primarily by Niu and Twitty (1953) who placed minute pieces of ectoderm in solution, and more recently by Becker, Tiedemann and Tiedemann (1959), and Yamada (1961) who kept the ectodermal explant flattened by mechanical means.

In the experiments of Niu and Twitty (1953), tiny pieces of urodele ectoderm, each containing about 15–20 cells, were cultured either simultaneously with normal inductor tissue without close contact, or in media previously conditioned by it. Later Niu (1958a, 1958b) used chemical fractions of heterogenous tissues. In all of these experiments, the ectodermal cells were partly differentiated. Niu reported neural cells, pigment cells and myoblasts, with a relatively high percentage of positive cultures, rising to 90 per cent in some experimental series. In series where extracts from different mammalian organs were used, different types of cell arrangement were noted, e.g., tubule-like aggregates, or neuroid tissue (Plate 6.4). Nevertheless, the conditions in these cultures still appear to be unfavourable for normal development of the cells, and consequently the differentiations are mostly poor when compared, for instance, to the neural crest cultures of Wilde (1955a, 1955b, 1956, 1959). This might be due either to the lack of certain nutritional factors, or to the small number of cells in the explants (see Wilde, 1961a). However, it might be a consequence of only a certain type of initiative stimulus being transmitted by the conditioned solution. (The chemical constitution of the solutions used in these experiments is dealt with separately in Chapter VII.)

The most interesting findings of Becker, Tiedemann and Tiedemann (1959), mentioned above, have been published only in the form of a brief, preliminary report, and some of their convincing slides were demonstrated at the International Embryological Conference in 1959. The curling of the ectoderm in hanging drop cultures was avoided either by means of a plasma or fibrin clot, or by a filter membrane. The inductor used was either chicken embryo extract, or a protein fraction thereof. In all series the ectodermal cells differentiated into nerve cells, melanophores, myoblasts, and in some instances formed aggregates of notochord-like structures (Plates 6.5 to 6.8). In a number of the slides demonstrated at the Embryological Conference, definite striated muscle cells were noted, as well as pigmented elements. A definite differentiation into the neural, neurectodermal and mesodermal directions had thus occurred under the conditions briefly described in the report, and accordingly provides strong evidence in favour of inductive interaction without cellular contact. It is however still possible that the embryo extract contained cytoplasmic material which coagulated under the conditions of experiment, and the results would thus be comparable to the implantation experiments whith serum, protein pellets, etc. (e.g., Yamada, 1950b; Kuusi, 1951b; Vainio, Toivonen and Saxén, 1958).

5. *Transfer of material from inductor to ectoderm*
  As it can be seen that at least certain types of induction can be obtained through porous membranes or by liquid medium, the question arises whether there is any evidence of an actual transfer of material from the inductor tissue into the responding ectoderm. It appears that three methods are available for following this possible transfer: direct histochemical or quantitative measurements of certain factors in these two tissues, labelling the inductor tissue by radioactive tracers, and demonstration of a transfer of antigenic material during induction.

  (a) *Chemical observations.* Certain histochemical observations were what originally prompted Brachet to present his theory of the transfer of material during induction. He studied the distribution of pyronin-stained basophilic granules in amphibian embryos during early gastrulation (Brachet, 1941a, 1941b, 1943). These granules lose their stainability after treatment with ribonuclease, and it has thus been suggested that the main constituent of these particles is RNA. Brachet could demonstrate a decrease in this granulation in the dorsal lip during its invagination, and a simultaneous increase in the granules in the overlying ectoderm. The author here saw definite evidence of an actual transfer of these RNA-granules during the process of induction. The question has recently been brought to the fore by Rounds and Flickinger (1958), by the employment of more accurate quantitative methods. The RNA content was spectrophotometrically measured from different fractions of homogenized dorsal lip (chordamesoderm) and ectoderm at different stages of gastrulation. The results (figure 33) show that the decrease of the total RNA in the invaginating dorsal lip, which had already been suggested by Brachet, can be confirmed quantitatively and correlated with invagination, i.e., with the time of induction. The increase of the

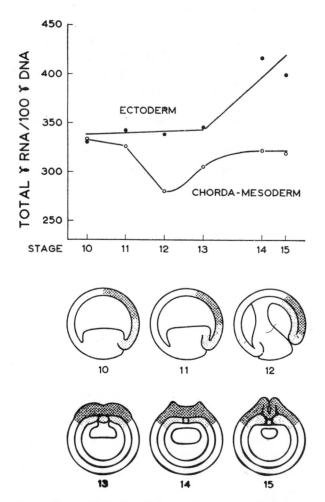

Figure 33. The total levels of ribonucleic acid per 100 gamma of
DNA for the ectoderm and the chordamesoderm during early
development of *Rana pipiens* embryos. The different stages
examined and the regions taken for RNA measurements are indicated in the figures. A definite increase in the RNA-content of the
ectoderm is noted after gastrulation. (After Rounds and Flickinger,
1958.)

ectodermal RNA, however, does not occur until later, in the early neurula stage. The main changes were observed in the residual fraction of the tissues, that is in the residue after an extraction with physiological saline and 10 per cent NaCl. When the authors compared these findings with the observations of Brachet, they deemed it possible that if an actual transfer of RNA into the ectoderm had occurred, then some of the RNA of the dorsal lip had been hydrolized and was present in the trichlor-acetic-acid soluble fraction of the ectoderm, which was discarded in the analytical procedure. However, one must conclude that an increase in the ribonucleic acid concentration of the ectoderm during its determination has not yet been confirmed, and is based only on Brachet's early data which have been criticized by some authors (Holtfreter and Hamburger, 1955).

Later, Brachet (1950b), by employing a vital stain of the inductor tissue, studied the transfer of material from the inductor. After several washings of the stained tissue he concluded that at least the major part of the remaining stain (neutral red) was attached to the cytoplasmic particles of the inductor, the soluble dye having been removed. After a brief contact between the stained inductor and competent ectoderm, stained material could be observed in the ectodermal cells, and the author believed that the microsomes were the only components of the stained material small enough to pass from cell to cell. In any case the result can hardly be considered as being a convincing demonstration of the transfer of microsomes during induction.

The hypothesis of microsomal transfer during induction and its significance to the induction process was further investigated by Brachet and his co-workers by the injection of microsomes from amphibian embryos into the ventral halves of amphibian morulae. However, the morphogenetic action of this treatment was very weak, and the few neural formations observed might have been occasioned by mechanical injuries (Brachet and Shaver, 1949; Brachet, Kuusi and Gothie, 1952; Brachet, 1960a).

Working *in vitro*, Benitetz, Murray and Chargaff (1958) added microsomes isolated from rat liver and kidney to cultures of rat fibroblasts and noted certain heteromorphic changes in these cells. The morphological picture and growth behaviour of the "induced" cells resembled those of nerve cells, but whether there was any question of reversible "modulation" or true differentiation needs further experimental data. Recently Ebert (1959b) used a mixed inoculum of microsomal fraction of heart muscle and Rous sarcoma virus, which was inoculated on the chorio-allantoic membrane of chick embryos. In 27 per cent of these experiments, striated muscle was identified in the tumour masses produced by the treatment. In control experiments either with pure virus inoculum or with pure microsomes, muscle tissue was never observed. This result and its theoretical background (see Ebert and Wilt, 1960) might prove to be of major importance, and we look forward to continued experiments at the Carnegie Institution.

(b) *Radioactive tracers.* The next approach to study of the transfer of material from inductor to the ectoderm was made by the use of inductors labelled with radioactive tracers. Ficq (1954a, 1954b) used C-14 labelled orotic acid or glycine for labelling the living organizer. She noted a definite transfer of labelled compounds to the reacting ectoderm, but simultaneously activity was found in the normal dorsal part of the embryo, and especially in the tissues which were metabolically most active. She concluded that some large-molecular substances (proteins or nucleic acids) diffuse from the organizer to the induced neural tissue. A number of similar experiments were then carried out at Waddington's laboratory (Waddington and Sirlin, 1954, 1955; Sirlin, Brahma and Waddington, 1956), and the living organizer was labelled with glycine-C^{14}. In correspondence with the results of Ficq, an incorporation of labelled material was observed in the induced structures, and especially in their nuclei. From the last mentioned fact, the authors concluded that at least a major part of the diffusion had taken place in the form of small molecules, and that no massive transfer of cytoplasmic structures had occurred. Subsequently, Waddington (1959) reported on new experiments, in which the living organizer had been replaced by an alcohol-treated, heterogenous inductor tissue (mouse kidney). In this case, the transferred labelled factors were seen to predominate in the cytoplasm of the ectodermal cells. It thus seems likely that the material had not diffused in the form of free amino-acid, but rather in large-molecular compounds. Kuusi (1959, 1960) labelled a mesodermalizing inductor, guinea-pig bone-marrow, with glycine-C^{14}, $Na_2S^{35}O_4$ and methonine-S^{35}. She confirmed the earlier findings of incorporation into the actively metabolizing tissues, but could show no specific accumulations in the induced structures. Further she demonstrated that the release of the labelled factors by the inductor was dependent on its

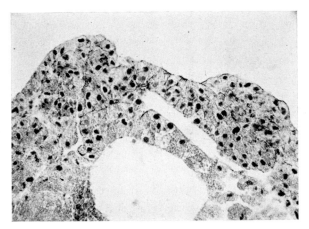

Plate 6.1. The chordamesoderm and the ectoderm of an Axolotl embryo have been separated by a porous membrane, preventing induction at the site of the membrane. On either side, neural tube-like formations have been induced. (Brahma, 1958.)

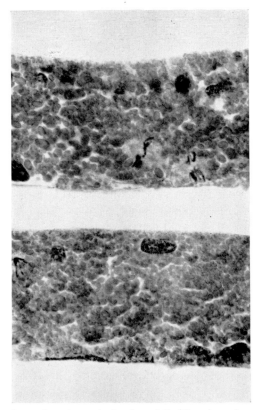

Plate 6.2. A section through the dorsal lip/filter/ectoderm-explants after 24 hours of cultivation. No visible material can be detected in the pores of the filter, and the tissue/filter-borders are sharp. (Saxén, 1961.)

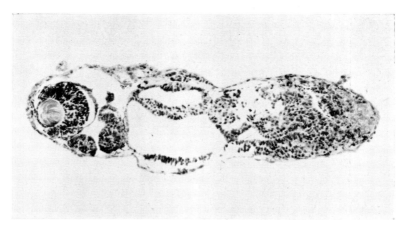

Plate 6.3. An ectodermal explant induced through a porous filter by the normal inductor tissue. Forebrain structures, an eye and a nasal placode can be seen. (Orig.)

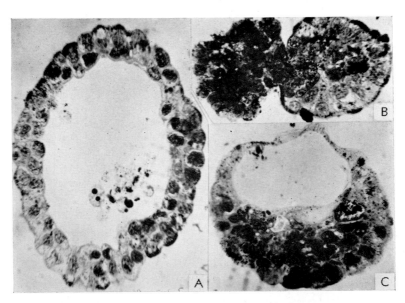

Plate 6.4. Different types of cell aggregates in cultures of ectodermal cells in "conditioned" medium. A tubule-like structure is shown in Fig. A, and neuroid aggregates in Figs. B and C. (Niu, 1955.)

location—when in good contact with ectoderm, the loss of radio-activity was rapid, but if buried in the host endoderm, the removal of the activity was slower.

Rounds and Flickinger (1958) made an extensive study of the same problem, using quantitative methods for determination of the radioactivity passing from inductor to ectoderm. They used different combinations of labelled, inductively active and inactive parts of the gastrula, with parts of a non-labelled gastrulae. The samples were cultured for 8 hours, following which medullary plate inductions were observed in experiments with an active inductor. The tissues were then separated, and from the non-labelled components, the radioactivity was counted from the fraction insoluble in trichloracetic acid (TCA) and from the nucleic acid fraction. The results (figure 34) show that there is observable a much higher transfer of activity into

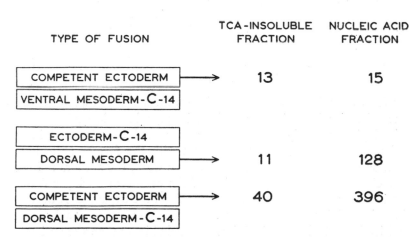

TYPE OF FUSION	TCA-INSOLUBLE FRACTION	NUCLEIC ACID FRACTION
COMPETENT ECTODERM / VENTRAL MESODERM-C-14	13	15
ECTODERM-C-14 / DORSAL MESODERM	11	128
COMPETENT ECTODERM / DORSAL MESODERM-C-14	40	396

Figure 34. Radioactivity of different tissues, originally not labelled, but fused with inductively active or inactive tissues labelled with C-14. The nucleic acid fraction and the fraction insoluble in trichloracetic acid are counted separately. The highest activity is to be seen in the nucleic acid fraction of competent ectoderm fused with inductively active, labelled dorsal mesoderm. (After Rounds and Flickinger, 1958.)

the induced ectoderm than into the non-induced one. At the same time, the calculations indicate that the nucleic acid fraction of dorsal mesoderm shows some radioactivity when cultured in contact with labelled ectoderm. The authors concluded that the results suggest

H

a passage of nucleoprotein molecules from the mesoderm into the ectoderm during induction.

To summarize the findings with radioactive tracers in induction it may be correct to state that there is strong evidence in favour of the transfer of material from inductor to the ectoderm both in the form of free amino acids, and obviously also in larger molecules.

(c) *Transfer of antigenicity*. In studying the question of the transfer of large-molecular material from one tissue to another, immunological methods seem to offer a suitable means. In their work mentioned above Rounds and Flickinger (1958) were the first to use serological techniques in the study of the problem. After 4 to 5 days of cultivation of chimaeric explants (*Rana pipiens* dorsal mesoderm × *Taricha torosa* competent ectoderm), the tissues were separated, and the salamander ectoderm tested for frog antigenicity, rabbit anti-frog gastrula serum being used. The *Taricha* ectoderm of these explants showed a 1/32 anti-*Rana* titre in contrast to the 1/8 titre of the non-treated *Taricha* gastrulae and neurulae. The authors interpreted these results as evidence of the passage of antigenic substances from the inductor to the ectoderm. They pointed out, however, that the contamination of the ectoderm of cells from the graft was not fully excluded. This was the subject of a later experimental series in which approximately 40 chimaeric explants were histologically studied, but no frog cells could be detected in the salamander ectoderm kept in contact with the former (Flickinger, Hatton and Rounds, 1959). In the same work, the authors followed the changes in the anti-frog titre of the ectoderm during a further period after removal of the frog tissue from the explants. A decrease in this activity could be observed after 2–4 days of subsequent cultivation, but the original titre was again higher than the anti-Rana activity of the control cultures, thus confirming their earlier findings. These results "tend to indicate that frog proteins are passing over into the salamander tissue" (Flickinger, Hatton and Rounds, 1959).

This study was followed by two independent reports on work in which heterogenous inductors had been used. Clayton and Romanowsky (1959) used alcohol-treated liver or bone-marrow as inductor, and tested the transfer of antigenicity into the ectoderm by means of fluorescence antisera. No massive transfer was revealed, but in two instances where the liver inductor had been in good contact with the ectoderm, a relatively strong fluorescence was observed in the cytoplasm and platelets of the ectodermal cells. Vainio, Saxén and

Toivonen (1960) also made use of alcohol treated bone-marrow of the guinea-pig as the inductor in explantation experiments. The inductor was removed after 1 or 3 hours, and the ectoderm washed, homogenized and tested for guinea-pig bone-marrow antigenicity. (Figure 35.) Here again the results suggested a transfer of antigenic, obviously large-molecular, substances. These investigations have been

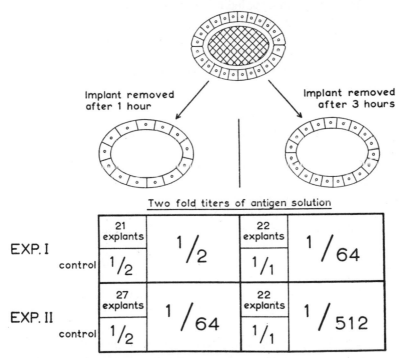

Figure 35. Transfer of antigenicity from guinea-pig bone-marrow implants to the reactive ectoderm of Triturus in explantation experiments. The antigenicity is determined by the ring precipitation test, utilizing rabbit anti-guinea-pig bone-marrow serum. In both experiments, the ectoderm which was in contact with the inductor tissues for three hours showed higher antigenic titres than the control explants (without inductor) and the explants in contact for one hour. (Vainio, Saxén and Toivonen, 1960.)

continued more recently mainly using fluorescence antisera (Vainio, Saxén and Toivonen, unpublished). When ectodermal sandwiches were opened three hours after implantation of a heterogenous inductor, and the inductor removed, fluorescent granules were observed in the ectodermal cells. Sandwiches opened after one hour did not show similar particles in the cells. Thus, here again there might be a true transfer of material, but the nature of these particles is still completely a matter for conjecture.

These three reports seem to support the concept of a transfer of large-molecular compounds from the inductor to the reacting ectoderm. Despite the morphological controls of Flickinger, Hatton and Rounds (1959) and of our own group, we do not think that a direct contamination by the inductor can be excluded. This might be possible by the employment of a combined filter-immunological technique, but at the present time we have no experience of this rather complicated method.

6. *Observations with an electron microscope*

In connection with discussion of the problem of diffusible inductive substances versus surface reaction, some observations should be made on the submicroscopical contact during induction. Eakin (1957) and Eakin and Lehmann (1957) studied the mode of contact between the chordamesoderm and overlying ectoderm in Xenopus-gastrulae. Large intercellular spaces were seen between the cells of these layers, but the cells were in contact by means of cytoplasmic bridges (Plate 6.9). In these cytoplasmic processes a separating membrane could be detected, but in some places this seemed to be broken and true anastomosis was possible. The authors came to the conclusion that apparently the macromolecular complexes of neural inductors could pass across such temporary anastomoses from the archenteric roof into the overlying competent ectoderm. Nieuwkoop (1959) and Weiss (1959) mentioned a similar picture during lens induction, and the second of these authors suggested that perhaps a "molecular bridge" is formed between the cells under these conditions. Similar interruptions of the cell membranes were recently reported by Ferris and Bagnara (1960), and the authors suggest that these "might facilitate the exchange of material between the opposed tissues and the intervening space".

However, these observations do not seem to be in complete agreement with some recent findings of Bellairs (1959) and Hunt (1961). The former studied the cellular contacts between the presumptive neural plate and the mesoderm during neural induction in the chicken. She could on each occasion demonstrate a definite intercellular matrix, 200 to 1000 Å in thickness, between the cells of the presumptive neural plate and those of the underlying chordameso-derm. Complete contact was never observable between the cell membranes, nor were any anastomoses noted. Similar observations were reported by Hunt (1961) from studies of the submicroscopical relations of cells during lens induction in the chicken. Between the cells of the optic cup and the epidermal cells of the lens anlage, an interepithelial space was always noted, with a width of the order of 1 to 3 microns. The spaces were filled with interepithelial material, and in addition to different submicroscopical structures, there were "clouds" stainable with PAS which undergo a decline after the inductive stage. From certain progressive changes in the abundance of RNP-particles in the reacting tissue components, Hunt (1961) has concluded that his study may corroborate the suggestion of McKeehan (1956) of an actual transfer of RNA during induction.

7. *Information from other inductive systems*

As has been pointed out by Waddington (1959), Weiss (1959) and many others, the various inductive systems might operate quite differently and thus no generalizations can yet be made. Nevertheless, it would be unwise not to make at least some comparison of the results of similar problems in different systems. Both here and in other connections, we shall see that in very many respects the results are similar, and might corroborate results obtained during primary induction.

As regards the importance of cellular contact in induction, the oldest data are those obtained in experiments with lens induction, and these were in fact the observations which originally led Weiss (1950) to his theory of surface reaction. He mentioned his own observations (1950) and those of McKeehan (1951) on the cellular arrangements in the lens placode. At the point of the contact between the reacting ectoderm and the optic cup, the ectodermal cells become elongated and oriented in a certain way which very much resembles the palisading of cells in early differentiation of the neural tissue. This is seen only at the point of contact, and was interpreted by Weiss as an induction at these points. This concept was further corroborated by the observations of McKeehan (1951), that the interposition of cellophane membrane between the optic cup and the ectoderm prevented induction of the lens. More recently, however, McKeehan (1958) re-opened the question by placing a thin sheet of agar jelly between the tissues, and on this occasion he noted normal differentiation of the lens, despite the separation of the cells. He concluded that the earlier negative results must have been due to factors other than lack of contact, and that his new observations did not support the theory of Weiss; they seemed to support the idea of diffusible inductive agents. A short while ago, lens-induction was studied by means of radioactive tracers by Sirlin and Brahma (1959), and these authors noted a relatively selective incorporation of labelled substances from the eye cup to the lens. From the distribution of the radioactivity (mainly its nucleus/cytoplasm ratio) the authors concluded that the transfer consists of both small molecules and more complex molecules or particles.

The most elegant demonstration of an induction without cytoplasmic contact is the well-known experimental series of Grobstein (Grobstein, 1953, 1955a, 1957, 1959a, 1959b, 1961a, 1961b; Grobstein and Dalton, 1957). Without going into details of these extensive investigations, the main results are noteworthy: 1. The normal differentiation of the tubules in mouse metanephrogenic mesenchyme is dependent on an inductive stimulus of the Wolffian duct (or some other tissues, under experimental conditions). 2. This stimulus passes a filter of an average pore size of the order of $0 \cdot 1 \mu$. 3. The stimulus operates over a certain distance, which is however limited to about 80μ. 4. No cytoplasmic material could be electron-microscopically observed in the filter. 5. Certain labelled factors cross the filter and are incorporated in the reactive mesenchyme. 6. The exact nature of these labelled substances is still unknown, but several characteristics in their transfer are similar to the transmission of the inductive effect (Plate 6.10).

As another example, we know that the ventral part of the spinal cord can *in vitro* induce cartilage from the somite cells of chick embryo, and this effect can pass a filter of an average pore size of $0 \cdot 8 \mu$ (Lash, Holtzer and Holtzer, 1957). Similar trans-filter action has been demonstrated in the development of the thymus gland (Auerbach, 1960) and as the technique is further developed, we shall certainly have other examples of trans-filter tissue interaction in the near future.

In a manner comparable to the experiments on cell-free fractions and implants in amphibian induction, some late inductions have been produced by tissue extracts or fractions. Lens has been induced by a protein extract from rabbit bone-marrow (Sasaki, Kawakami, Mifune and Tamanoi, 1957), otic mesenchyme is induced to form cartilage by an extract (Benoit, 1960) and the induction of feather germs can be produced by an extract from brain tissue (Sengel, 1961).

8. *Conclusions*

On the basis of the numerous observations presented, there are two main theories of embryonic induction to be discussed; the theory of a transfer of active substances between the tissues and the hypothesis of a surface reaction. There is a real temptation to make use of the evidence of all the different inductive systems, but—as mentioned earlier—it might not yet be time to make generalizations. Accordingly, discussion is here limited to the different results concerning primary induction only.

Many of the experimental findings just presented speak in favour of an actual transfer of substances during induction (labelled grafts and detection of a transfer of antigenicity) and suggest induction without cellular contact (culturing in conditioned medium, trans-filter experiments). Nevertheless, one should bear in mind the observation of Eakin (1957) of the obvious anastomoses between the tissues during normal development. It thus seems that some kind of compromise would be possible between the two theories, which are in fact only partially contradictory. The suggestion by Weiss of the necessity of a cellular contact does not exclude the possibility of an actual transfer of inductively active factors, and the observation that this contact is unnecessary under experimental conditions does not, on the other hand, mean that this is the case during normal development. In other words, at present it seems probable that the inductive stimulus is transmitted by diffusible agents, and to achieve the optimal conditions for this transmission, the cells should be in close contact during normal invagination of the inducing dorsal lip.

In conclusion, it must be stressed in discussion of the importance of "contact" in inductive interactions that the term is still somewhat ill-defined and very widely used. Furthermore, new techniques, electron-microscopy in particular, have perhaps changed our ideas of this term. In a narrow sense contact can be referred to as "fusion of cytoplasm" (Hunt, 1961) or "immediate juxtaposition and touching of bodies with no intervening space or other material" (Grobstein, 1961a). The other extreme would be a diffusion of inductively active molecules across a "free space", and we should like to end this chapter with a quotation from Grobstein (1961a): ". . . while these interactions can proceed over distances far too great to be spoken of as contact in the original sense, we need not and probably should not, assume the opposite extreme, i.e., that they can proceed across a "free space", one in which there is no order and molecules diffuse freely carrying specificity in intra-molecular pattern alone. Intermediate possibilities range from spatial or temporal patterns of a single molecular species through complexes of several molecular species of successively higher order, to viroid particles of sufficiently high organization to replicate or to direct syntheses".

VII

Chemistry of Inductive Agents

1. *Introduction*

As was stated in Chapter I, the demonstration of the inductive effect of killed tissues (Bautzmann, 1932) led to the assumption that this action was caused by specific chemical agents, the inductors or evocators. This marked the beginning of intense research work seeking such specific agents—work which is still in progress. This research can be divided into two different phases: from 1932 to 1938 two groups of investigators in particular were seeking a specific inductor by the employment of tissue fractions and purified chemicals as implantation material. Following a large number of contradictory and puzzling findings and hypotheses, enthusiasm died. This was a result of the discovery that the problem was much more complicated than had been originally thought, and that instead of one, small-molecular factor, it was obvious that several active agents were involved in the process of induction. The other finding which caused dismay was the demonstration of a neural differentiation of the ectoderm after toxic, and certainly not specific, treatment (see Autoneuralization). It was not until the end of the 'forties that the problem of the chemistry of the inductive agents was again raised by some teams of optimistic embryologists. This research, which was engaged in even more intensively and comprehensively than the first "biochemical Odyssey" (Herrman, 1960), was from the first concentrated on certain large-molecular factors which played a part in the inductive process. On detection of a number of inductively active heterogenous tissues, these became the main source for fractionation of the active factors, and experiments which made use of small-molecular and toxic chemicals were left to one side. As a result of this research work, a voluminous literature has come into being, and only the main results can be referred to here.

As yet, there may be no reason for discussion of whether or not this type of chemical research will solve the problem of induction, but before we examine the results, the main defects in research on these lines should be mentioned. In these chemical investigations extracts and fractions from different sources are tested for their inductive capacity, and the results relate to certain morphological changes which are usually seen 10–14 days later in the responding tissue. But what occurs between the two stages is practically unknown, and consequently only some causal relationships between the treatment and definite morphogenesis can be noted. How many of these changes are actually caused by the inductor tested, and how many result from the properties of the responding tissue and from the subsequent tissue interactions following the primary stimulus, cannot be determined. That is why so much space has been devoted to the responding tissue and the mode of action of the inductive agents, despite the scantiness of the information available on these points. It seems to us that at present the most important thing is to learn more about the mechanism and the first steps of differentiation, but there is no doubt that the results of biochemical analysis of the active factors will be of great value in this research. The fact that our main attention has to be focused on the *process of induction* and into the *reactive system*, has recently also been stressed by the pioneers of the chemical approach (Kuusi, 1957b, p. 86; Hayashi, 1959a, p. 265; Brachet, 1960a, p. 251; Yamada, 1961, p. 48).

In addition to these two phases, which differ not only in time but also in the mode of thought entailed and in theoretical background, a third, very recent and important, type of chemical research deserves note. This is concerned with the specific environmental factors controlling the development and differentiation of organ rudiments *in vitro*. These investigations were begun originally in England by Honor B. Fell in her work on organ rudiment culture. This research was subsequently continued by Miss Fell herself and her school, and in several other laboratories, mainly in France (Etienne Wolff and his school), in the United States (Grobstein, Moscona etc.) and in the Netherlands (Gaillard). However, this work and its findings are beyond the scope of this book, and only certain points concerning the small-molecular, "inductive" factors will be accorded brief discussion.

After this general presentation of the problem, there seems to be every reason to follow the recent classification of Ebert (1959b), who divides morphogenetic stimuli into three categories: 1. Nonspecific stimuli, 2. Specific small-molecular stimuli, and 3. Specific macromolecules and particles.

2. Non-specific stimuli

From 1932 to 1938, as mentioned above, an intensive search was made for a specific inductor substance or evocator. This work was mainly carried out by two teams, one in England, the other in Germany. Although most of the results of these investigations are out-of-date as regards the chemical nature of the inductive agents, they require some discussion.

Needham, Waddington and Needham (1934) started by testing the inductive capacity of different chemical fractions made from Amphibian neurulae. The most active fraction seemed to be the unsaponifiable part of the ether or petrol–ether extract, and the authors thus concluded that the active factor might be a *sterol*. These findings were later confirmed by Waddington, Needham, Nowinski, Needham and Lemberg (1935) by the employment of extracts from adult amphibian tissues. The fact that certain polycyclic hydrocarbons similar to the sterols were inductively active (Waddington and Needham, 1936, Shen, 1939, 1942) has been considered as supporting the "sterol theory" (Brachet, 1944).

Simultaneously the German group reported that the inductive action of tissues was not affected by the extraction of lipids from the tissue. In contrast to the view held by the British team, they also demonstrated that certain organic acids were inductively active (oleic acid, linolenic acid and other fatty acids, thymonucleic acid and muscle adenylic acid). On the basis of these extensive experimental data, the German group came to the conclusion that the inductive stimulus was occasioned by *acids* (Saure-Reiz). (Fischer and Wehmeyer, 1933; Fischer, 1935; Fischer, Wehmeyer, H. Lehmann, Jühling and Hultzsch, 1935; H. Lehmann, 1938).

In addition to the active chemicals reported by these two groups, a number of other chemical compounds were reported to be inductively active: the cephalin fraction (Barth, 1934), methylene blue (Waddington, Needham and Brachet, 1936), some inorganic compounds (kaolin, silicon, etc.) (Okada, 1938) and certain dyes (Beatty, de Jong and Zielinski, 1939). The first quantitative approach in the field of embryonic induction was embodied in the experiments of Shen (1939). As inducing agent, he used 1 : 2 : 5 : 6-dibenzanthracene-endo-succinate, earlier known as a carcinogen, and tested for its inductive capacity by Waddington (1938). Solutions of different concentrations of this hydrocarbon were used, and egg albumen was added to form the implantation mass. The results are shown in figure 36. Here again there seems today every reason to disagree with the author, and to conclude that the "inductive" action was in fact occasioned by a toxic, cytolysing effect. The fact that higher concentrations of the active agents used did not cause neuralization may be compared with the observation of Karasaki (1957a) that treatment leading to higher degrees of cytolysis can prevent neuralization.

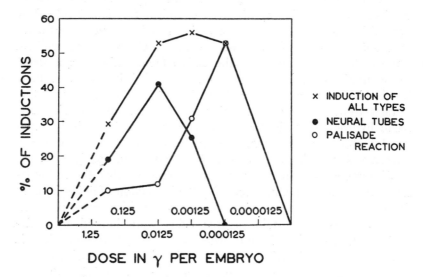

Figure 36. Relationship between the concentration of 1, 2, 5, 6-dibenzanthracene-α, β-endosuccinate concentration in implanted egg albumen and the percentage of "induced" structures obtained. (After Shen, 1939.)

After these results, it became evident that there were *too many* factors which caused differentiation of the ectoderm under experimental conditions. In 1936, Waddington, Needham and Brachet presented a theory of the action of these factors, explaining the variety of the active agents by their capacity to release the true "evocator" present in the ectoderm, ". . . it can always be held that the substance tested simply unmasked or activated the natural evocator already present in the competent tissue". The subsequent demonstration of autoneuralization (Chapter IV) proved the validity of their theory in many respects, and is in fact not very different from the hypothesis of Holtfreter (1948b) presented on page 74.

3. *Specific small-molecular stimuli*

In many respects, the work of Charles Wilde Jr. has provided us with basal facts and concepts of certain induction-like processes (Wilde, 1955a, 1955b, 1956, 1959, 1961b). Because of the importance of his findings, and of the methodological and theoretical excellence of this experimental series, the results will be presented here in some detail.

Wilde (1955b) started by developing a superior technique for culturing cells of Urodelan ectomesenchyme *in vitro*. When ecto-mesenchymal cells of young Urodelan embryos (Harrison's stage 11–14) were cultured in the presence of the correct non-mesodermal inductor tissue, very good differentiation of the normal derivatives of the neural crest was obtained. Based on the suggestion of Willmer (1951) that all cells derived from the neural crest may have a meta-bolism concerned with tyrosine, Wilde (1955a) started experiments with phenylalanine, which will normally replace tyrosine in verte-brates. His working hypothesis was: "The differentiation of neural crest derivatives, especially pigment cells and ectomesenchyme, is dependent upon a metabolic sequence localized in the presumptive region using phenylalanine or tyrosine as a key substrate. Should this metabolism be sufficiently disturbed, differentiations of these cells from the neural crest would not occur." A suitable means for such an experimental disturbance of the metabolism was provided by the structural analogues of phenylalanine acting as antimetabolites by competing with it as a substrate for specific enzyme (like sulphon-amides for para-aminobenzoeacid). Wilde used a number of such structural analogues of phenylalanine by adding them to his basal medium (a protein-free nutrient medium). His first results are summarized in figure 37. As can be seen from this original figure, three types of inhibition of the neural crest differentiation were observed in experiments with different antimetabolites: 1. General inhibition of cyto-differentiation (differentiation of somite mesoderm was also inhibited in control experiments), 2. Inhibition of the differ-entiation of ectomesenchyme (control cultures of somite mesoderm differentiated normally into striated muscle), and 3. Specific in-hibition of melanogenesis and of the differentiation of pigment cells. As the author carefully concluded, these results "appear to establish a causal relation between phenylalanine metabolism and cellular differentiation of the neural crest type."

In his next step, Wilde (1956) reverted to normal development, and enquired what was the source of the phenylalinine necessary for neural crest differentiation, and whether the reactive material could synthetize this molecule from exogenous precursors. From his earlier experiments, he knew that both phenyllactic acid and $\beta-2$ thienylalanine acted as antimetabolites and inhibitors of the neural

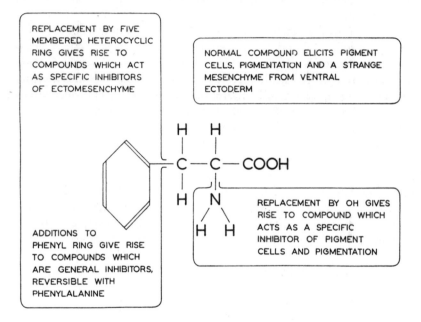

Figure 37. Structural formula of phenylalanine and the changes in its structure leading to inhibition of development and differentiation of neural crest material *in vitro*. (Wilde, 1955a.)

crest differentiation. The first was a specific inhibitor of melanogenesis, and the second inhibited the differentiation of ectomesenchyme. On the other hand, the two compounds presented below possess all the portions of the phenylalanine molecule, and if the reactive material were capable of exchanging portions of the two molecules, phenylalanine could be synthetized (figure 38).

This inhibition was presented by Wilde (1956) in the form of two equations:

1. $\dfrac{\text{neuroepithelium}}{\text{phenyllactic acic}} \rightarrow$ Inhibition of pigment cell differentiation

2. $\dfrac{\text{neuroepithelium}}{\beta\text{-2 thienylalanine}} \rightarrow$ Inhibition of ectomesenchymal differentiation

When both these antimetabolities were added to the culture medium, the following equation demonstrated the experiment:

3. $\dfrac{\text{neuroepithelium}}{\text{phenyllactic acid} + \beta\text{-2 THA}} \rightarrow$ Total inhibition of differentiation

In other words, the result indicated a summation effect of the two structural analogues of phenylalanine. Thus the responding neuroepithelium was obviously not capable of synthesizing phenylalanine from the two compounds. To test the normal inductor tissue, the archenteron roof for this capacity, the following experiment was carried out:

4. $\dfrac{\text{neuroepithelium} + \text{mesoderm}}{\text{phenyllactic acid} + \beta\text{-2 THA}} \rightarrow$ Normal differentiation

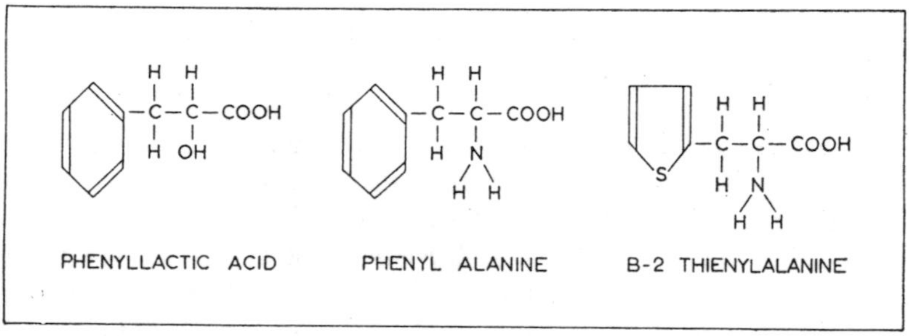

Figure 38. Structural formula of phenylalanine and of the two structural analogues used in the experiments by Wilde (1956).

It thus seems highly probable that the mesoderm of the archenteron roof present in the culture had been able to synthesize phenylalanine from the precursors, and had thus overcome the inhibition of cytodifferentiation (equations 1–3). Subsequent experiments with similar combinations of mesoderm and other inhibiting precursors gave corresponding results.

One can conclude from these experiments that the normal inductor tissue, the dorsal mesoderm, is capable of synthesizing a certain factor which is necessary for the normal development of the overlying neural crest. Furthermore, there seems good reason to think that during normal development this factor (phenylalanine) is released by the mesoderm into the microenvironment of the differentiating neural crest cells, and will thus control their differentiation. There is accordingly some justification for agreement with Wilde (1956): "The type of chemical activity expressed by archenteron roof cells and its effect upon the co-cultured neural crest cells is similar to embryonic induction."

The question was now whether there are other similar examples of the morphogenetic action of definite small-molecular factors. Naturally enough, a variety of chemical compounds have been tested during embryogenesis *in vivo* or for cytodifferentiation *in vitro*. Many of these factors have displayed inhibiting or teratogenic action either as a general effect or as a somewhat more specific action upon certain types of tissue. Deficiency of vitamins or an excess of certain vitamins leads to abnormal growth, and differentiation of tissues and similar effects have been obtained with certain hormones, antimetabolites, drugs, etc. The best example of such a morphogenetic effect is perhaps the mucous metaplasia of chick epidermis in the presence of excess vitamin-A (Fell, 1953; Fell and Mellanby, 1953; Weiss and James, 1954, 1955). The first mentioned authors cultured rudiments of chick skin in a medium enriched by vitamin-A, and noted a metaplastic change of the epithelium. In contrast to the squamous epithelium of the control cultures, a mucus-secreting and often ciliated epithelium developed. In certain respects this change seemed, however, to be reversible: when the explants were transferred to normal medium, the basal cells again formed squamous epithelium, whereas the metaplastic, cuboidal cells were not changed. To study the reversibility of these changes (true differentiation versus modulation) Weiss and James (1954, 1955) exposed dissociated cells from the skin of 7th and 8th day chick embryos to vitamin-A for a short time, and subsequently transferred the explants to normal medium. In these experiments, the reaggregated cells after a 15 min. vitamin-A treatment showed no signs of keratinization or squamous differentiation, but were morphologically more like the cuboid cells described by Fell and Mellanby (1953). The non-treated control cultures again developed into keratinizing squamous epithelium. When later a booster dose (repeated vitamin-A treatment) was given to the treated cells, these were transformed into typical cuboid, mucus-secreting cells. The authors thus concluded that

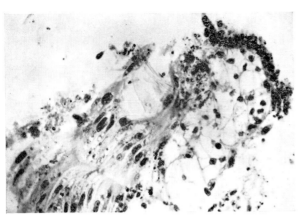

Plate 6.5. A ten-day-old flat explant cultured in a medium containing chick embryo extract. Notochord and somites have been induced from the competent ectoderm. (Courtesy: Dr. Ursula Becker.)

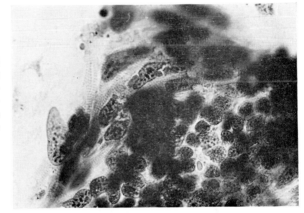

Plate. 6.6 A twelve-day-old ectodermal explant showing definite striated muscle. Inductively active protein extract has been added to the culture medium. (Courtesy Dr. Ursula Becker.)

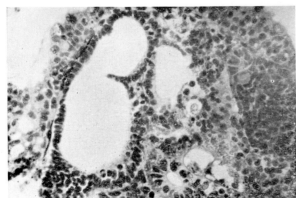

Plate 6.7. Neuroid structures in an extodermal explant cultured in the presence of a protein extract for 12 days. (Courtesy: Dr. Ursula Becker.)

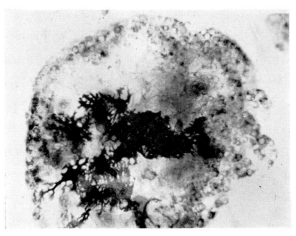

Plate 6.8. A ten-day-old living explant showing differentiation of melanopohres and xanthophores. Chick embryo extract has been added to the culture medium. (Courtesy: Dr. Ursula Becker.)

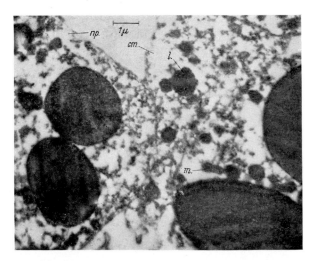

Plate 6.9. An electron micrograph showing close cellular contact between the presumptive neural plate (np) and the chordamesoderm (cm) in an amphibian embryo. (Eakin and Lehmann, 1957.)

the brief treatment with vitamin-A had switched the cellular mechanism of differentiation into an alternative pathway. The morphological change might thus be considered as determination, and the effect of vitamin-A may be compared to induction.

In both of these experimental series, the main criteria for cytodifferentiation was the morphological change in the cells. In both cases, also the production of certain chemical compounds was observed (pigment granules, or keratin versus mucous substance) and this might be considered as a demonstration of the development of a specific metabolism, which always has to be the basic change during morphogenesis, ... "the cells respond by adapting their metabolism to the substrates provided, and this defines their future biochemical and morphological differentiation" (Wilde, 1956). As an example of such a change in the metabolism induced during normal development, the extensive works of Wilt (1959) may be mentioned. He studied the conversion of the photopigments in the visual cells of amphibian larvae during metamorphosis, and demonstrated that this was done by thyroxine, which obviously acts as a tissue-specific stimulus for this process in the eye.

The two examples presented here, the role of phenylalanine in the differentiation of the neural crest, and the effect of vitamin-A upon the differentiation of the epidermis, show that at least in some cases small-molecular factors of the environment of a developing tissue can control their differentiation. The mechanism of this process is not yet fully elucidated, and its relation to normal embryonic induction is still obscure. The importance of these observations is, however, indisputable, and as will be seen from the following part of this chapter, understanding of the mechanism of neural and mesodermal inductions is far from the stage achieved by Wilde in his experiments relating to determination of neural crest.

4. Specific macromolecules

(a) *Introduction.* The experiments of Fischer, Wehmeyer, H. Lehmann, Jühling and Hultzsch (1935), as well as those of H. Lehmann (1938), focused attention on the large molecular factors involved in the primary induction. Lehmann (*op. cit.*) observed that both nucleoproteins and nucleic acids were inductively active, but when the "nucleotide" fraction was purified and the proteins removed, the activity of the preparations was lost. Subsequently, Barth (1939a) and Barth and Graff (1943) obtained strong inductions

I

with protein samples from different tissues (calf brain, amphibian gastrulae, etc.), and the nucleoprotein fraction seemed to be the most active.

The role of RNA in primary induction was now taken up by Jean Brachet in particular. After Dalcq (1941) and Needham (1942) had presented their "infective" theory of induction (see page 91), Brachet formulated his working hypothesis by suggesting that the "infective" particles were in fact RNA-rich microsomes. Several experimental results seemed to corroborate this hypothesis of the importance of RNA in the induction process (Brachet, 1940, 1941a, 1941b, 1942, 1943, 1944). Histochemical observations during normal gastrulation suggested a transfer of RNA from the invaginating dorsal lip into the reacting ectoderm (see page 99), implants treated with ribonuclease lost their inductive effect, and the inductive capacity of different ribonucleoprotein samples was apparently proportional to their RNA content. There was thus strong evidence in favour of the importance of RNA in induction, but more recent experiments have provided some contradictory results. The treatment of preparations of the inductor tissue with ribonuclease has on many occasions proved ineffective; these results will be dealt in more detail subsequently. Brachet himself (1959, 1960a) pointed out that his war-time results with ribonuclease might be explained as being due to a contamination by proteolytic enzymes of the ribonuclease preparation then available. As regards other evidence, for example the relation between the RNA content of an inductor and its inductive effect, little work has been done. Kuusi (1951b) could not demonstrate such a relation between the RNA-content of inductors and their inductive capacity. When testing the inductive action of normal and regenerating liver, we could observe no significant differences in their inductive capacity, despite a definite increase in RNA-content during regeneration (Saxén and Toivonen, 1958). This was also true when HeLa-cells, from different cultures and with very different amounts of RNA, were tested (Saukkonen, Toivonen, Saxén and Vainio, unpublished).

Before we further embark on discussion of the chemical nature of the inductive agent, there seems to be every reason to discard the use of the singular in connection with the active compounds involved in the primary induction. This problem will be dealt in more detail in Chapter X, but already the extensive experiments of Chuang (1939) and Toivonen (1938b, 1940), which demonstrate the tissue specificity of the inductive action of heterogenous tissues, strongly suggest the existence of at least two types of active agent. Results corroborating this idea were further obtained by comparing the effects of implanting tissues in fresh condition with those obtained after heat treatment. Following heat treatment the spinocaudal induction type could not be observed (Chuang, 1939, 1940). The main tissues used in these experiments were the liver and kidney, and the same sources were used in later fractionations and experiments dealing with the chemical nature of inductive agents. The main work in this field has been carried out in Nagoya (Yamada *et al.*), in Heiligenberg (Tiedemann *et al.*), in Cologne (Engländer *et al.*), in the Rockefeller institute (Niu) and in our laboratory (Toivonen, Kuusi *et al.*). The Japanese group in particular has provided very important information during the last five years.

(b) *First fractionation experiments.* The first approach to separation of the different inductive agents was made by Toivonen and Kuusi (Toivonen and Kuusi, 1948, Toivonen, 1949a, 1949b, 1950, Kuusi, 1951a, 1951b). Starting from the two heterogenous tissues mentioned above, different fractions were obtained, and these yielded different regional inductive effects (figure 39). Guinea-pig liver tissue was known to be an almost pure inducer of archencephalic structures after alcohol treatment, and this action proved to be stable during heating at 70–90°. Extraction with petroleum–ether, as well as dialysis, removed this agent from the inductor tissue, whereas the fatty acid fraction of the extraction showed an archencephalic action. In contrast to certain earlier observations mentioned in connection with unspecific factors, the sterol fraction was not active as an inductor. The non-dialysable part of the tissue showed a weak tail-inducing capacity. When kidney of the same animal was used as starting-point, this tissue being known as an inducer of spinocaudal structures, this activity was lost after heat treatment, but instead in some cases the tissue induced archencephalic structures. Extraction with petroleum–ether affected the inducing capacity of the kidney to a certain extent. Hindbrain structures were not observed after extraction, and the spinal cords in the induced tails were smaller. Consequently the mesodermal structures, especially the somites, were more frequent and larger.

These results were interpreted as corroborating the concept of two chemically distinct inductive agents or groups of agents: the archencephalic inductor was thermostable, soluble in petroleum–

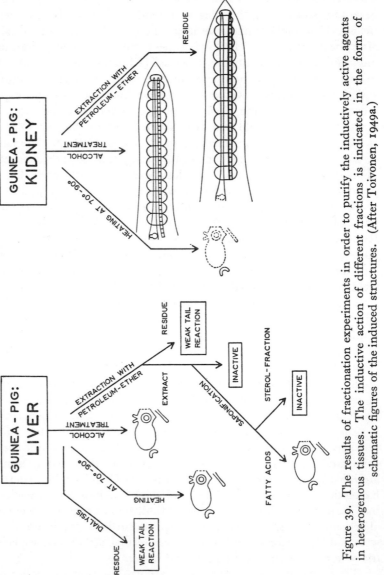

Figure 39. The results of fractionation experiments in order to purify the inductively active agents in heterogenous tissues. The inductive action of different fractions is indicated in the form of schematic figures of the induced structures. (After Toivonen, 1949a.)

ether and dialysable, whereas the spinocaudaudal agent was insoluble in organic solvents, thermolabile and non-dialysable.

The separation and characterization of these agents was continued by Kuusi in extensive series (Kuusi, 1951a, 1951b, 1953). In addition to the testing of nuclear fractions, RNA-samples etc., she used fractionating centrifugation of the tissue homogenates. Her main results may be summarized as follows: Liver tissue contains soluble agents responsible for archencephalic inductive action, and a weak inductive capacity was also demonstrated in the granular fractions. This was mainly of a deuterencephalic-spinocaudal type. The kidney tissue, after removal of the granular fraction, showed definite spino-caudal activity, but here also the other fractions were not fully inactive. It appears that the archencephalic activity is associated with the soluble fractions and large-granular fractions, whereas the spino-caudal inductive action was most definite in the small-granular fractions.

In addition to these fractionation experiments, Toivonen and Kuusi (1948) and Kuusi (1951a, 1951b) were the first to use enzyme treatments for separating the two agents (the original experiments with ribonuclease of Brachet (1942) have already been mentioned). Toivonen and Kuusi (*op. cit.*) used trypsin and pepsin treatment, and could achieve an almost complete disappearance of the spino-caudal induction. Kuusi (1951a, 1951b) presented some contradictory results concerning the importance of RNA in the induction process. Ribonuclease treatment did not seem to affect either the spinocaudal inductive action of kidney tissue nor the archencephalic action of the liver. However, these series were small and not quite conclusive, but the following year saw their confirmation by Brachet, Kuusi and Gothie (1952) and by Kuusi (1953), who used tobacco mosaic virus after an almost complete extraction of RNA with perchloric acid. The results of Kuusi (1951b) led her to the conclusion that there are chemically distinct factors responsible for archencephalic and spinocaudal inductions. The former might be connected to the RNA-rich granular fractions, and the latter is obviously a protein.

After these observations, there seemed to be enough evidence for at least two chemically distinct inductive agents with different inducing capacities. The original idea of an archencephalic and a spino-caudal agent seemed, however, no longer to be valid, and according to our concept and terminology, the two agents are responsible for neural and mesodermal inductions respectively. Thus in what follows the terms "neuralizing principle" and "meso-dermalizing principle" will be used. It has to be stressed, however, that we are still dealing with suggestions and hypotheses, and the presence of a third regional inductive system, the deuterencaphalic inductor (Tiedemann, 1959a, 1959b) cannot be excluded. In addition, there is no evidence that there is only one active agent in these systems, and there might be a variety of chemically dissimilar agents yielding the same inductive effect. This is especially true when working with heterogenous inductors. Furthermore, there is the possibility of these agents being changed into one another during chemical or physical treatment, as suggested by Yamada (1958a, 1958b, 1959). However, the information available on these two active principles will be discussed separately.

(c) *The neuralizing principle.* In all the investigations made during the 'thirties dealing with the chemical characterization of the inductor or evocator, attention was focused on the neuralizing capacity of the fractions and tissues used. This was also the case with the earlier works of Brachet (1942, 1944). It has already been stated that his original concept of the role of RNA in the neuralizing process may not be valid, in view of the repeated experiments made with ribonuclease, where this was demonstrated as exerting no effect on the neuralizing capacity (Kuusi, 1951a, 1951b; Brachet, Kuusi and Gothie, 1952; Kuusi, 1953; Engländer, Johnen and Vahs, 1953; Yamada and Takata, 1955b; Hayashi, 1955, 1956, 1959a; Vahs, 1957; Engländer and Johnen, 1957). The most conclusive of these experiments appears to be the recent one by Hayashi (1959a). He started with a purified ribonucleoprotein sample from liver tissue, and treated it with ribonuclease. The results are demonstrated in figure 40. According to his estimations the ribonuclease treatment removed more than 99 per cent of the original RNA, and it seemed very unlikely that the small amount of RNA remaining in the sample could have been responsible for the inductive capacity, which did not differ from the activity of the original sample. There thus seems to be a weight of evidence to demonstrate that the RNA-part of the ribonucleoprotein is not indispensable to its neuralizing capacity. In this connection, it may be worthy of note that all these results are obtained with *heterogenous* inductors, and they might thus not be directly applicable to the *normal organizer*.

Somewhat contradictory results have been reported by Niu

(1953, 1955, 1956, 1958a, 1958b, 1960) whose work, employing a new and elegant method, will be described in more detail. The method, originally developed by Niu and Twitty (1953), has already been referred to (page 96): presumptive ectoderm of different urodele species was cultured in a modified Holtfreter solution, with no proteins or amino acids. In order to preclude the curling of the ectoderm, and to expose the uncoated inner surface of the cells to the medium, very small pieces containing only 15–20 ectodermal cells were cut out and grafted in hanging drops. In the first experiments, normal dorsal lip tissue was used as the source of the inducing agent, together with the posterior portion of the medullary plate and notochord from older embryos. When a large piece of these

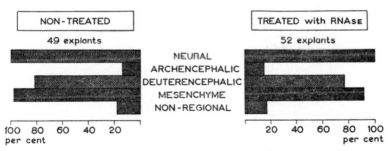

Figure 40. The inductive action of a purified liver nucleoprotein sample (left), and of the same sample after treatment with ribonuclease removing more than 99 per cent of the RNA. (After Hayashi, 1959a.)

inductor tissues and a tiny piece of ectoderm were cultured simultaneously, in a hanging drop, a high proportion of differentiation of the ectodermal cells was observed, amounting to 90 per cent in the best series. In addition to pigment cells, nerve fibres and myoblasts were noted, whereas differentiation of control explants in the absence of inductor tissue was very rare and probably due to cytolysis of some of their cells. In subsequent experiments, the presence of the active factor in solution was demonstrated by culturing the explants in "conditioned" medium: after 10 days' cultivation of the inductor tissue, this was removed and replaced by pieces of competent ectoderm. After a minimum of 24 hours' exposure to this medium, differentiation of the explant was noted. In older cultures, reared in the same medium for 12–16 days, differentiation of up to 60–70 per cent of the explants was noted, and the differentiated cell types were again the same; pigment cells, nerve cells and myoblasts. Niu (1955, 1956) now began to analyse the "conditioned" medium by different methods: 20–30 pieces of inductor tissue were cultured in depression slides, and the conditioned salt solution was collected at intervals of 7–10 days and analysed. The absorption spectra of one such series are shown in figure 41. Niu (1955, 1956) pointed out that the inductor substance, in his explantation experiments, may have been released during the first 7–16 days of cultivation, and

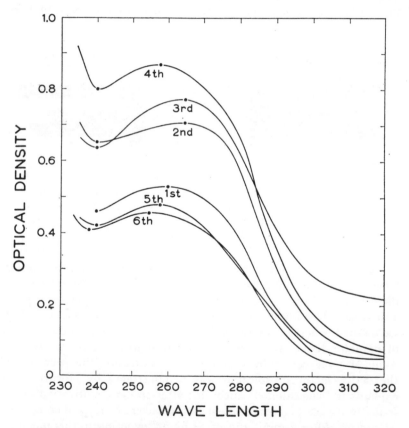

Figure 41. UV absorption spectra of the culture media "conditioned" by *A. tigrinum* dorsal lip. Medium from the first to sixth batches collected at 7–10 day intervals. (After Niu, 1956.)

was accordingly present in the medium of the first and second collections. The behaviour of the ectodermal explants was somewhat different in younger cultures (corresponding to the first collection), and in older cultures corresponding to the second collection of analyzed medium. The difference in the absorption maxima between these two media (258 mμ, 265 mμ) might have been due to the presence of two of more different inductor substances. Furthermore, the absorption spectra suggest the presence of *nucleoproteins*. The fact that the active agents were nondialysable, and that both RNA and proteins were present in the solution (colour test) corroborated the suggestion that nucleoproteins constituted the active factor. However, the results obtained with ribonuclease and chymotrypsin did not yield quite conclusive data. The former "greatly reduced" the inductive activity of the medium conditioned in experiments with *Taricha torosa*, and when ribonuclease and desoxyribonuclease were added simultaneously, the induction was totally inhibited. The same combination of enzymes, however, was used in experiments with *Triturus rivularis*, and the inductive action did not vanish. Furthermore, chymotrypsin had no effect in the experiments with *T. torosa*, but in *T. rivularis*-explants it completely prevented induction. These results could not be interpreted, but Niu (1956) stated that the effect of these enzymes on the reacting cells themselves could not be excluded in these experiments.

Later, Niu (1958a, 1958b) used samples of RNA prepared from various adult tissues, and tested their activity under similar experimental conditions. If RNA-samples from calf kidney or thymus were employed, differentiation of the ectodermal cells was observed; as a most interesting point, Niu mentioned that the type of differentiation varied in the different experimental series. It is possible that there is a certain resemblance between the normal structure of the inductor source and the differentiation observed (e.g. kidney—tubule-like structures, thymus—thymus-like bodies). It has to be added, however, that the differentiations were generally poor, and much work is still needed to prove this type of "organ specificity" of the RNA. In the experiments with thymus RNA, the cells were nerve-like or pigmented, and in addition formed mesenchyme in about 70 per cent of the cases; when subsequently implanted into older hosts, "thymus-like" bodies were developed. The experiments were continued by testing the changes in the inductive capacity after enzyme treatments. It proved that trypsin prevented the induction completely, but when estimating the activity of the trypsin it was noted that only 26 to 59 per cent of the protein was removed from the sample. The complete inactivation was thus difficult to explain. Because the effect of trypsin on ectodermal cells is well known (dissociation), Niu (1956) suggested that the prevention of induction was caused by a direct effect on the responding system. The concept was corroborated by retention of normal inductive action after the addition of an equimolar concentration of soya bean inhibitor (which alone is not active as inductor). Treatment with ribonuclease greatly reduced the inductive action of the samples (Niu, 1958b, 1960), but this result is contradictory to most recent findings concerned with the effect of ribonuclease on inductive capacity. However, on the basis of his extensive experiments, Niu (1958b) concluded that there is a correlation, and that the protein compound might be only "a stabilizer, a carrier or an agent to facilitate the entrance of RNA into the cells." Yamada (1961) has recently repeated these experiments on the inductive action of the thymus-RNA. The results were, however, negative in all series.

It is not yet possible to explain these apparently contradictory findings. Without casting any doubt on the importance of the new method of Niu (*op. cit.*) and of his results, we are inclined to consider the results of the Japanese authors (see below) as being more conclusive. The differentiation of the very small pieces of ectoderm in the cultures of Niu does not seem to be very good; this might be explained by their being too small (see Wilde, 1961a). As long as there is no definite organ rudiment formation, or no specific histochemical features in cells *in vitro*, it is apparently difficult to distinguish between true differentiation and "modulation" (Weiss, 1947). As the case most familiar to us, we may mention certain "modulations" in cultures of continuous cell lines. When HeLa-cell or cells from continuous amniotic line are transferred from a culture medium containing fresh, untreated serum, to a medium containing heated serum or amino acids only, their shape is definitely changed from being epithelial-like to fibroblast-like, and they then often possess long, axon-like outgrowths. After return to the original culture medium, this form often maintained throughout a prolonged cultivation of several months, will change back to the original epithelial-like shape. At the same time, there are definite changes in growth behaviour of the cells. (E. Saxén and Penttinen, 1956, 1961 ; Penttinen, E. Saxén, L. Saxén, Toivonen and Vainio, 1958;

Toivonen, Saxén and Vainio, 1960). There are other similar, well-known cases of reversible modulations due to non-specific environmental conditions of cells *in vitro*, and some changes observed by Niu might belong to this category. Without doubt, the method of Niu and Twitty (1953) is most elegant, but the results are difficult to interpret, as pointed out by Tiedemann (1959b), who was not very successful in an attempt to repeat the experiments. On the other hand, analysis of the medium conditioned by normal inductor tissue may yet prove of great importance, and it is still one of the very few attempts to arrive at chemical characterization of the active factor in *normal inductor tissue*.

The most successful investigators concerned with the fractionation and purification of the neuralizing agent have been the Japanese workers at Nagoya. Their results have recently been presented in more extensive form (Yamada, 1958a, 1958b, 1961), but a short review of the main results should be given here.

In their early work ribonucleoprotein was isolated from the heterogenous inductors used by Toivonen (1940), i.e. liver and kidney tissues of adult guinea-pigs (Yamada, Takata and Osawa, 1954; Yamada and Takata, 1956; Hayashi, 1956). The ribonucleoprotein was precipitated by streptomycin sulphate from a 0·14 saline extract of the homogenized tissues, dialyzed, washed and finally precipitated with cold ethanol. Its inductive capacity was tested in explantation ("sandwich") experiments using *Triturus pyrrhogaster* gastrula ectoderm. The results of these experiments are summarized in figure 42. As Yamada (1958b) pointed out, the most interesting observation might be that ribonucleoprotein samples isolated from two different tissues by identical techniques yielded distinct inductive actions, which corresponded to the original "tissue specific" effect of these tissues (here the similar results of Niu (1958a) and Kawakami and Yamana (1959) need to be remembered) (Plates 7.1–7.3). It has further to be noted that in addition to the definite inductive capacity of these fractions, also the non-nucleoprotein fraction was inductively active in both series. This fact is of importance in later discussion of the "specificity" of the neuralizing principle. The same "overall" nature of the archencephalic, and in part as regards the other regional inductors had already been observed in the fractionating experiments of Kuusi (1951a).

The ribonucleoproteins obtained by streptomycin sulphate-precipitation were further purified by ultracentrifugation, using forces from 100,000 × g up to 170,000 × g for one hour. The supernatant and the sediment were tested separately for their inductive action (Hayashi and Takata, 1958; Yamada, Hayashi and Takata, 1958). The results are shown in Table 2.

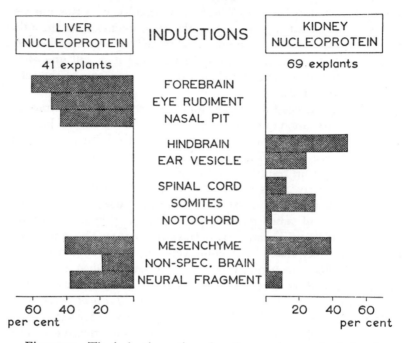

Figure 42. The inductive action of nucleoprotein samples isolated from guinea-pig kidney and liver tissues. (After Yamada, Takata and Osawa, 1954; Yamada and Takata, 1956; Hayashi, 1956.)

It is clear from these results that all the fractions proved to be neuralizing, yielding both archencephalic and deuterencephalic inductions. However, it appears that the archencephalic activity is mainly in the sediment, and weaker in the non-sedimenting sub-fractions representing the bulk of the ribonucleoprotein. It is interesting to note that inductive activity could not be "purified" by this treatment, and that all fractions showed both archencephalic and deuterencephalic effects. The fact that the archencephalic inductive actions are not correlated to the amount of RNA in the preparation is demonstrated in the liver series; a decrease of the

	Ribonucleoprotein fractions obtained by ultracentrifugation ($100 \cdot 000 \times g$, 1 hr)			
	KIDNEY		LIVER	
	Super-natant	*Sedi-ment*	*Super-natant*	*Sedi-ment*
RNA-P μg/mg. protein-N	358·7	124·6	92·7	10·2
Induction percentage	99	99	100	94
Archencephalic inductions	11	28	34	55
Deuterencephalic inductions	66	83	71	9
Spinocaudal inductions	29	18	—	—

TABLE 2. Inductive actions of ribonucleoprotein fractions further purified by ultracentrifugation. (After Yamada, Hayashi and Takata, 1958; Hayashi and Takata, 1958.)

RNA to one-tenth did not affect the archencephalic activity; on the contrary it appeared to increase.

The Japanese author now continued with comprehensive investigations in which the effect of enzyme treatment on these preparations was tested. The experiments with ribonuclease have already been mentioned (Hayashi, 1959b). In confirmation of the earlier results of Toivonen and Kuusi (1948), Hayashi (1958) obtained a progressive inactivation of the inductive effect of liver ribonucleoprotein sample after prolonged treatment with pepsin at pH 4 (figure 43). The same ribonucleoprotein preparation was also treated with trypsin, different times of treatment being employed. A complete disappearance of both deuterencephalic and archencephalic inductive action was noted after 120 min. (figure 44).

Finally, the works of the Heiligenberg-team have to be presented. Before discussion of their results, it must be stressed that this group seems to have some ideas regarding deuterencephalic inductions which differ from ours. In contrast to our neuralizing and meso-dermalizing agents, they prefer to speak of archencephalic, deuter-encephalic and spinocaudal agents in addition to a mesoderm inductor (Tiedemann, 1959b; Tiedemann, Tiedemann and Kessel-ring, 1960). Whether or not specific deuterencephalic and spino-caudal inductors exist, cannot yet be decided, but according to our hypothesis, deuterencephalic formations are developed as a result of an initial stimulus by both neuralizing and mesodermalizing agents, and this is also true in the formation of spinal cord. How this

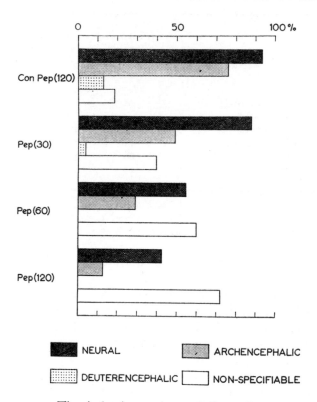

Figure 43. The inductive actions of liver ribonucleoprotein samples treated with pepsin at pH 4 for different periods of time (30, 60 and 120 min.). In the control samples (ConPep), an aliquot of the nucleoprotein solution was adjusted to pH 4 and incubated for 120 min. at the same temperature as the pepsin-treated samples. (After Hayashi, 1958.)

can be reconciled with the results of Tiedemann and his group is discussed below.

In the main, the German team used 9-day chick embryos as the source material for their experiments (von Woellwarth, 1956b; Tiedemann, 1959a, 1959b; Tiedemann and Tiedemann, 1957, 1959b; Tiedemann, Tiedemann and Kesselring, 1960). By extraction with pyrophosphate buffer or by $Ca(OH)_2$, and subsequent acidification of the extract, a sample was obtained from the nuclear fraction which induced almost purely deuterencephalic structures, sometimes accompanied by trunk and tail inductions. A similar active factor was obtained by extraction with 1 M NaCl at pH 7·2. After further purification of this fraction, the authors concluded that the factor was obviously not bound to the DNA of the nuclei, but probably to ribonucleoproteins or nuclear proteins (Tiedemann, 1959a, 1959b). The deuterencephalic inductive capacity of these preparations was definitely reduced by trypsin treatment but not

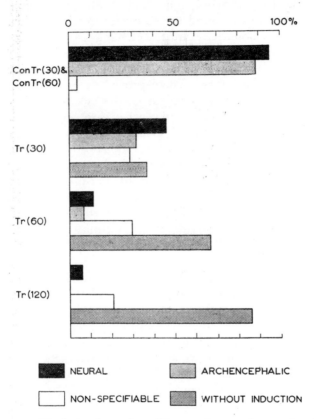

Figure 44. The inductive action of liver nucleoprotein samples after treatment with trypsin for 30, 60 and 120 min. Controls as in Figure 43. (Hayashi, 1958.)

completely abolished. (Tiedemann, Tiedemann and Kesselring, 1960). In these experiments, the trypsin was inactivated by soya bean inhibitor before the sample was implanted and thus a direct effect of the enzyme on the responding cells was excluded.

Archencephalic activity was obtained in the same fractions, *but not until the sample had been briefly heated at* 100°, which was explained as possibly being the consequence of an inactivation of an inhibitor of archencephalic inductor. Chemically, it has not yet been possible to separate the archencephalic and deuterencephalic agents (Tiedemann, 1959b).

Because the archencephalic and deuterencephalic inductive agents seemed to be bound to the nucleoprotein fraction, and not inactivated by ribonuclease treatment but with protolytic enzymes, there again seemed to be definite evidence for the importance of the protein part. This was further tested by using purified RNA-preparations as inductors. These proved to be very weak neural inductors, and their activity might be due not to the RNA but to the small amount (up to 1 per cent) of protein remaining in the preparations (Tiedemann and Tiedemann, 1957). The results thus corroborate the earlier similar observations of Yamada and Takata (1955a) and are in close agreement with the experimental results of Niu (1958b), in which the addition of non-inducing protein to a RNA-preparation definitely increased its inductive effect. The conclusiveness of experiments with purified samples of RNA is diminished, however, by the many technical difficulties which arise when working with this water-soluble and very labile molecule.

The role of the protein component was further investigated by blocking some groups of the protein molecules. The archencephalic factor seemed to be resistant to treatment with thioglycolic acid, which inactivates the mesodermalizing agent (Tiedemann and Tiedemann, 1956, 1957). It is interesting to note that after treatment of deuterencephalic-mesodermalizing fraction, its action was changed into an archencephalic-deuterencephalic inductive effect. The change is very similar to that observed by Kuusi (1953) after treatment of deuterencephalic-spinocaudal-inducing kidney tissue with formol.

(1) *Discussion.* In trying to draw some conclusion from the substantial amount of experimental data and information just presented, certain main questions need consideration. The first, and most important question might be the justification of the whole problem, in other words are there specific chemical factors responsible for a neural differentiation of the undifferentiated ectoderm? This question has in fact been treated already in connection with autoneuralization or

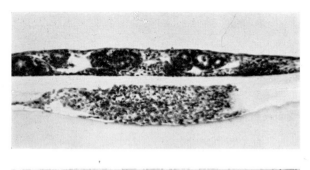

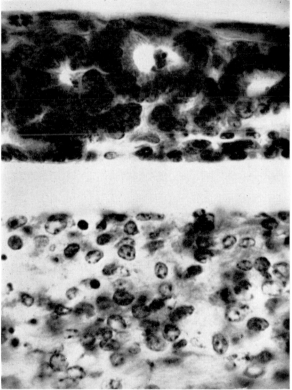

Plate 6.10. A microscopical view of trans-filter induction of mouse metanephrogenic mesenchyme. A definite induction of tubules is obtained through a porous membrane, spinal cord tissue being the inductor. Both pictures are from the same culture, fixed after four days of cultivation (metanephrogenic mesenchyme above, spinal cord below). (Courtesy: Dr. Clifford Grobstein.)

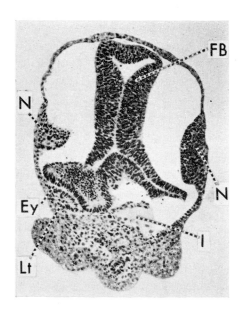

Plate 7.1. An archencephalic induction obtained by liver nucleoprotein sample (forebrain (FB), eye-rudiment (Ey), lentoid (Lt), nose (N), and the implant (I).) (Hayashi, 1959b.)

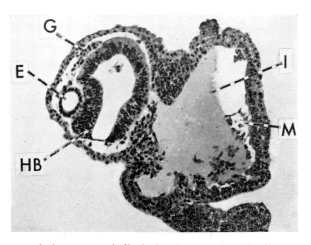

Plate 7.2. A deuterencephalic induction obtained by liver nucleoprotein sample. (Hindbrain (HB), ear vesicle (E), ganglion-like formation, mesenchyme (M), and the implant (I).) (Hayashi, 1959a.)

differentiation without an inductor. As was seen, neuralization can be stimulated by non-physiological treatment damaging the responding cells, which obviously contain all the agents necessary for neuralization. Some of the results presented in this chapter might be relevant to this "unspecific" category, e.g. the induction by fatty acid fraction (Toivonen and Kuusi, 1948). On the other hand, most of the recent experiments with adequate controls, and often ultra-purified fractions, might not be deemed unspecific. Furthermore, the inactivation by proteolytic enzymes is an indication that large molecules are involved in the process, and these are unlikely to be wholly non-specific.

On turning to the neuralizing activity of tissues and fractions, the next question must be: are there several chemically distinct agents yielding similar inductive actions, and, secondly, is the regionality of the central nervous system caused by several different agents with different inductive effect (e.g., deuterencephalic inductor, spinal cord inductor, etc.)? As regards the first part of the question, no answer can yet be given. However, in view of the great variety of tissues, fractions and preparations yielding the same inductive effect under experimental conditions, it seems most improbable that there could be only one specific, obviously large-molecular agent responsible for this action. This, again, is related to the old question of the significance of such experiments, because there is hardly any evidence that we are here dealing with the same agents involved in normal neural induction during gastrulation. This problem is discussed at the end of this chapter.

As for the second part of the question, the existence of several neuralizing inductors with different regional inductive effect, we would refer to the preceding chapter in which the different theories are discussed. In this connection we will look only at the evidence of the existence of agents such as are obtained in the chemical fractionation of the inductor tissues. As already mentioned, Tiedemann (1959a, 1959b) seems to be the main defender of a "deuterencephalic" inductor. According to the two-gradient theory (page 174), the hindbrain is formed as a result of a simultaneous action of neuralizing and mesodermalizing principles (Lehmann, 1950; Yamada, 1950b; Toivonen and Saxén, 1955a, 1959b; Saxén and Toivonen, 1961), and most chemical embryologists today seem to agree with the theory of two main principles (Brachet, 1960a; Kuusi, 1961; Yamada, 1961). As his main chemical evidence for the deuterencephalic agent,

K

Tiedemann (1959a, 1959b) reported findings on treatment with thio-glycolic-acid. This chemical, as stated above, inactivates the meso-dermalizing principle, but not the deuterencephalic. After such treatment of a mesodermal-deuterencephalic inducing fraction, its inductive effect was changed, so as to give in addition to deuterence-phalic structures definite archencephalic formations in 44 per cent, which means that the mesodermal-deuterencephalic inductor was changed to archencephalic-deuterencephalic inductor. According to our hypothesis, this change can be produced by inactivating most of the mesodermal principle thus causing a shift in the neuralizing/meso-dermalizing ratio. As we have recently demonstrated, a very small amount of mesodermalizing agent is sufficient to produce deuterence-phalic induction in the presence of the "archencephalic" or neuraliz-ing principle. Thus, the results of Tiedemann and Tiedemann (1956, 1957) just referred to, can be explained as being the consequence of very small amounts of active mesodermalizing agents remaining in the sample after thioglycolic-acid treatment. In fact, there is men-tion in this same paper by Tiedemann (1959b) of findings which cor-roborate our theory. After stating that archencephalic and deuter-encephalic activity are both found in the same fractions, he went on to say that the archencephalic activity could be demonstrated "aber erst nach kurzem Erhitzen unserer Fraktionen auf 100° oder Behand-lung mit thioglykolsaurem Natrium." In our terms the mesodermal component was inactivated from the "deuterencephalic inductor" and its neuralizing component then acted alone. As far as we can establish, accordingly, there does not seem to be enough chemical evidence for the existence of a specific hindbrain inductor. However, its existence cannot be excluded with certainty, and will be touched upon later in the light of some other experiments.

Finally, compilation of the data on the chemical nature of the neuralizing factor is necessary. The long chain of experiments which started from the observations of H. Lehmann (1938), to the recent, extensive and conclusive series of Hayashi (1958, 1959a), seems to indicate that neuralizing activity is found in ribonucleoproteins. The question then arises whether it is the protein or the nucleic acid com-ponent which is responsible for the inductive potentiality of these preparations. The fact that ribonuclease treatment seems to be with-out effect, at least in the majority of experiments (see Hayashi, 1959a), together with the repeated observations that neuralizing capacity can be inactivated by proteolytic enzymes (see Hayashi,

1958) seems to indicate that certain *neuralizing inductive capacity is bound to the protein part of the ribonucleoproteins*. Much work is, however, needed before we can say more of the chemistry of neural differentiation.

Even more obscure is the "overall" nature of the neuralizing principle. All the fractionation experiments have shown that despite the definite inductive action of the nucleoprotein fraction, there always remain certain inductive properties in the other fractions as well. Whether this means that we are still dealing with "unspecific" stimuli, or with a general contamination by the neuralizing factors, remains an open question. The most probable explanation at this stage is that there is a great number of components which possess certain active radicals leading to neural differentiation under experimental conditions.

(d) *The mesodermalizing principle.* The first suggestion of a specific factor responsible for the induction of mesodermal structures was made by Chuang (1939, 1940) and Toivonen (1940). Later, Toivonen (1953a, 1953b) demonstrated that this effect could be obtained in an almost pure form when the bone-marrow of adult guinea-pig was used as an inductor.

From the beginning the information concerning the chemical nature of this agent (or these agents) was more uniform and less confusing than that related to the neuralizing principle. The main reason for this may have been that unspecific mesodermalization or "automesodermalization" of the reactive material was not achieved, and consequently "inductions" produced by toxic or non-physiological treatments did not confuse investigators. Furthermore, the protein nature of the mesodermalizing principle seems to have been quite evident from the very beginning of the search for this factor.

As in the discussion in the neuralizing factor, the terminology and ideas of the mesodermalizing principle are not uniform. As pointed out on a number of occasions above, and as will be discussd in more detail in the concluding chapter, the existence of deuter-encephalic and spinocaudal inductors is not proved, and in our view these regional inductions are caused by a simultaneous action of neuralizing and mesodermalizing principles. The practical difficulty which stems from this is that we can never be sure exactly what we are looking for when deuterencephalic or spinocaudal inductions are obtained as a result of the inductive action of certain fractions or samples. Is there a combination of agents with different inductive actions, or a specific inductor for this particular region. Fortunately, most of the teams working on the mesodermal inductor are today getting almost pure mesodermal reactions, and consequently the term "mesodermal inductor" is widely used (Tiedemann, 1959b; Brachet, 1960a, Yamada, 1961; Kuusi, 1961).

(1) *Inactivation of the mesodermalizing principle.* Before giving an account of recent work done in the purification of the meso-dermalizing factor, the numerous ways of inactivating this agent will be discussed.

Chuang (1939, 1940) was the first to employ short term heat treatment for examination of the changes in the inductive action of tissues. After being boiled for 5 minutes, the tissues had lost their capacity to induce spinocaudal structures, and after a prolonged heat-treatment deuterencephalic inductive activity had also disappeared. His observations were first confirmed by Hama (1944), and subsequently by several investigators using heterogenous inductors (Okada, 1948; Toivonen, 1949a, 1949b, 1954a, 1954b; Vahs, 1955; Yamada, 1959, etc.). It should here be mentioned in this connection that there are certain opposing opinions on the "unmasking" of the neuralizing principle (archencephalic inductive action) observed in such experiments after heat-treatment of an original spino-caudal-inducing inductor (Yamada, 1958a, 1958b, 1959; Yamada and Takata, 1955a). These concepts are discussed at the end of this chapter.

Apart from short-term heat treatment, several other inactivating treatments have been used for the mesodermalizing principle. Kuusi (1951a, 1953) bound the amino groups of the inductor tissue with formol or Na-nitrite, and observed a disappearance of spinocaudal inductive action accompanied by a definite decrease in deuterence-phalic inductive capacity. Similar formol-experiments were made by Lallier (1950), who used normal inductor tissue. After formol-fixation, the blastopore lip lost its inductive action almost completely, and only occasional small neural inductions were noted.

Ethanol-treatment was used in an extensive series by German workers testing the inductive action of several tissues of guinea-pig and mouse (Engländer, Johnen and Vahs, 1953; Engländer and Johnen, 1957; Vahs, 1957). The results were very similar when different organs with different organ-specific inductive actions were used. As one example can be cited the series with alcohol-treated guinea-pig kidney tissue, presented in figure 45 (Engländer and Johnen, 1957): in less than two weeks, there was a definite weakening in the spinocaudal inductive capacity, accompanied by a progressive strengthening of the archencephalic inductive action. On testing the same phenomenon in mouse tissues, Vahs (1957a) noted the first changes even after 9 to 12 hours, and after three weeks of alcohol-treatment significant changes were no longer to be observed. Similar

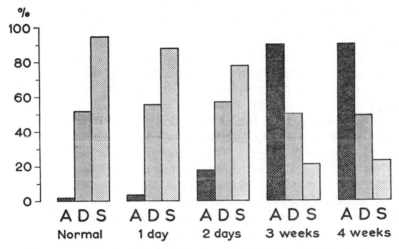

Figure 45. Gradual changes in the original spinocaudal inductive action of guinea-pig kidney tissue during prolonged alcohol treatment. (After Engländer and Johnen, 1957.)

progressive changes were noted in all tissues with an original spino-caudal action, whereas tissues inducing primarily archencephalic structures showed no definite alterations in their inductive capacity. The results were accordingly interpreted as a change in the spino-caudal inductor, and consequently in the ratio between spinocaudal and archencephalic inductors. Recently, Kuusi (1957a) reported similar changes after short treatment with butanol. In this connec-tion, the recent results of Kuusi (1961) seem to be very important and interesting. Instead of alcohol or heat treatment, she used urea to denature her mesodermalizing (and neuralizing) bone-marrow extract. Despite a complete and irreversible denaturation of the proteins following this treatment, only a very slight change was noted in the regional character of the inductor towards more cranial inductive effect of denaturation by long-term alcohol treatment and heating to 70–90°, it thus seems that the denaturation of protein-compounds in the mesodermalizing inductor cannot alone explain the inactivation of its activity—certain of her results even seem to indicate that a light or reversible denaturation will increase the inductive capacity of heterogenous tissues (Kuusi, 1960, 1961). Kuusi (1953) examined the effect of acetylation on the inductive effect of kidney tissue. After mild acetylation with acetic anhydride, she obtained a weakening of the inductive capacity of the inductor tissue, but the regional character of the effect was not altered from the original spinocaudal type.

In a series of experiments, Tiedemann and Tiedemann (1956, 1957, 1959a) studied the effect of performic acid, thioglycolic acid and acetylation on the mesoderm inducing capacity of their protein samples. Treatment with these acids and acetylation with acetic anhydrid resulted in a total inactivation of the mesodermalizing principle, whereas strong acetylation with ketene reduced the total induction rate by 50 per cent, without changing the regional character of the induction. The mechanism of these effects is not known; the performic acid may have oxidized certain sulphur-containing amino-acids, and the thioglycolic acid is known to break the S-S-bindings. The effect of the acetylation may partly be due to the acetylation of free amino and hydroxyl groups, partly to changes in the solubility of the proteins tested (Tiedemann, 1959b).

Finally, the effect of enzyme treatment should be noted. Treatment of tissues or tissue fractions possessing a spinocaudal inductive action with ribonuclease appears to have no effect on their inductive action (Kuusi, 1951b; Hayashi, 1955; Engländer and Johnen, 1957; Vahs, 1957). In contrast, treatment with proteolytic enzymes (trypsin, pepsin) has often been shown to inactivate both spino-caudal and deuterencephalic inductive actions (Toivonen and Kuusi, 1948; Yamada and Takata, 1955b; Hayashi, 1958; Tiede-mann and Tiedemann, 1955, 1956; Tiedemann, Tiedemann and Kesselring, 1960).

The results of these investigations into the inactivation of deuter-encephalic and spinocaudal (mesodermal?) inductive capacity are summarized in Table 3. Certain unpublished observations of Toivonen on the effect of oxidation of kidney tissue by peroxide are included in the table.

Certain conclusions can be drawn from the experimental results presented in Table 3. First of all the results seem to indicate that the inactivation of the inductive effect is caused by denaturation or splitting of protein. Secondly, the "sensitivity" of the deuterence-phalic inductive agent seems to be very similar to that of the spino-caudal inductor, with the exception of the thioglycolic acid, which will be discussed separately. Two explanations seem possible: either

| | EFFECT OF THE TREATMENT | |
	Deuterencephalic inductive capacity	Spinocaudal inductive capacity
Heating at 55°	(+)	+ +
Heating at 70–90°	+ +	+ +
Formol	+ +	+ +
Ethanol 1–2 weeks	(+)	+(+)
Butanol	(+)	+
Urea	−	(+)
Oxidation	−	−
Thioglycol acid	(+)	+ +
Performic acid	?	+ +
Acetylation	?	+
Ribonuclease	−	−
Carboxypeptidase	−	−
Pepsin	+ +	+ +
Trypsin	+ +	+ +

+ + strong effect   (+) weak effect
+   medium effect   −   no effect

TABLE 3. The effect of different pre-treatments of the inductor upon its deuterencephalic and spinocaudal inductive effects. References are given in the text.

the deuterencephalic inductor is a protein, like the spinocaudal one, or the deuterencephalic reactions are produced by a simultaneous action of a labile, protein-like mesodermal agent and a more stable neuralizing agent, as previously suggested in different connections. The observation that after most of the treatments which inactivate the spinocaudal and mesodermal, as well as the deuterencephalic inductive capacity, the archencephalic capacity remains in the inductor and is frequently even strengthened, seems to corroborate the second possibility.

The mechanism of inactivation caused by different forms of treatment is unknown. Apart from the concepts of Tiedemann (1959b), already presented, Kuusi (1953) and Lallier (1950) have stressed the importance of free amino groups which are obviously bound by their nitrite and formalin treatment. Recently, Kuusi (1957b, 1959, 1960, 1961) dealt with the possible mechanism of inactivation following denaturating treatment (heat, alcohol, urea). She stressed the significance of the physico-chemical changes in the implant which obviously followed these treatments. The solubility of the implant will certainly be altered after a denaturating treatment, and consequently the "release" of the inductively active factors is probably altered. Furthermore, digestion of the implant by the enzymes of the host tissues may play an important role, and the hardening of the implant, for instance after long term alcohol fixation, may result in a decrease in this activity. These ideas are corroborated by her observations, that the release of basophilic material and labelled compounds from the inductor is dependent on both the type of pre-treatment and the location of the implant.

There is one further point to be stressed here: almost all of the inactivation experiments are carried out with heterogenous inductors, and the information concerning the inactivation of the normal organizer tissue, the blastopore lip, is scanty. Nevertheless, the few data we have indicate that there are definite differences between the sensitivity of the agents present in the normal inductor and that of heterogenous agents. Thus both heat and alcohol treatment inactivate the mesodermalizing capacity of the dorsal lip, but this occurs much more rapidly than in the heterogenous inductor tissues (e.g., Rollhäuser-ter Horst, 1953). The same lability of the meso-dermalizing principle in the normal inductor tissue was shown in the denaturation experiments by Okazaki (1955). Whether this was due to a chemical difference between the mesodermalizing agents in normal and heterogenous inductors, or to other differences between the embryonic and adult tissues, cannot yet be concluded. Some unpublished findings of Kohonen in our laboratory appear to indicate that there also exist certain differences in the heat-tolerance of the mesodermalizing principle between different heterogenous tissues.

(2) *Purification of the mesodermalizing principle.* In the first attempts at characterization of the mesodermalizing principle, it was noted as being thermolabile, non-dialyzable, not extractable with organic solvents, but at least partially soluble in aqueous solutions (Toivonen and Kuusi, 1948; Toivonen, 1950; Kuusi, 1951a, 1951b). These characteristics, together with the mode of inactivation by

different pre-treatments just reviewed, hinted strongly at large molecular factors, obviously proteins. Subsequently, much work has been done to purify and isolate the proteins responsible for spino-caudal and mesodermal inductions. The main part of this work has again been carried out by the Japanese team at Nagoya University, in the Heiligenberg Institute, and by Kuusi in our laboratory. These experiments have recently been summarized by the authors in a number of reviews (Kuusi, 1957a, 1957b, 1961; Yamada, 1958a, 1958b, 1961; Tiedemann, 1959b; Tiedemann and Tiedemann, 1959b).

Since Toivonen (1953a, 1953b) demonstrated that guinea-pig bone-marrow was an almost pure mesodermal inductor, this has been the source of the different fractionations of Yamada and his group, as well as in recent research undertaken by Kuusi.

Kuusi (1957a, 1957b) started from an extract obtained from the bone-marrow by $M/100$ phosphate buffer at pH 7·4, and subsequently centrifuged for 10 minutes at 2,000 r.p.m. In testing the inductive action of the centrifuge fractions, she noted spinocaudal inductions and formations of trunk-mesodermal type in both the sediment and the supernatant. After extraction the residue also gave some inductions of the same general type, although the activity was weaker. In discussing these results Kuusi (1957b) stated that the mesodermalizing inductor was an "overall" factor in her fractions, and it seems probable "that different compounds, having the same property—e.g., a structural factor—may cause the same reaction in the test material."

Before giving some account of the results of the extensive series of experiments carried out by Yamada and his team, mention should be made of his ideas on the products of mesodermal induction. In all the earlier investigations concerned with induced mesodermal structures, they were simply called "mesodermal" and when combined with spinal cord, they were usually called spinocaudal. Yamada (1958a, 1958b) proposed that, in fact, there are two types of mesodermal structures to be distinguished: "trunk-mesodermal" formations such as trunk somites and notochord, nephric tubules and blood cells, and "spinocaudal" formations, represented by tail somites and notochord and spinal cord. The former type of induction product is typical in experiments with bone-marrow of the guinea-pig, rat and mouse (Toivonen, 1953a, 1953b; Saxén and Toivonen, 1956; Toivonen and Saxén, 1957; Kawakami and Mifune, 1955,

1957, etc.). Typical spinocaudal inductions are obtained, for instance, by kidney tissue as inductor (Toivonen, 1940; Yamada and
Takata, 1955b, etc.), certain continuous cell lines grown in fresh
serum (Saxén and Toivonen, 1958b; Saxén, Toivonen and Vainio,
1961) and certain protein samples from the anterior pituitary of the cow
(Tiedemann, 1957). This "trunk-mesodermal" reaction of Yamada
seems to correspond to our "pure mesodermal" inductive action.

Yamada (1958a, 1958b) started from an extract obtained with
0·14 M NaCl from guinea-pig bone-marrow. The ribonucleoproteins
were precipitated by streptomycin sulphate, dialyzed and tested for

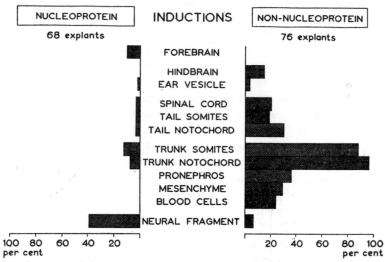

Figure 46. The inductive action of the nucleoprotein fraction of
guinea-pig bone-marrow (left), and the activity of the fraction
non-precipitable with streptomycin sulphate. (After Yamada,
1958b.)

their inductive capacity in the form of alcohol precipitate. In contrast to similar ribonucleoprotein samples from kidney tissue (Yamada
and Takata, 1955a, 1956), the preparation showed only a very weak
inductive action of all regional types. The fraction which could not
be precipitated with streptomycin sulphate, containing only about
3 per cent of the RNA-phosphorus obtained in the ribonucleoprotein
sample, proved, however, to be a potent inducer of formations which
were mainly trunk-mesodermal (figure 46 and plate 7.4).

The tissue extract was further fractionated in accordance with the scheme presented in figure 47. After centrifugation for one hour at 100,000 × g, the supernatant was precipitated by pH 4·7, centrifuged at a lower speed, and dialyzed. The content of the dialysis bag was separated into a soluble fraction and a precipitate, and both of these were tested separately for their inductive capacity. In contrast to the very weakly inducing SD and SP fractions (figure 47), these

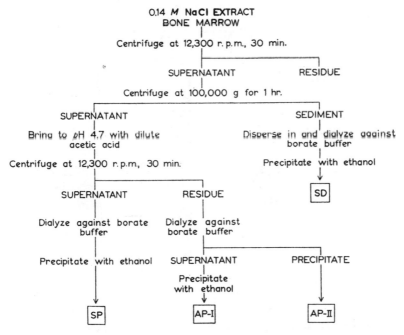

Figure 47. Yamada's (1958b) scheme for fractionation of the guinea-pig bone-marrow extract. The supernatant fraction (A-P-1) was further purified and separated into five components by electrophoresis.

two acid-precipitable fractions proved to be strong inducers of trunk mesodermal structures. The supernatant fraction of the dialyzed samples (AP-1) was used for further purification. When centrifuged for one hour at 220,000 × g, both the sediment and the supernatant gave the same mesodermal inductive actions. On study of the same fraction in electrophoresis, five components were recognized and the two slower-moving ones were tested in the usual manner. In figure 48 are shown the inductive actions of the original tissue extract, the acid-precipitable fraction *AP*-1 and the two electrophoretically separated components *D* and *E*. The strong mesodermal effect of this purified sample (*DE*) can be noted (Plate 7.5), the inductive effect of the faster-moving components is not yet known, and further progress in this respect, as well as in the characterization of the active components, will be followed with great interest.

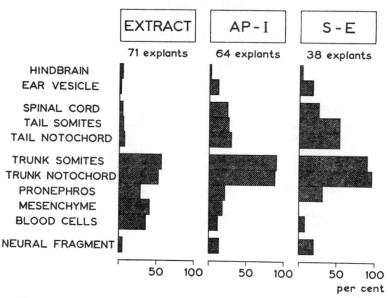

Figure 48. The inductive actions of an extract from guinea-pig bone-marrow, its acid-precipitable fraction (figure 47), and of two components (S-E) electrophoretically separated. (After Yamada, 1958b.)

Tiedemann and Tiedemann (1956) obtained from 9-day-old chick embryos a granular fraction which showed spinocaudal and deuterencephalic inductive action. This fraction was further purified with ammonium-sulphate precipitation, extraction by phenol and fractionation with pyridine (Tiedemann and Tiedemann, 1959b). When tested in implantation experiments, the inductive effect of this sample was of the trunk-mesodermalizing type, and the neuralizing capacity was almost removed, manifesting itself by inducing short spinal cords or neural strands (Plate 7.6). In extensive studies made in order to characterize the chemical composition of this preparation, the authors arrived at the following data: The maximal *UV*-absorption was at pH 3·6 278 mμ (figure 49), and in electrophoresis, at the same pH, a major component and small, slowly-moving component were noted. The strongly mesodermalizing major component was obviously still a mixture of several proteins or polypeptides (electrophoresis in veronal buffer). The molecular weight for this sample was calculated at 40,000–50,000 from the sedimentation and viscosity measurements.

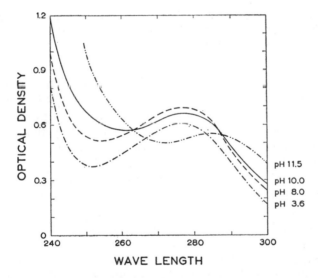

Figure 49. The UV absorption spectra of the mesodermalizing fraction obtained by the phenol-pyridin process. (After Tiedemann and Tiedemann, 1959b.)

In a second series of experiments, Tiedemann and Tiedemann (1959b), purification was started from an acetone-dried powder of chick embryos. A fraction which displayed relatively strong mesodermalizing capacity was obtained after extraction with 95 per cent acetic acid, and subsequent precipitations with acetone, ether and pyridine. The inductive effect of this fraction, as well as that of the fraction obtained after the phenol-process, is shown in Table 4.

| | INDUCTION PERCENTAGE | |
	Phenol process 93 exp.	Acetic acid process 83 exp.
Total	77	66
Trunk formations	76	65
Tail formations	42	42
Not defined	22	20
Spinal cord*	28	58
Brain formations	0	0

TABLE 4. Secondary structures induced by two protein samples in implantation experiments (Tiedemann and Tiedemann, 1959b). (* According to the authors the spinal cord was often a short and thin neural strand, expecially in the phenol-series.)

(3) *Discussion.* By way of brief summary of the information available on the mesodermalizing system, it can first be stated that there is obviously an agent or group of agents leading under experimental conditions to the mesodermalization of competent ectoderm. These agents are large-molecular, obviously proteins, and are present in a variety of heterogenous tissues. Whether there is only one specific protein, a mixture of such molecules, or a large quantity of different large-molecular factors responsible for the same morphogenetic effects, cannot yet be stated. Nevertheless, it does not seem very probable that there is only one and the same mesodermalizing protein present in all the different tissues examined.

The question of the existence of different inductors responsible for the different regional inductions (deuterencephalic, spinocaudal) has already been mentioned in different connections, and a number of theories in this respect are presented in the last chapter of this book. Here, only the chemical data will be discussed. In dealing with the chemical nature of the neuralizing principle, we suggested that the deuterencephalic effect might be brought about by a combined action of the neuralizing and the mesodermalizing agents. This according to our theory holds true with the spinocaudal inductions.

In figure 45 (page 137) some results were given of the alcohol-inactivation of the spinocaudal effect (Engländer and Johnen, 1957). The results showed that, parallel to the disappearance of the spinocaudal inductive action during long-term alcohol treatment of an inductor tissue, its capacity to induce archencephalic structures becomes stronger. Several experimental findings have indicated the same phenomen when the spinocaudal and mesoderm-inducing capacity have been progressively inactivated by treatment by chemical and physical means (e.g., Okada, 1948; Vahs, 1955; Kuusi, 1957a; Saxén and Toivonen, 1958). On examination of these experimental results, the same sequence of changes in the inductive action is always visible: SPINOCAUDAL-DEUTERENCEPHALIC-ARCHENCEPHALIC. In some experiments, however, the change produced has been the opposite. Toivonen (1949a) showed that guinea-pig kidney after alcohol treatment was an inducer of typical spinocaudal structures and deuterencephalic formations. After extraction with petroleum ether, the deuterencephalic inductive action disappeared completely from the residue, and simultaneously the capacity to induce spinal cord had become definitely weaker. Thus the regional inductive action of the kidney tissue had changed from a deuterencephalic-spinocaudal action to a mesodermal-spinocaudal type. The same change was recently demonstrated by Tiedemann and Tiedemann (1959b) during purification of the mesodermalizing agents. Crude granular fraction obtained from the chick embryos yielded a typical spinocaudal inductive action, producing complete tails with spinal cord. After subsequent fractionations, a sample was acquired whose inductive action was of the trunk-mesodermal type, small neural strands being induced but occasionally.

These progressive changes in the inductive effect of heterogenous inductor were recently investigated by Yamada (1958a, 1958b, 1959). He examined the inductive action of guinea-pig bone-marrow which had been exposed to steam for various periods of time. The results (figure 50) show that in addition to a general weakening of the inductive action, its regional character is changed progressively from "trunk mesodermal" type, through spinocaudal and deterencephalic inductive capacity, to purely archencephalic action. Yamada (*op. cit.*) suggested that this might be due to a chemical change in one and the same inductive agents, the trunk-mesodermal factor: "It appears not improbable that the protein molecule responsible for the regional induction undergoes a progressive change in configuration under diverse experimental conditions, and this change is reflected in the progressive change in its regional effect" (Yamada, 1958a). The results may, however, be explained on the basis of our "two-gradient" hypothesis (Toivonen and Saxén, 1955a): The original inductor

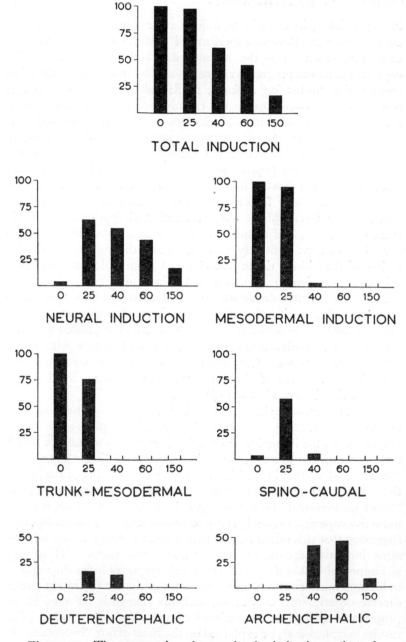

Figure 50. The progressive changes in the inductive action of guinea-pig bone-marrow tissue when exposed to steam for 25, 40, 60 and 150 sec. (After Yamada, 1959.)

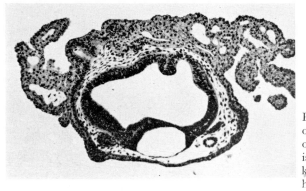

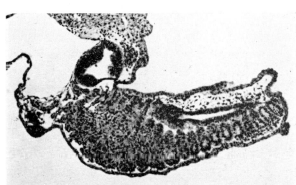

Plate 7.3. Two examples of the inductive action of nucleoprotein sample isolated from guinea-pig kidney. Above: Large hindbrain vesicle with an ear vesicle and mesenchyme. Below Definite myotomes and a spinal cord. (Yamada, 1958a.)

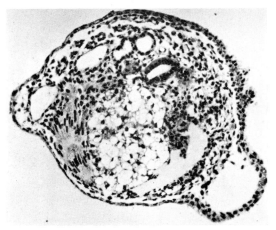

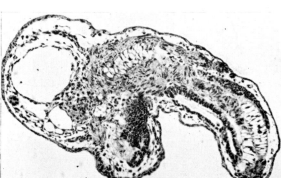

Plate 7.4. An ectodermal explant induced by non-nucleoprotein fraction of guinea-pig bone-marrow. Notochord, myotomes and pronephric tubules are seen. (Yamada, 1958a.)

Plate 7.5. An ectodermal explant induced by the *S-E* fraction. Induction of notochord, myotomes and spinal cord is to be noted. (Yamada, 1958b.)

Plate 7.6. Two examples of Triturus-larvae induced by implantation of a protein sample obtained through the procedure of Tiedemann and Tiedemann (1959b). Tail-like formations showing mesodermal structures and a small spinal cord are observable in both cases. (Orig.)

tissue is a very potent mesodermal inductor, "masking" the weak neuralizing capacity. After progressive inactivation of this mesodermalizing action, the neuralizing capacity is "unmasked", thus resulting in combination of the two active principles in different ratios with different "combined" effect. The progressive change can consequently be put in the following formula:

very strong mesodermalizing capacity + weak neuralizing capacity →
  mesodermal induction
strong mesodermalizing capacity + weak neuralizing capacity ⸱→
  spinocaudal induction.
medium mesodermalizing capacity + strong neuralizing capacity →
  deuterencephalic induction
weak mesodermalizing capacity + strong neuralizing capacity →
  archencephalic induction.

Accordingly, the results of Yamada (1959) could, in our view, be explained as *a progressive elimination of the mesodermalizing capacity, resulting in an "unmasking" of the stable neuralizing principle.* In fact, we have recently experimentally produced a similar progressive change in the inductive action of an implant, but in the *opposite direction.* This was done by adding various amounts of spinocaudal inductor to a pure archencephalic inductor (see Chapter X) (Toivonen, Saxén and Vainio, 1961; Saxén and Toivonen, 1961).

Recently another Japanese team has presented their experimental results, along with a hypothetical explanation of the findings (Kawakami, Iyeiri and Sasaki, 1960). They studied the inductive effect of different fractions obtained from chicken embryo extract either by centrifugation or by chemical fractionation. From the centrifugal fractions, the nucleoprotein-rich microsomal fraction proved to be a potent spinocaudal inductor, but the other fractions were almost without inductive activity. On the other hand, the non-nucleoprotein fraction separated by streptomycin sulphate treatment yielded a similar spinocaudal activity, whereas the nucleoprotein fraction induced structures of the archencephalic region. The seemingly contradictory findings, demonstrating a similar inductive action in the nucleoprotein-rich granular fraction and in the non-nucleoprotein fraction, led the authors to an interesting hypothesis. They suggested that the spinocaudal inducing granules were covered by a non-nucleoprotein substance, obviously a protein, responsible for the

L

spinocaudal-mesodermal activity, and "masking" the archencephalic capacity of the nucleoproteins demonstrated in this fraction after separation with streptomycin sulphate. In the light of the chemical data presented in this chapter and the subsequent discussion, another and less complicated explanation seems to be offered. The granular fraction of Kawakami, Iyeiri and Sasaki (1960) could be compared with the "combined" inductors possessing both mesodermalizing and neuralizing agents. As a result of their combined action, the archencephalic inductive action of the neuralizing principle is "masked", and more caudal neural structures are induced. After inactivation or elimination of the mesodermalizing factor (heat-treatment, alcohol, etc.), the archencephalic activity is "unmasked", and can be compared with the action of the Japanese authors' nucleoprotein fraction after separation from the non-nucleoprotein, spinocaudal protein. Obviously a short-term heat treatment of their granular fraction would lead to similar "unmasking" of the archencephalic activity.

5. Conclusions

As regards the lively research work going on to characterize the chemical nature of the inductive agents, one may ask whether it might not be still too early to try to identify factors and molecules whose mode of action, specificity and importance to normal development are far from clarified. "The main problem remains the same, what does happen in the *reactive* system when it is submitted to the action of such abnormal inducing agents?" (Brachet, 1960a). There is no doubt that interest has to be focused more and more upon the *induction process* itself, but the chemical investigations just described have provided us with very important information to be made use of in future research. There is today strong evidence for the fact that we have to look for several inductive agents with different specific actions, and that these agents are obviously large-molecular, protein-like factors. Among others, substances of the ribonucleoprotein group seem to be responsible for neuralizing stimuli under experimental conditions, and under the same conditions mesodermalization of the competent ectoderm is initiated by environmental proteins. There still remains the question of the importance of such agents in the *normal development* of the embryo, and especially in the control of differentiation. There is no evidence for resemblance of the chemical constitution between the inductive active factors isolated from heterogenous tissues and the similar active agents obviously present in the inducing blastopore lip. On the other hand some observations with devitalized normal inductor speak against such an assumption (Okazaki, 1955). However, these active fractions and samples from heterogenous inductors give us a suitable means of studying the problem of differentiation and its environmental control mechanisms, and it has to be stressed that their morphogenetic action leads to differentiation which is very similar to that in normogenesis (Toivonen and Saxén, 1955b). There is, therefore, no reason to neglect the importance of the attempts at chemical characterization of the inductive agents, but at the same time it has to be remembered that this type of research can hardly solve the most complicated problem of primary induction. None the less recent advances in the chemical study of certain secondary inductions look very promising, and justify an optimistic attitude (see Wilde, 1959).

Finally, we wish to refer to the very recent review of Tuneo Yamada (1961), in which he presents some quite new results, although in part preliminary, arrived at by the very active Japanese team working at Nagoya (only some of these results are included in our book). Yamada has developed a new method of culturing isolated presumptive epidermis as flat explants, and has thus been able to test certain fresh samples of the subcellular components of amphibian tissues. Without going into details of this new approach, we may state that the preliminary results of the Japanese school look very promising, and their combination of certain chemical results with observations of the changes in the submicroscopical structures of the cells may offer a new way of approach to the problem of the chemistry of the inductive agents.

VIII

An Immunological Approach
to the Problem of Induction

1. *Introduction*

It can hardly be said that there exists any unique way of approaching the problem of tissue interaction in differentiation. Among the disciplines applied, immunology offers many techniques which might be considered promising, if one is concerned with a problem of the synthesis of macromolecular substances and their transfer between tissues. It would be most important to determine by the use of available immunological techniques whether the transfer of antigenic substances between interacting tissues is connected with the temporal appearance of new morphological patterns, along with the problem of typical "new" antigenicity of these patterns themselves.

The use of heterogenous inductors, in interaction between two antigenically unrelated tissues, probably gives more scope for the study of antigenic transfer during induction, particularly since the inductor can just as well be a piece of dead tissue as some isolated fraction of tissue material. What follows is a discussion of some of the aspects of this interaction as studied by immunological means (c.f. Chapter VI).

The points upon which stress is laid in this short survey are in many respects merely suggestive as in this connection very few studies have been published. This is by no means true of "immuno-embryology" in general, which has been amply and thoroughly reviewed by Ebert (1959a) and others (Woerdeman, 1955; Tyler, 1955; Nace and Clarke, 1958; Brachet, 1960a; Dalcq, 1960).

2. *The appearance of new antigenic specificities upon primary induction*

Without entering upon a detailed examination of the studies undertaken, we can make brief reference to a number of experiments designed to determine the antigenic characteristics of our induction model. We intend to refer in particular to those studies which demonstrate changes in the developmental pathway when certain antigenic groups of early amphibian material are affected *in vivo* by antibodies. As regards the most extended and illustrative studies of the "immuno-embryology" of chick and sea urchin in embryo and organogenesis, the reader might recall several recent monographs and papers (Perlman and Gustafson, 1948; Perlman, 1953, 1954; Perlman and Perlman, 1957; Holtzer, Marshall and Finck, 1957; Edds, 1958a; Ebert, 1959a).

The precipitin test has been used by several authors to examine the synthesis of new serological specificities during early amphibian development (Cooper, 1948; Flickinger and Nace, 1952; Clayton, 1953). There is little doubt that several new antigenic patterns appear during gastrulation and neurulation, as shown by Clayton in her exhaustive paper. The profound changes in the metabolism of amphibian embryo at these times, and the relevance of increased RNA synthesis during gastrulation should be borne in mind (Brachet 1960a, 1960b). Accordingly the appearance of new antigens might be one step in the genetic determination of changes in cell metabolism rather than bear any relevance to epigenetic differentiation at the molecular level.

It has been a popular suggestion, in considering the interactions of contiguous cell surfaces, that antigen-antibody-like interactions between adjacent cells are involved (Weiss, 1947, 1955). If one admits the importance of these surface contacts to cellular differentiation, then every form of approach which allows them to be investigated arouses immediate interest. Several papers have appeared which report the further development of the cell, or cell group, after attack by immune sera. One must recall the most stimulating papers of Spiegel (1954a, 1954b, 1955) with findings of sponge cell re-aggregation being affected by antisera. Among the workers interested in amphibian embryogenesis, several have applied what is, in principle, the same technique. Flickinger and Nace (1952), Clayton (1953), Nace (1955), Inonue and Ishikawa (unpublished) and Nace and Inonue (1957) have tried to affect amphibian development by the application of specific antisera to growth media. The results were fascinating but anomalous. The most extensive of these papers is that by Ishikawa and Inonue, summarized briefly by Edds (1958a). The results indicate that once certain antigenic groups have been

154

PRIMARY EMBRYONIC INDUCTION

affected by immune sera, the development of the cell groups is totally inhibited (homologous antisera) or "changed" (heterologous antisera). One feels tempted to believe that some re-chanelling of the developmental pathway has occurred on the cells being attacked by heterologous antisera, but several arguments speak against this: (i) the total amount of active antibody in the culture medium determines whether the effect upon the cell is cytolytic, inhibitory or stimulating; (ii) at the time of administration of antibody, some of the treated cells might be richer in antigens, and the antisera have merely a selective affect; (iii) finally, antibody molecules at the cell surface or in the cell may, perhaps, introduce new information into the cell's metabolism, and might themselves affect its subsequent development. The last of these points may have some bearing on the problem of the re-chanelling of affected cells, since it has been shown in our laboratory (Vainio, Toivonen and Saxén, 1958) that some material in plasma and sera is active in causing gastrula ectoderm to differentiate.

We are still far from an understanding of the patterns of antigenic activity in early embryogenesis. There seems to be no close relationship between the appearance of certain antigens and corresponding morphological patterns. We have learned a great deal concerning the appearance of lens antigens from the Dutch school (Woerdeman, 1953, 1955), particularly from the studies of ten Cate and van Doorenmaalen (1950), which amply demonstrate that lens antigen appears at a time when the lens is only a placode in chick and frog embryos. By following the lens protein by means of specific antisera conjugated to fluorescent material, van Doorenmaalen (1958) and Flickinger (1958a) showed lens antigen as being present also in areas other than the placode region. If we add to this what is known of the appearance of some other specific markers, actin and myosin, in muscle differentiation (Ebert, 1959a) we may with due caution make the brief statement that several specific tissue antigens exist in early morphogenesis. Some of these antigens are widespread, some early localized in the region of the appropriate organ primordia. There is obviously some variation in the appearance of these antigenic markers in various organs of the same individual (Ogawa, 1958), which makes the interpretation of the bearing of these antigens on morphogenesis even more difficult. Some more recent immunological techniques, such as immune electronmicroscopy, might produce important information in this connection.

3. *Immunological attack upon interaction by heterogenous inductors*

One straightforward means of investigating the action of heterogenous inductors would be that of using antibodies. A simple way of doing this would be the preparation of antibodies against known inducing tissues, and permitting them to prevent or otherwise affect the action of the inducing tissue. This has been done by Vainio (1957). He prepared rabbit antisera against guinea pig liver, kidney, and bone marrow, and applied them to fresh pieces of these organs, which he then treated with cold alcohol and implanted into the blastocoele of newt gastrulae. A summary of these studies is given in figure 51. It seems clear that all the antisera had an effect upon bone-

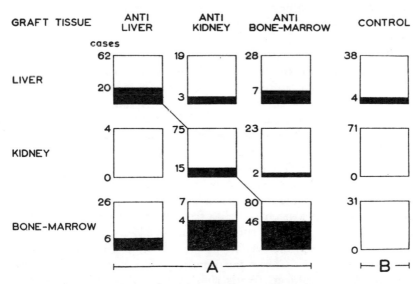

Figure 51. Inhibition of induction of heterogenous inductors produced with homologous antisera. Black area = percentage of cases where no induction was obtained, although the inductor tissue was present and in contact with the ectoderm. (*A*. Heterologous or homologous anti-guinea-pig organ sera used. *B*. Normal rabbit sera used as controls.) The homologous series are connected by lines. (After Vainio, 1957.)

marrow which made it incapable of affecting ectoderm. Normal rabbit serum lacked this effect. Without embarking upon further discussion of these studies, we should like to comment on these results, which

Vainio provocatively entitled the inhibition of "complementary interaction".

There had obviously been a number of antigens involved in the material used in previous studies for immunization. Vainio (un-published) has demonstrated at least 4–5 precipitation bands in gel diffusion. This makes it likely that several antigens are attacked by these antisera, and one might assume that surface antigens are con-cerned, as in these sera high titre of guinea-pig haemaglutinins were demonstrated. Furthermore, one would assume (quite tentatively) that this would also affect the release of any material from the cells into extracellular spaces, which again might cause an inhibition of inductive activity in this material. Nevertheless, it is still important to bear this technique in mind; it could be applied to more highly purified inductive material, and to the soluble inductor of Tiedemann and Tiedemann (1956) in particular.

It is surprising that the technique described is so little used in studies of the problem of inductive interaction. It is not necessary to delve far to find examples of experiments in which the biological activity of macromolecules, or a complex of macromolecules, has been subjected to interference by antibodies. If a virus is considered as being too large to be a good example, hormone-antibodies (such as insulin antibody) will serve the purpose. It is, of course, difficult to find a suitable antigenic marker in induction studies as far as tissues from one and the same animal are concerned. On the other hand, heterogenous combinations are available, and one would suggest the immunological approach as being fruitful in re-aggregation experi-ments in which unrelated species are involved.

The principle of intervening in late induction with tissue antisera has been applied by Clarke and Fowler (1960), lens induction being employed as an object. Antiserum against adult chicken lens in-hibited the inductive action of optic vesicle enclosed in competent ectoderm. The possibility was suggested that the reactive patterns in optic vesicle, similar to those in adult lens (Langmann, Schale-kamp, Kuyken and Veen, 1957), are normally transferred to the ectoderm and can bring about lens induction. In this system the same reservations as those presented in connection with Vainio's studies apply. The rabbit antisera prepared were obviously not absorbed, and one would suggest that the effect of antisera upon the optic vesicle included that of rabbit anti-chick. The specificity of the antiserum was controlled by showing that it did not interfere with development of the optic vesicle. However, the experiments do not provide convincing evidence that the material transferred from the optic vesicle to the ectoderm (McKeehan, 1958) is the object of the action of antibodies.

4. *Conclusions*

The aim of this short chapter was to show something of what has been done with immunological techniques in studying primary induction, and what in our opinion most immediately remains to be done. A study of primary induction, as is true of many other aspects of biology, lacks clear indications of the line to pursue, but in this field much confusion is due to what are termed factors and agents causing induction. Thus, each step closer to chemical definition of these "agents" serves to improve the possibilities for the use of immunological tools. Once biochemical determination of the substances active in primary induction has been achieved, the specificity and sensitivity of immunological methods will help to localize the transferred material along the lines outlined in this chapter. Furthermore, some relevant information could be obtained on the mechanism of interaction itself by study of the phenomenon with antibodies prepared against the reactants.

IX

Conceptions of Primary Induction
and their Experimental Basis

1. *Introduction*

Since the first experiments of Hans Spemann and his school, which were presented in Chapter I, it has become evident that in discussing the process of primary induction we are dealing with a completely new biological phenomenon which is hardly comparable with any of the other known activities of cells, tissues or biologically active factors. It is both a most fascinating field of experimentation and is open for theoretical considerations, speculations, and even for non-biological philosophy, thus being comparable with the alchemy of the fifteenth century, and, perhaps, with the cancer research of today. Consequently, while a great quantity of literature has been produced, after thirty years of intense research work the problem is still open, and the object of controversial opinions. Nevertheless there seems to be a certain convergence of the primarily very different theories of the induction process, and it may be that the present situation is less chaotic than it was some ten years ago.

The presentation and classification of the very great amount of experimental data obtained during this research work, and their interpretation in particular, is by no means an easy task. Moreover, when such a survey is made by authors who are themselves working on the problem, and who have presented their own theory of the process, it may not always be possible for them to adopt a neutral attitude to opposing ideas, and especially as most of the experimental evidence can be considered as supporting several of the theories (as will be seen below). In the following survey, accordingly, the main theories of the process of induction are presented in the light of the original experiments which have led the different schools to their hypotheses, and only subsequently are they discussed in the light of other experimental results. When this is done, and the original ideas of different authors are presented, it has to be borne in mind, however, that these conceptions were based on experimental data available some twenty years ago, and in most cases, as will be seen in the Discussion, the authors have later modified their ideas.

2. Quantitative hypothesis

Before demonstration of the chemical nature of the induction process, Child (1929, 1941) made an attempt to explain determination by his metabolic gradients by means of a "physiological dominance" of the animal pole. Although many chemical investigations have demonstrated the existence of such gradients (see Chapter II) in the distribution of certain compounds, as well in the metabolic activity of the different parts of the embryo, the main merit of Child's hypothesis may be its stimulatory effect upon a variety of subsequent investigations.

The most important of the theories obviously stimulated by the conceptions of Child (1929), was the gradient theory of Dalcq and Pasteels (1937, 1938). This theory was originally based upon certain observations made after the rotation of fertilized amphibian eggs which were then kept in abnormal orientations with respect to the gravitational field. These experiments, known as "Schultze's rotation", were carried out by Penners and Schleip (1928a, 1928b) and by Penners (1929), and later repeated by Pasteels (1938).

When a fertilized amphibian egg is kept in an abnormal position between two glass slides, the distribution of yolk is altered. Subsequently, the blastopore is formed in a new position which always corresponds to the margin between the accumulated yolk mass and the area of cells less loaded by yolk granules. However, in some experiments the rotation led to the formation of two blastopores and invaginations, and consequently two more or less complete embryos developed (figure 52a). These two blastopores appeared either on the opposite margins of one larger yolk mass, or, if the rotation had led to the separation of two smaller yolk islands, on the margin of each of them. It was further noted that the blastopore developed earlier and the invagination started first from the margin closer to the grey crescent, and this was only later followed by invagination from the more peripherally-situated blastopore (figure 52b). It was thus evident that the site of the blastopore was determined by two factors: the distribution of the yolk and the position of the grey crescent. The stimulatory effect of the grey crescent seemed to be strongest at its centre, and decreased from here towards the periphery, thus forming a "gradient" in the dorso-ventral direction.

These observations suggested the existence of two gradients in the normal embryo (Dalcq and Pasteels, 1937, 1938): a caudocranial gradient following the distribution of the yolk, and a dorso-ventral gradient which was correlated with the grey crescent. The latter seemed to be bound to the thin cortical layer of egg, which is not affected in rotation experiments though these alter the distribution of the yolk, and consequently change the "yolk gradient". The authors further suggested that there occurred certain reactions, obviously chemical in nature, between the components of these two

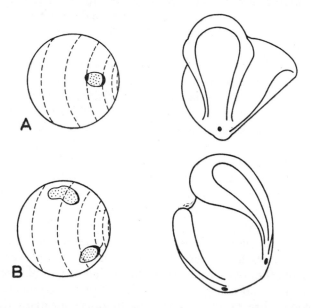

Figure 52. Results of "Schultze's rotation experiment". Formation of yolk-islands (left) with secondary blastopores (black) leading to the development of secondary neural plates (right). (After Dalcq and Pasteels, 1937.)

gradients leading to the formation of a hypothetical active factor, "organicine". This factor, distributed in the developing egg in the form of a gradient, was the actual determining factor leading to different "morphogenetic potentials" of different regions in the embryo. The amount of this agent was determined by the two factors,

the yolk gradient (V) and the cortical gradient (C), but it was suggested that the C/V-ratio plays a role in the determining stimuli.
The segregation of the different organ primordia was due to their
having different values of the CV- and C/V-stimulations, and consequently the areas with the same amounts of "organicine" (or CV
and C/V) become determined in the same direction. Thus, for
instance, as different mesodermal structures have different values, a
decreasing field of the determining stimuli leads first to formation of
the notochord, followed by somite development and finally by a
transformation into mesenchymal tissue (figure 53). During gastru-

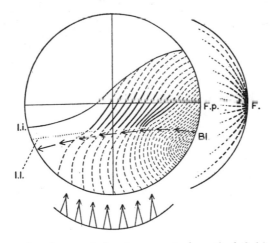

Figure 53. A scheme of the dorso-ventral cortical field (F) and
the yolk gradient (arrows) suggested by the theory of Dalcq and
Pasteels (1937). The lines indicate the C-V concentration necessary for invagination (Bl—site of the blastopore). (After Dalcq and
Pasteels, 1937.)

lation, the areas richest in organicine (the dorsal lip region) come into
contact with the ectodermal cells containing less organicine (presumptive neural plate area). This leads to diffusion of the active
agent from the invaginated dorsal lip into the overyling ectoderm,
and to synthesis of organicine in the latter tissue. The organicine
thus seems to be able "to catalyse its own synthesis *in vivo*" (Dalcq,
1941). The determination of the central nervous system, neural crest
and epidermis is now again due to different thresholds to the determining stimulus forming a gradient in the ectoderm.

In this connection, it is not possible to go into details of this theory and its experimental basis. The theory has been later modified to a certain extent by Dalcq (1947, 1960), and we will return to these modified conceptions in conjunction with the discussion on the different theories. Subsequent experiments, made in order to corroborate the quantitative hypothesis, particularly the centrifugations by Pasteels (1939c, 1940, 1953a, 1953b, 1954) are also described below. Here, it might be stated that this all-embracing hypothesis has repeatedly been criticized (e.g., Rotmann, 1943; Eyal-Giladi, 1954; Holtfreter and Hamburger, 1955, etc.), and it seems no longer valid in its original form. However, several points of this quantitative theory have been adopted in subsequent theories—even by the present authors, who originally started from a quite contrary theory (see below). Some current ideas of the different quantities and ratios of inductivity active agents and of threshold values for different organs do not, as a matter of fact, differ very much from the original ideas of Dalcq and Pasteels. However, their suggestion of the existence of only one inductively active factor does not seem to be in accordance with our present knowledge.

3. Qualitative hypotheses

Simultaneously with the presentation of the quantitative hypothesis, Chuang and Toivonen started their extensive experiments on very different lines, leading them to a conclusion different in principle from those of Dalcq and Pasteels and similar to those already presented by Holtfreter (1934a).

Both Chuang (1938, 1939, 1940) and Toivonen (1938b, 1940) used heterogenous inductors (see Chapter V), and tested their properties in implantation experiments. Their main findings can be presented in a very brief form.

Chuang (op. cit.) used as inductor material mouse kidney tissue and liver tissue from Triturus. After testing their original inductive action, he tested them after different periods of heat treatment in boiling water. The results he obtained with the kidney tissue are presented in figure 54. The diagram shows that the original effect of this tissue was an archencephalic-deuterencephalic inductive action, and that mesodermal structures were noted in up to 40 per cent of cases. Boiling for 1 second did not affect this activity, but after 5 minutes of treatment the mesoderm-inducing capacity was almost completely lost, and during prolonged treatment the brain-inducing capacity was also progressively decreased. Later similar experiments with liver tissue of the newt yielded similar results (Chuang, 1940). From these observations, the author concluded that there is obviously more than one inductive agent: "that the meso-dermal formations are produced by specific, chemical agents which react differently to boiling from the inductive factors producing neural formations." (Chuang, 1939, translated.) He pointed out that this difference could not be a quantitative one.

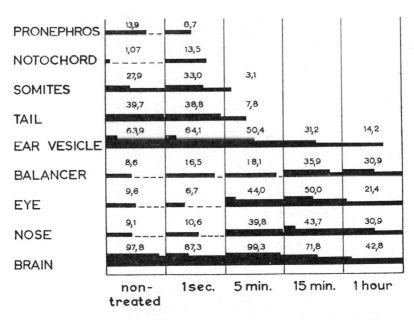

Figure 54. The percentages of different inductions obtained with mouse kidney tissue as inductor. In addition to non-treated kidney, the same tissue was used subsequent to boiling for various periods of time. (After Chuang, 1939.)

Toivonen (1938, 1940) examined a great number of different heterogenous tissues from fishes, reptiles, birds and mammals. There is no need to repeat the results here—most of them have already been given in Chapter V. The main result demonstrated in figure 55 was that there were definite differences in their inductive action, some being inductors of mainly forebrain structures and the cor-responding sense-organs (archencephalic inductors of Lehmann,

1945), some inducing hindbrain structures and ear vesicles (deuterencephalic inductors), whereas certain tissues yielded an inductive
action of more caudal and particularly mesodermal structures (spinocaudal inductors). Toivonen (1940) concluded that these differences
in "tissue-specific" inductive action can be explained only by the
presence of "several inductive agents with different action".

This qualitative hypothesis of Chuang and Toivonen seemed
to be quite contrary to the quantitative theory presented above, and
was followed by ten years of lively competition between the two
theories. However, before we examine the large amount of experimental work stimulated by these theories, and the evidence obtained,
there are some more recent theories and models of primary induction
which need brief presentation.

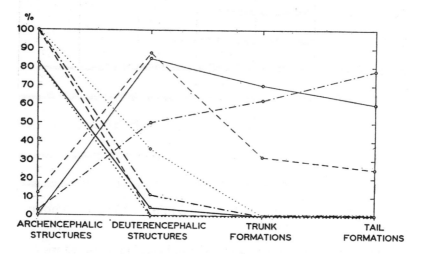

Figure 55. Diagram demonstrating the differences in the tissue
specific inductive agents of heterogenous inductors. The percentages of different regional types of inductors are given for seven
different heterogenous inductors. (After Toivonen, 1940.)

4. The double-potency theory

Meanwhile, a third type of experimental series was carried out in
Tokio by Yamada (1939a, 1939b, 1940). He studied the differentiation of pieces of amphibian neurulae, explanted in isolation or in
combination with different homogeneous tissues. The results of
experiments with the ventral mesoderm of young Triturus neurulae

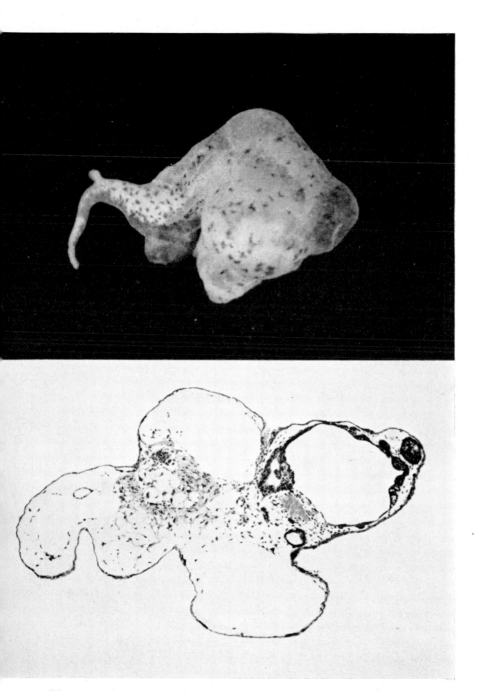

Plate 9.1. An external view and a section of an explant induced by liver+bone-marrow tissue, resulting in a quite complete "embryo". A tail-like formation with myotomes and notochord is seen on the left (bone-marrow effect), and on the right, around the liver implant can be identified forebrain structures with an eye. (Toivonen and Saxén, 1955b.)

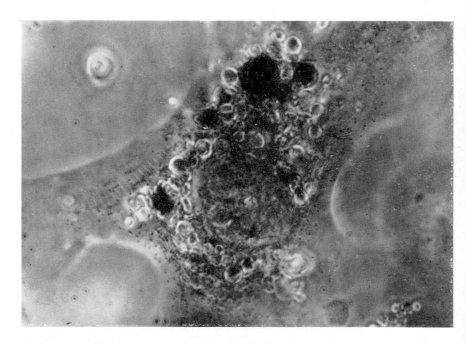

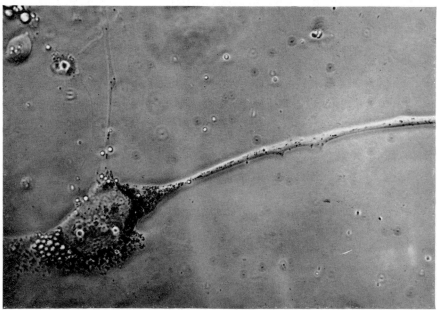

Plate 10.1. Two examples of "confused" cells developed from
disaggregated washed cells in microdrop cultures containing
approximately 25 cells. Above: A cell showing muscle striation
and synthesis of melanin granules. Below: A neuron-like cell with
an intense melanin synthesis in the cell body. (Courtesy: Dr.
Charles E. Wilde, Jr.)

are shown in figure 56: when the prospective somite material was cultured alone, it formed more ventral structures, mainly nephric tubules and occasionally muscle fibres. This was also true of the prospective kidney material, which in addition to its prospective tissue again formed more ventral structures, i.e., blood islands. If, on the other hand, these areas were explanted in combination with notochord-material, the result was a dorsalization of their differentiation: The prospective blood forming area formed nephric tubules

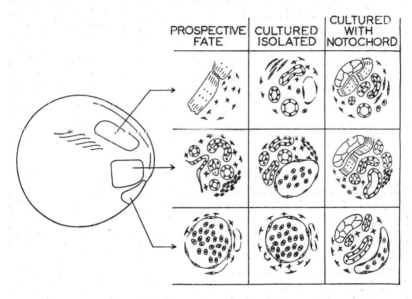

Figure 56. Differentiation of explanted pieces of mesoderm from different regions when cultivated either as isolated explants or as explants combined with notochord. (After Yamada, 1940.)

and the prospective kidney mesenchyme gave rise, in addition to kidney tissue, to somites. From results of this type, Yamada (1940) formulated a theory of "morphogenetic potential" in which the highest potential was represented by muscle differentiation. This potential could be increased experimentally by explanting with noto-chord-material and by the effect of its "Chordafactor". The theory of Yamada bears a definite resemblance to the quantitative theory of Dalcq and Pasteels (1937, 1938), but has subsequently undergone certain changes, as have all the different conceptions presented above.

M

After a long interruption, Yamada did not return to this theory until 1947 in Japanese, and not until 1950 in English. With reference to some observations on the importance of morphogenetic movements (to be mentioned later), and to certain experiments with protein fractions as inductors, he presented his theory of "double potentials". According to this hypothesis, the development of each part of the embryo is dependent on two "potentials", a dorsoventral potential (P_{dv}) and a cephalo-caudal potential (P_{cc}). The process of "embryonic induction" is actually a shift of the P_{dv} into a more dorsal direction (dorsalization) and is mediated through chemical factors, dorso-ventral mediators (M_{dv}). On the other hand, the activity responsible for the cephalo-caudal segregation of tissues (cephalo-caudal mediator or M_{cc}) is a mechanical one occasioned by the dynamic conditions of the active and reactive tissues. Due to the combined or simultaneous actions of these two mediators, both dorso-ventral and cephalo-caudal segregation are induced. M_{dv} acting alone (as in the archencephalic region of normal embryos) leads to differentiation of archencephalic structures, and only in combination with the mechanical M_{cc} is the regionality of the central nervous system determined.

Yamada (1950b) explained by this theory certain results obtained with heterogenous inductors. If the M_{cc}-activity is bound to the *structure* of these implants, the results of Chuang (1939, 1940), for instance, could be explained as a destruction of this structure by heat, followed by a shift towards archencephalic activity (M_{dv}), which is not bound to this structure. In subsequent investigations, Yamada was one of the first to extract the "mesodermalizing factor", or M_{cc}, from heterogenous tissues. This result might weigh against his hypothesis of the mechanical nature of this activity, but he has explained this by a suggestion that the activity is connected with the *structure of the protein*. (Yamada and Takata, 1955a.)

5. *Activation-transformation theory*

In a series of very fine experiments carried out in 1952–58, P. D. Nieuwkoop obtained results which led him to his own modification of the conception of induction. In several respects, this can be considered as a compromise between the earlier theories. Before we present his ideas, a description of the new operation technique developed by Nieuwkoop *et al.* (1952) is necessary.

In order to test the inductive action of different regions of the gastrula, and to follow the process of induction in the reactive tissue,

Nieuwkoop *et al.* (1952) used ectodermal "folds" implanted in the dorsal midline of young gastrulae (figure 57). Because of the inductive action of the host, these folds of competent ectoderm differentiated into successive zones of different neural, mesectodermal and epidermal structures, which were analyzed microscopically. Figure 58 shows a typical example of such a fold implanted in the hindrain region of the host: the most apical part has remained undifferentiated, in the following proximal zone mesectodermal differentiations

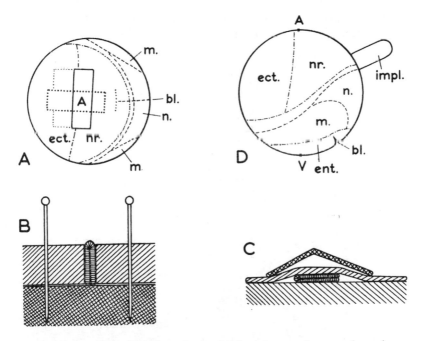

Figure 57. The "fold"-method of Nieuwkoop. An extodermal strip is cut away from the presumptive epidermis (*A*), folded between two pieces of agar (*B* and *C*), and implanted into different regions of gastrulae (*D*). (After Nieuwkoop *et al.*, 1952.)

(pigment cells and connective tissue) are obtained, and the most proximal part of the fold has differentiated into definite brain structures. If folds are implanted in different regions of the host, it can be shown that this most proximal part always differentiates into neural structures corresponding to the regional structure of the host at the level of the fold. The more distal parts of the folds show neural

differentiations more anterior to the level of the fold, usually forebrain structures. In the most posterior folds, implanted in the trunk
or caudal spinal cord of the host, this differentiation into forebrain
structures by the distal part of the fold was, however, only occasionally seen, and those structures which did not correspond to the
implantation level represented hindbrain structures.

These results led to the presentation of a new working hypothesis
by Nieuwkoop *et al.* (1952), but before an account is given of this,
certain additional results of Nieuwkoop and Nigtevecht (1954)
deserve mention. Instead of examining the neuralization process in a
longitudinal fold, the authors used flattened ectodermal pieces. Two

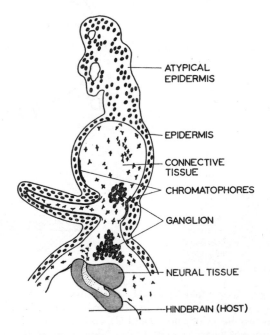

Figure 58. Differentiations in an ectodermal fold implanted at
the hindbrain region of a gastrula. (After Nieuwkoop *et al.*, 1952.)

pieces of competent ectoderm were pressed against each other, and a
piece of inductor (living notochord) placed in the centre of this
"sandwich". The result of a gradual spreading of the inductive
stimulus in the folds was confirmed by this means. Differentiation

started in the immediate vicinity of the inductor, and after a subsequent two weeks of cultivation this area usually showed differentiation into hindbrain structures. Nearer the periphery, the neural structures represented forebrain formations and the corresponding sense organs, whereas the parts nearest the periphery remained undifferentiated (figure 59).

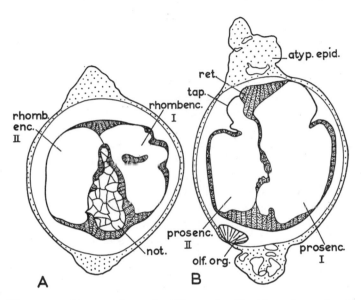

Figure 59. Two sections of a "flat explant" with a piece of notochord as inductor. Close to the inductor, deuterencephalic formations have been induced; nearer to the periphery the secondary structures are of the archencephalic type, the periphery parts on the extreme of the explant remaining undifferentiated. (After Nieuwkoop and Nigtevecht, 1954.)

The theory presented by Nieuwkoop on the basis of these experiments suggests two successive phases in the induction process. The first is regarded as a general stimulus leading to the manifestation of the differentiation properties of the ectoderm. This tendency is evidently presented all over the prospective neural plate, and leads to differentiation of *archencephalic structures*. In a reference to the earlier results of autoneuralization (Chapter IV), Nieuwkoop *et al.* (1952) concluded that this "activating principle liberates prosencephalic differentiation tendencies in the whole area of ectoderm in which activation is brought up to threshold." The nature of this activating principle still remains an open question, as does the mode of its spreading, but in the light of the latter experiments of Nieuwkoop and Nigtevecht (1954) it is evident that it is an external stimulus, and in their experiments emanates from the notochord material. Furthermore, this activating system determined the total size of the neural formations, and the response to this seems to be of the all-or-none-type (Nieuwkoop *et al.*, 1955; Hori and Nieuwkoop, 1955; Nieuwkoop, 1958).

According to the theory in question, the regional segregation of the central nervous system is due to a subsequent wave of differentiative action, called *"transformation"* which "is a quantitative process, through which, with increasing strength of action, progressively more caudal differentiation tendencies appear" (Nieuwkoop, 1955). Segregation within the central nervous system is now due to the balance between "intrinsic, autonomous prosencephalic differentiation tendencies and extrinsic 'caudal' influences." (Nieuwkoop *et al.*, 1952). A schematic representation of this hypothesis applied to the folding experiments is shown in figure 60.

As pointed out by Nieuwkoop *et al.* (1952), the theory seems to account satisfactorily for the facts of normal development: during the invagination of the dorsal lip the whole area of prospective neuroectoderm will gradually be "activated" by it, and a subsequent wave of transforming influence will segregate this activated neural tissue into different parts of the central nervous system; the most cranial part is not exposed to this stimulus and continues its differentiation in an archencephalic direction. This temporal aspect seems to be confirmed by the investigations of Eyal-Giladi (1954), to be presented later in connection with the "time factor" (page 194). Some other experiments carried out at the Hubrecht laboratory which confirm the ideas of Nieuwkoop *et al.* (1952) are also presented in the following chapters (Sala, 1955a, 1955b; Johnen, 1956a, 1956b; Nieuwkoop *et al.*, 1955b). For discussion of the theory, the reader is referred to the original papers of Nieuwkoop (1955a, 1955b, 1958).

As noted from this account of the activation-transformation theory, and as pointed out by Nieuwkoop himself (1952), the hypothesis bears a certain resemblance to the quantitative theory of Dalcq and Pasteels (1937, 1938), particularly as regards the "field effects" of the neuralizing stimulus. On the other hand, the suggestion of two stimuli, activation and transformation, seems to bear a close resemblance to the ideas of Chuang (1940) and Toivonen (1940) as well as to the two mediators of Yamada (1950b). How far the differences in these conceptions are only terminological is discussed in the next chapter.

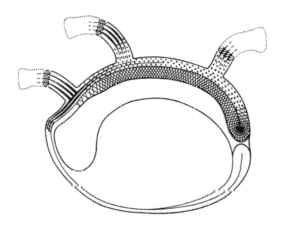

Figure 60. A summary of the results obtained with the "fold" method, and explained in the light of the activation-transformation hypothesis of Nieuwkoop. The folds are divided into three regions: Distal region remaining undifferentiated (pointed line), intermediate region showing mesectodermal inductions (slightly hatched) and proximal regions differentiating into neural structures (continuous lines). The primary activating action leads to differentiation into an archencephalic direction, and in the most proximal part of the folds this is followed by a transforming action of the "mesodermal substrate" resulting in differentiation of deuterencephalic structures (indicated by crosses). (After Nieuwkoop, *et al.*, 1952.)

6. *The two-gradient theory*

The qualitative theory of Chuang (1940) and Toivonen (1940) suggested different inductive agents for neural and mesodermal differentiations. The first fractionations of heterogeneous inductors (Toivonen and Kuusi, 1948; Toivonen, 1949b, 1950) along with some subsequent chemical experiments appeared to corroborate this idea. In testing the inductive action of guinea-pig bone-marrow, Toivonen (1953a, 1953b) demonstrated for the first time an almost pure mesodermalizing activity in implanted materials. These observations, together with the findings of Toivonen (1940), were used in planning the following experiments.

The experimental series to be described was stimulated by the suggestion of Lehmann (1950) concerning the combined effects of two types of inductors with different actions. His conception can briefly be presented in the form of three equations:

(i)   Much archencephalic + little spinal → archencephalic effect.
(ii) Relative much archencephalic + relative much spinal → deuter-encephalic effect.
(iii) Little archencephalic + much spinal → spinal effect.

As a result of some findings in 1950–1954 (e.g., the detection of purely mesodermal activity), the conceptions of Lehmann (1950) can be somewhat modified, and the term "spinal" replaced by "mesodermal activity". This idea was subsequently tested by an experimental combination of such effects (i.e., combination of archencephalic and mesodermal inductive agents). This was carried out by a simultaneous implantation of liver and bone-marrow tissue of the guinea-pig (Toivonen and Saxén, 1955a, 1955b). The results demonstrated in figure 61 show that when these two tissues of different

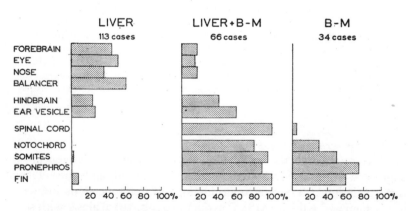

Figure 61. The simultaneous inductive action of two heterogenous inductors with different actions. Guinea-pig liver and bone-marrow tissue were implanted either alone or simultaneously, and a combined action was noted in the latter case. (After Toivonen and Saxén, 1955b.)

inductive action are combined and implanted simultaneously, their combined effect is not a simple summation of their effects, but one that is definitely new, i.e., spinal cord is induced in a higher percentage of cases in comparison than with the two original tissues (Plate 9.1). We believe that the effect of the combined inductor can be explained as a manifestation of three different "fields" of stimuli upon the competent ectoderm (figure 62). Two of these

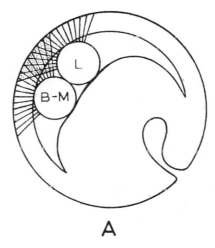

A

Figure 62. A scheme of the implanted liver and bone-marrow pieces in the blastocoel. The scheme suggests three different "fields" of inductive action: A neuralizing "liver field", a meso-dermalizing "bone-marrow field", and between them a field in which the two effects overlap (combined action). (After Toivonen and Saxén, 1955a.)

are the original "fields" of the two inductor tissues, and the third represents the area in which these fields overlap each other and result in a combined effect. On the other hand, this combined effect is a graduated field in which the two effective principles are represented in different amounts—an idea once again obviously stimulated by the old conceptions of determining fields (Child, 1929; Dalcq and Pasteels, 1937, 1938; Yamada, 1950b; Nieuwkoop, 1950; Nieuwkoop et al., 1952). These conceptions are demonstrated in a very schematic form in figure 63. According to this two-gradient hypothesis, there are two active principles involved in the induction process—one leading to determination of mesodermal structures, and the other

controlling the neuralization of the ectoderm and leading to archencephalic induction if acting alone. Both effects are suggested as being
strongest in the dorsal midline of the normal inductor tissue, and
weaker ventrally, as in the hypothesis of Yamada (1950). The
neuralizing principle, according to our theory, is not changed in the
cephalocaudal direction, whereas the mesodermalizing principle is
lacking in the most anterior part corresponding to the region of the

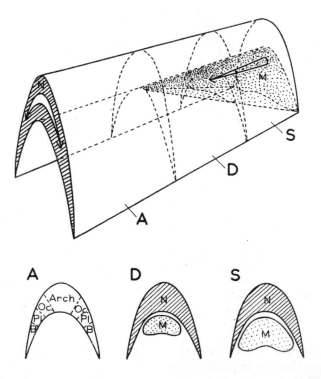

Figure 63. A schematic representation of the two-gradient hy-
pothesis. *M*, mesodermalizing action; *N*, neuralizing action,
A, archencephalic inductions; *D*, deuterencephalic inductions;
S, spinocaudal inductions. (After Toivonen and Saxén, 1955a.)

prechordal plate, and increases gradually in the caudal direction. In
consequence of the combined action of these two principles, different
hindbrain structures, as well as spinocaudal formations, are induced.

On comparison of this model with earlier ideas, there are several common features observable. Two active principles in gradient form were suggested both by Yamada (1950b) and Nieuwkoop *et al.* (1952), and the existence of neuralizing and mesodermalizing principles by Chuang (1940) and Toivonen (1940). During subsequent experiments, some minor modifications to this model were presented by the authors (Saxén and Toivonen, 1961), but as a whole it still seems to explain most of the results obtained in studies of primary induction.

7. Concepts of regionally specific inductors

In all the theories presented earlier, the regionality of the central nervous system was regarded as the product of quantitative differences in either one agent (organicine) or in the ratio of two active principles ($M_{dv} + M_{cc}$, activation-transformation, neuralizing-mesodermalizing principles). Nevertheless, some authors still suggest the existence of regionally specific inductors, and the main protagonist of this concept is the team working at Heilingenberg under the leadership of one of the pioneers of amphibian embryology, Otto Mangold.

The main evidence for this concept comes from a series of isolation experiments, in which the presumptive neural ectoderm or the already visible neural plate were explanted (Mangold and von Woellwarth, 1950; von Woellwarth, 1951, 1952). The neural area was isolated from embryos of different ages: gastrulae with a small yolk plug, gastrulae with a closed blastopore, and neurulae with a closed neural tube. The explants in the first group showed differentiations of the neural crest type, and only occasionally poorly differentiated brain vesicles. In the second group, most of the explants showed differentiations of the archencephalic type (brain parts and corresponding sense organs) whereas the deuterencephalic inductions were relatively rare and poorly differentiated. At the time of the closure of the neural tube, the isolated fragments develop into well differentiated brain vesicles representing both forebrain and hindbrain structures with corresponding sense organs.

In discussing these results, von Woellwarth (1952, 1956a) concluded that they did not support the idea that the first step of induction is a general "neuralization" followed by a subsequent segregation of the brain parts. In contrast, they seemed to demonstrate the fact that the induced explants were given their final destiny from the beginning. The short time of induction in the younger series was considered responsible for the "weak neural induction", leading to the formation of neural crest derivatives or less-differentiated fore-brain structures. This direct determination of competent ectoderm to become different parts of the central nervous system is due to regionally specific inductors, "two or three spatially separated differentiation centres" (von Woellwarth, 1956a, transl.). However, to some extent the author seemed to agree with the earlier concepts of fields and quantities of these inductors, and pointed out that the neural crest is obviously induced by a weak inductive action.

From these observations, as well as certain chemical data (presented in Chapter VII), Heinz Tiedemann (1959b) agreed with these ideas, and stated that the theory of the combined action of two inductors leading to the differentiation of hindbrain structures might not be valid.

This concept of the regionally specific inductive agents has already been discussed in connection with the chemical fractionation experiments, and will be reverted to later. As a typical example of the quite complicated situation in this kind of work, it may be mentioned that experiments very similar to those by von Woellwarth (1951, 1952) were carried out by a student of Nieuwkoop, Mrs. Eyal-Giladi (1954). The results fully confirmed the above observations, *but were considered as giving evidence in favour of Nieuwkoop's hypothesis*. We may add that our own two-gradient hypothesis presented above might well explain these results, as well as those of Yamada.

X

Theories in the Light of Experimental Data

1. *Introduction*

After presentation of the main theories on the process of induction, they need discussion in the light of various experimental data. Let us first consider the possibilities of such an experimental analysis of the theories. When studying a dynamic, continuous process such as the determination of the embryo and its controlling mechanisms, the best method would be to follow the process by methods permitting continuous registration, but in the case of embryonic induction this is hardly possible. An inductive stimulus can only be recorded by the subsequent morphological differentiation of the reactive tissue—the very few exceptions of results obtained by means of histochemical, submicroscopical or immunological methods do not yet permit of any generalizations, but may be promising for future research. Thus, today we cannot follow the process with exactitude, and its results cannot be examined until several days or weeks have elapsed from the actual stimulus. We must therefore be satisfied with time-slice pictures of the process, obtained by an experimental division of the process into successive steps. This course of action has repeatedly been used in studies concerning the distribution of inductive activity in the embryo, in investigations related to the time factor in the induction process, as well as experiments made to elucidate changes in the competence of the ectoderm. Another, quite original line of approach to the problem is the centrifugation of fertilized eggs— originally stimulated by the rotation experiments and examined on many occasions by Jean Pasteels (1941–1954). Furthermore, the chemical fractionations presented in Chapter VII have provided us with valuable data on the mechanism of the induction. Our modification of the two-gradient hypothesis was originally based on experiments with certain combined inductors, and recently this type of experiment has been continued.

Finally, we must revert to what was said above. The results of all the experiments suggested above were not studied until several days after the actual inductive process, which, however, normally takes place in a few hours. Consequently, we cannot exclude a variety of subsequent factors which influence the development between the process to be analyzed and the final differentiations obtained. In addition to true experimental errors due to such environmental conditions (culture medium, temperature, etc.), the role played by the initial mass of developing tissue and late interactions between tissue rudiments have to be discussed.

2. *Centrifugation experiments*

A particularly interesting approach to studying the changes in the "morphogenetic potential" of the ectoderm was made by Jean Pasteels in his centrifugation experiments (Pasteels, 1947a, 1947b 1947c, 1953a, 1953b, 1954). After some minutes of centrifugation at 460 g, the roof of the blastocoele of young gastrulae or old blastulae will collapse, and under certain circumstances this part of the ectoderm will subsequently form a coherent mass and develop into secondary structures (figure 64). This phenomenon has been demonstrated in several anuran and urodelan species (Rana, Xenopus, Pleurodeles, Amblystoma, Bufo) (Pasteels, 1953a, 1953b; Karasaki and Yamada, 1955), whereas in Discoglossus the "reaction" is weak, and in three Triturus-species tested so far, secondary formation could not be obtained after similar centrifugation (Pasteels, op. cit.). The sensitivity to centrifugation is limited to a very short period from the late blastula to the early gastrula: after the blastopore has become crescent-shaped centrifugation is no longer capable of altering the normal development of the ventral ectoderm. Even during this period of "competence" certain differences in the results can be obtained, dependent upon the stage at which the centrifugation was effected, and both quantitative and qualitative variations can be achieved in the secondary ventral structures. The most sensitive period is restricted to the earliest stages of gastrulation (Pasteels, 1953b; Karasaki and Yamada, 1955).

As a result of centrifugation during the sensitive period of the species such as is mentioned above, the collapsed blastocoele roof will differentiate into quite complex spinocaudal structures, often accompanied by hindbrain vesicles. In addition to spinal cord, the caudal structures are represented by notochord, myotomes and nephric tubules. These secondary structures are always cephalized in the same direction as that of the host, but are usually less organized, forming complex tissues resembling those obtained by heterogenous inductors.

That the changes in the ectoderm leading to an altered differentiation really do occur during centrifugation or immediately thereafter, was shown by Pasteels (1953a). Immediately after centrifugation, the collapsed blastocoele roof was excised, and all trace of attached endodermal cells removed. Following this the ectoderm was cultured in isolation as an explant, or transplanted either homo- or

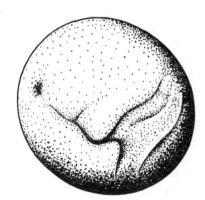 

Figure 64. A collapsed roof of the blastocoel following centrifugation (left), and a young neurula showing the formation of a secondary neural plate from the collapsed part of the roof. (After Pasteels, 1953a.)

heteroplastically into non-treated hosts. Both methods of cultivation led to the formation of definite spinocaudal structures similar to those obtained in the original experiments.

In discussion of these results, Pasteels (1954) concluded that factors responsible for archencephalic, spinocaudal or mesodermal inductions, are present within the ectoderm, but "are ineffective in normal development". The author was inclined to explain his results on the basis of the quantitative theory of Dalcq and Pasteels (1937, 1938, page 159). Thus the centrifugation might be comparable with the original rotation experiments which led the authors to the presentation of the quantitative theory. In both instances, the secondary structures are developed as a result of changes in the "morphogenetic potential" of the ectoderm. Pasteels (1954) further stressed that the "activation" of the ectoderm in these experiments seemed to be an intrinsic process comparable with the autoneuralization obtained by "subcytolytic" treatment. Experiments made by Karasaki and Yamada (1955) included some intended to test the validity of the last mentioned suggestion, and their results did not appear to corroborate it. These authors, after confirming the results obtained by Pasteels with whole blastulae and gastrulae of their Japanese species, centrifuged pieces of presumptive ectoderm isolated *before* this treatment. Of 85 such explants made from two pieces of isolated ectoderm centrifuged according to the method of Pasteels, none displayed any neural or mesodermal differentiations, and only epidermis and occasional sucker cells were identified. In order to investigate the autonomous capacities of the ectoderm to differentiate, pieces of competent ectoderm were exposed to high pH, known to cause cytolytic changes followed by autoneuralization (Chapter IV). As in the earlier similar experiments, Karasaki and Yamada (1955) noted differentiation of archencephalic structures, but never the formation of spinocaudal tissues similar to those obtained after the centrifugation of whole embryos. Hence, the authors concluded that their results did not support the conception of Pasteels (1954) as to a direct activation of the ectoderm following centrifugation.

Furthermore, we have pointed to another possible explanation of these interesting observations of Pasteels (1947–1954). As a consequence of the collapse of the blastocoele roof, it came into contact with the endodermal cells, and during the later stages also with the material of the invaginated dorsal lip. There thus exists the possibility that an actual induction by this material occurs (Toivonen, 1954b; Toivonen and Saxén, 1955b). As Dalcq (1960) pointed out recently, there are, however, several features in the centrifugation experiments which are difficult to explain in the light of "normal" induction: the period of sensitivity to the centrifugation is not in accord with the competence for neural and mesodermal inductors, the secondary structures always lack archencephalic formations, and the secondary structures are less organized than are embryos obtained in experiments with normal inductors. There is one further point to be added to these comments of Dalcq (1960). In the experiments of Pasteels (1953a) in which the ectoderm was excised immediately after centrifugation, the time of contact between the ectoderm and the underlying tissue could not be more than some 15 minutes; however, a spinocaudal-mesodermal induction produced by living inductor requires a much longer period of contact (Johnen, 1956a). The process taking place during centrifugation can therefore hardly be compared with normal induction, but if the findings of Karasaki and Yamada (1955) are borne in mind, it is quite evident that without an external stimulus the ectoderm is not capable of becoming mesodermalized. Therefore the most probable explanation—although a very superficial one—is that during the process of centrifugation certain active agents are transferred inside the embryo into the reacting ectoderm. This transfer is not comparable with normal, active induction, but is a consequence of passive movements due to the centrifugation—on this point, our view is in close correspondence with the explanation of Pasteels (1954). Nevertheless, we do not think that this must be explained in the light of quantitative changes in one active agent, but rather it involves the active transfer of several inductively active agents.

3. The time factor in the primary induction

(a) *Distribution of inductive activity during normal development*

As stated in Chapter IV (page 59), there do not seem to be regional differences in neural competence within the presumptive epidermis and neural plate, and its "morphogenetic potential" is evenly distributed. It thus becomes evident that its segregation into different regions of the central nervous system must be due to an uneven distribution of determinative stimuli in its environment—a fact noted in all the different conceptions presented above. It is accordingly quite natural that this distribution of inductive activity has been the object of interest since the very beginning of the research work concerned with induction.

The first attempt at mapping out the inductively active district in the embryo was made by Bautzmann (1926). He showed that in the gastrula stage this activity was limited to a quadrant above the blastopore, the dorsal lip. Bautzmann performed his experiments on urodeles, and subsequent investigations with anuran species showed certain differences (Schechtmann, 1938; Raunich, 1940). Following this first attempt, a number of investigators have dealt with the same problem; it seems without doubt the most important means of trying to elucidate the process of normal induction. Several methods have been used, following two principal lines: either small fragments of inductor tissue have been isolated at different steps of development

N

and tested against competent ectoderm, or induction has been followed *in vivo* by the isolation of reactive material at different stages of induction, to follow their differentiation during subsequent cultivation *in vitro*. Despite certain discrepancies in the results obtained by these different methods, we have today quite a clear picture of the development of inductive capacity during gastrulation, and the distribution of this activity in the dorsal lip and invaginated archenteron roof tissues.

The experiments of Spemann (1931) had already demonstrated certain differences in the regional inductive capacity of parts of the organizer tissue (see Chapter I), and subsequent investigations made by Mangold (1933b) definitely demonstrated the justification of Spemann's division into "head organizer" and "trunk-organizer". Mangold (1933b) implanted different sections of the archenteron roof into the blastocoele of young gastrulae, and demonstrated their regionally different inductive effects. As will be seen below, this method has certain disadvantages, and the regional influence of the host, clearly demonstrated by Chuang (1939) and Toivonen (1940), cannot be excluded. Hence Holtfreter (1936, 1938b) used the explantation method to test these differences between the different regions of the inductor tissue. He distinguished between head and trunk organizers, and demonstrated their different distribution in the blastopore lip: the more anterior parts induced head structures (brain and sense organs), whereas the more posterior parts induced trunk or tail formations (figure 65). A more detailed study of the distribution of the inductive activity suggested that even the area of "head organizer" could be divided into partially overlapping fields of more specific determining stimuli, leading to the determination of specific sense organs in small explants (figure 65). "This seems to indicate that even at the gastrula stage the head organizer is not actually an equipotential entity but is subdivided into specialized inductors, although distinct boundaries between them do not seem to exist." (Holtfreter and Hamburger, 1955.)

The temporal changes in the inductive capacity of dorsal lip tissue were the object of special study by a Japanese team and by Gallera in 1947–60. The Japanese team presented the results of extensive experimental research work in a series of publications in 1942–1953 (Okada and Takaya, 1942a, 1942b; Okada and Hama, 1943, 1944, 1945a, 1945b, 1948; Hama, 1947, 1949, 1950a, 1950b; Takaya, 1953a, 1953b). These authors used both implantation and explantation methods, and removed sections of different regions of the inductor tissue at different stages of gastrulation and neurulation. The most important of their findings was the demonstration of a definite change in the inductive action of the dorsal lip tissue during gastrulation: before invagination, the whole dorsal lip area induced merely trunk and tail formations, and only in explantation experiments was a certain tendency by the most anterior part of the dorsal lip to induce forebrain structures noted. In implantation experiments, even the prospective prechordal area induced spinocaudal and mesodermal structures before its invagination. After the beginning of invagination, the inductive activity was qualitatively changed: the most

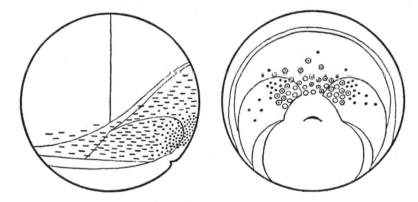

Figure 65. Distribution of the "head organizer" (dots) and of the "trunk-tail organizer" (dashes) in a young Urodelan gastrula (left). On the right, the figure indicates the localization of areas capable of forming ears (dots), noses (circles), and eyes (circles with dots). Holtfreter and Hamburger, 1955, after Holtfreter, 1938b.)

anterior part of the archenteron roof, the prechordal plate, lost its capacity to induce deuterencephalic and spinocaudal structures, and instead induced archencephalic formations (forebrain and sense organs). Similar changes were noted in the notochord-forming potency of the dorsal lip tissue: before invagination the whole dorsal lip tissue was able to form notochord when isolated and wrapped in ectoderm. After invagination, this potency was lost, and only the one or two most caudal fifths of the archenteron roof were capable of forming notochord. It is interesting to note that in these experiments the neural structures induced from the ectoderm wrapped in the inductor tissue seemed to have a close relationship to the notochord-forming potency of the inductor tissue: "Whereas the archencephalic organs such as forebrain and eyes were formed only in the absence of the notochord, in its presence all the neural organs produced were deuterencephalic or spinal cord" (Takaya, 1953a).

In an attempt to elucidate these obviously progressive changes in the inductive capacity of the dorsal lip tissue, the authors compared the inductive action of fresh implanted pieces of inductor with those cultured in isolation for different periods of time. When an isolated fragment of the anterior part of the uninvaginated dorsal lip tissue was cultured in Holtfreter-solutions for more than 20 hours (a time corresponding to the loss of its caudal inductive activity *in vivo*), a change of its action was again noted. Before such cultivation (fresh implanted) it induced deuterencephalic and spinocaudal structures, but after cultivation in salt solution, the inductive action was purely archencephalic, as *in vivo* after the same period. It thus appears that the changes are not due to the invagination, but can be considered as an autonomous "maturation" of the inductor tissue.

These temporal variations of the inductive activity were also examined by Gallera in a series of experiments (Gallera, 1949, 1951, 1952, 1958, 1959, 1960), by the employment of both implantation and explantation methods. In his first series (1949) he compared the inductive action of the prechordal zone taken from young gastrulae, preneurula stages and from neurulae. In confirming the results of the Japanese team, he noted that the uninvaginated prechordal territory only occasionally induced archencephalic structures, but usually complex formations with head, trunk and tail structures. After invagination, the prechordal plate induced only archencephalic structures, accompanied by certain endodermal derivatives of the head. These observations, along with some subsequent experimental results of his defect operations (Gallera, 1951, 1952), confirm the data of the Japanese team, and show the changes in the inductive capacity of the archenteric roof and their obvious importance to the normal segregation of the overlying neural plate. The results recently obtained by Gallera (1958, 1959, 1960) are in accordance with these observations, and will be dealt with in more detail in connection with the "time factor".

These changes may be finally examined against the background of some vital dye experiments made by Okada and Hama (1945b) (figure 66). The dorsal lip was stained with vital stain at two different stages of gastrulation, at the beginning of the invagination, and some hours later at the stage of a crescent shaped blastopore. The stained zone at stage I corresponds roughly to the "head-organizer" of Spemann, the later zone being identical with the "trunk-organizer"

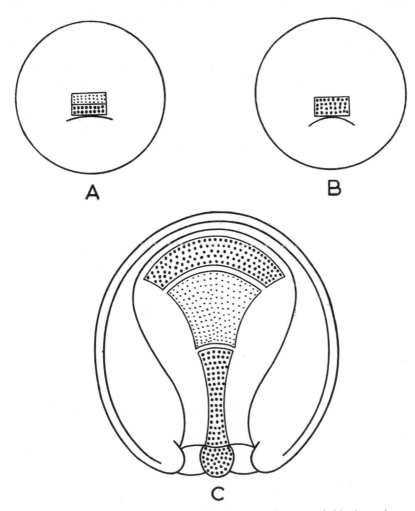

Figure 66. A scheme of the vital dye experiments of Okada and Hama (1945b). The dorsal lip tissue was stained at an early gastrula stage (A) and at a somewhat later stage (B). Figure C shows the distribution of the stained material in the archenteron roof of a neurula.

When the stained specimens were examined at the neurula stage, it was noted that the whole archenteron roof had developed from the material stained at the early gastrula stages, so that the head region corresponded to the two areas stained at stage I, and the trunk-tail region corresponded to the area stained at the crescent shaped gastrula stage. When these territories were now tested *after* invagination, they yielded a different inductive action, corresponding to the original "head" and "trunk" inductors of Spemann. It is thus established that the archenteron roof develops from a quite minute territory of the dorsal lip, and it appears that in comparison with the "trunk" inductor the "head" organizer area undergoes a much wider distribution. This observation might have a most important significance, and could be partly responsible for the changes in the inductive action during this process of invagination (page 229).

The regional inductive capacity of the archenteron roof has been tested in a great number of experiments, many different techniques being employed. Mangold (1933b) and ter Horst (1948) used an isolation and implantation method, von Woellwarth (1951, 1952) isolated different territories of the neural plate and cultured them *in vitro* (page 175), and the fold technique of Nieuwkoop *et al.* (1952) provided valuable information on the same subject (page 171). Moreover, the experiments of the Japanese team described above, as well as the works of Gallera (1947–1960) and Eyal-Giladi (to be treated below), have demonstrated the regional differences in the inductive capacity of the archenteron roof. All these results seem to be in close accord, and they might be summarized in view of the more recent results of Sala (1955a, 1955b), as well as the very similar observations of ter Horst (1948).

Ter Horst (1948) and Sala (1955a, 1955b) used transverse fragments of the archenteron roof, and tested their inductive activity in sandwich explants—ter Horst divided her archenteron roof into five, Sala into four territories, and the latter author further tested four "transitional" zones which included material from two neighbouring regions in each case. In her series, ter Horst (1948) was mainly interested in the induction of the central nervous system, and the main results are demonstrated in figure 67. In comparison with some results, already presented, the neural tube and muscle inductions by the most anterior part of the archenteron roof are unexpected. This is explained by the fact that this territory obviously did not represent the prechordal plate proper, but when cultured in isolation differentiated into notochord in a high percentage of cases. This fact explains the definite "caudalization" of the inductive products for instance when compared with Sala's results. He divided the archenteron roof into four sections (and the "transitional" areas), in which the most anterior fourth corresponds to the prechordal plate. His results, demonstrated in figure 68, confirm the earlier observations of the Japanese authors, as well as those of ter Horst (1948), and

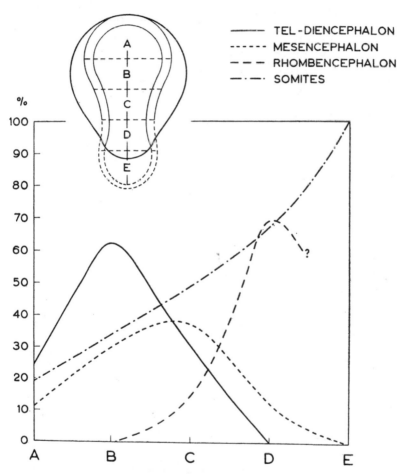

Figure 67. The incidence of different types of induction in experiments in which different territories of the archenteron roof were used as inductors. (After ter Horst, 1948.)

display a definite caudo-cranial "gradient": The prechordal plate was a pure archencephalic inductor, the two sections corresponding to the anterior and middle part of the notochord induced both fore-brain and hindbrain structures, and the middle part, in addition to

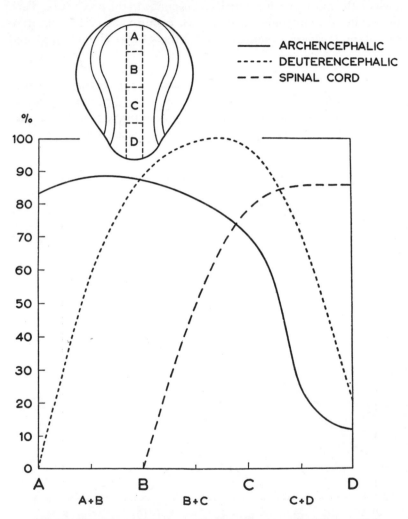

Figure 68. An experiment corresponding to that illustrated in Figure 67. The inductive action of four territories of the archenteron roof was examined, as well as that of three transitional areas. (After Sala, 1956b.)

these, spinal cord. The posterior notochordal section induced brain structures only occasionally, but spinal cord in a high percentage of cases. From these results, Sala (1955a) presented a hypothetical "two-gradient" system as an active principle in the archenteron roof (figure 69), and following to Nieuwkoop *et al.* (1952), he called these "activating" and "transforming" principles. Further to the qualitative analysis of the induced structures, Sala (1955a) made some

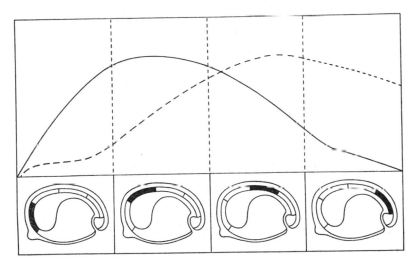

Figure 69. The "two-wave" theory of Sala (1955a). Black areas in the archenteron roof show the different regions tested for the inductive capacity. Continuous line = activation, spotted line = transformation.

observations on the size of the secondary formations. He stated that there is a maximum size of the induced neural structures which corresponds to the area of the first half of the anterior notochordal area, and from here the size of the structures decreases towards both ends of the archenteron roof.

All the above-mentioned investigations demonstrate the presence of a certain regional difference in different caudocranial sections of the archenteric roof, and show that their inductive capacity corresponds to the segregation of the overlying neural plate. Information on similar differences in longitudinal sections is more scanty, and the most accurate data are published by Raven and Kloos (1945).

Raven and Kloos (1945) divided the anterior notochordal area of the archenteron roof into two median and two lateral pieces, as demonstrated in figure 70, and these pieces were implanted in the

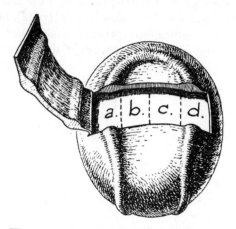

Figure 70. The operation scheme of Raven and Kloos (1945) for study of the distribution of the inductive capacity in the archenteron roof.

usual way. The results of their rather small series showed, as known from the earlier works, that the medial parts induced brain formations, accompanied by neural crest derivatives (ganglion cells, pigment cells, cartilage). On the other hand, the two lateral strips which did not induce a true central nervous system still induced neural crest derivatives. The authors were inclined to the conclusion that the results corroborated the ideas of the quantitative hypothesis; "The results indicate that the primary determination of neural plate, neural crest and epidermis is brought about by the differences in concentration of one and the same substance". (It is interesting to note in this connection, that a very similar mediolateral weakening is obtained in the inductive action of the medullary plate, cf. Waechter, 1953; Tiedemann-Waechter, 1960.) Taken with the results of the "transverse" differences in inductive action, it seems quite evident that in the archenteron roof there exists a real gradient in both caudocranial and medio-lateral directions.

The question now arises as to the extent to which this graduated distribution of inductive capacity is responsible for the normal segregation of the central nervous system. The first experiments in this respect were carried out by Hall (1937), who transplanted the posterior-(trunk) organizer of an old gastrula into the region of the anterior dorsal lip (head-organizer) and noted a suppression of the development of the brain. Waddington (1941) made corresponding observations with young anuran-gastrulae after reversal of the anterio-posterior axis of the organizer area: after this operation normal gastrulation was disturbed, and the regional inductive action was hardly noted. Waddington (1941) and Waddington and Yao (1950), felt that this disturbance might be correlated to the very rapid gastrulation of the anuran species used (Discoglossus), and later repeated the experiments with urodele species (Waddington and Yao, 1950). A similar reversal of the organization centre in young *Triturus alpestris* embryos did not affect development, and complete normal embryos were obtained. The same result was obtained when the anterior and posterior organizer were exchanged. Even at the late gastrula stage (Harrison stage 13), the regulation of the anterior-posterior quality of the inductive action of the archenteron roof seems to be possible. If at this stage an extra archenteron roof is placed between the ectoderm and the archenteron roof of the gastrula in a reversed condition (figure 71), normal morphogenesis is hardly

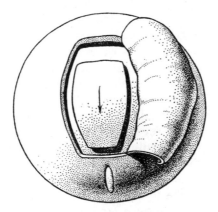

Figure 71. The operational scheme of Waddington and Yao (1950), in which an extra archenteron roof is placed, reversed, between the ectoderm and the archenteron roof.

affected. The findings of Holtfreter (1944a) and Deuchar (1953) are in close agreement with these observations. Holtfreter (1944a) studied the inductive effect of the blastopore lip after its cells had been disaggregated by alkali treatment, and subsequently reaggregated. This disaggregation certainly led to the abolition of any "inductive fields" responsible for the segregation of the induced structures, but when tested in implantation experiments, these reaggregates were able to induce a quite symmetrical and well organized nervous system. Before these results are discussed, the work of Deuchar (1953) has to be presented. She pointed out that Holtfreter (1944b) had used the dorsal lips of young gastrulae, in which the regional properties of the organizer tissue are still not fixed and are therefore modifiable (Hall, 1937; Okada and Takaya, 1942a, 1942b; Waddington and Yao, 1950). Furthermore, in these implantation experiments the influence of the host could not be excluded. Deuchar (1953) accordingly used pieces of the archenteron roof of older gastrulae (Harrison's stage 12–12½), and their inductive action was tested in explantation experiments. When the archenteron roof was divided into three transversed sections, and separate tests made, no definite differences were found in their inductive capacity, and their inductive power was low. On the other hand, when the mass of inductor tissue was increased to correspond with the mass of the archenteron roof by the employment of three similar thirds in the same explant, the inductive effect was definitely stronger, and there were then certain regional differences demonstrable which corresponded to the differences already described. After disaggregation of the same thirds, no such regional differences were observed, but when the archenteron roof was disaggregated as a whole, its inductive effect after reaggregation did not differ significantly from the normal, non-disaggregated, inductor tissue. The author explained this by assuming that these regional differences in the inductive capacity of the archenteron roof are reversible, "and can be re-established after they have been experimentally disturbed" (Deuchar, 1953). According to the author, these data can be explained by the existence of an anterior-posterior concentration gradient.

We should here like to stress the observed differences between species noted in Waddington's (1941) and Waddington and Yao's (1950) experiments. As mentioned above, the anuran dorsal lip does not seem to be able to re-establish its inductive capacity after an experimental reversal of its anterior posterior axis, whereas this is possible in Triturus both after similar reversal (Waddington and Yao, 1950), and after disaggregation of the dorsal lip tissue (Holtfreter, 1944b; Deuchar, 1953). These results seem to be in close agreement with the observations of Okada and Takaya (1942a, 1942b), demonstrating an earlier "maturation" of the inductor tissue in anurans followed by an earlier segregation into "tail"- and "trunk"-type inductor.

The large amount of experimental data given above may be summarized very briefly: the inductive action of the normal organizer tissue, the archenteron roof, shows definite regional differences. These can be demonstrated both in caudo-cranial and dorso-ventral directions, and they seem to correspond to the segregation of the overlying neural plate. In urodeles, this regionality is established during invagination and is still modifiable at late gastrula stage.

(b) *The time factor in primary induction.* In discussing a dynamic process such as primary induction during gastrulation, it is necessary to consider the time factor. Consequently in the previous chapters the role of time has often been briefly mentioned. Here some further information will be given, and a more detailed presentation made of some experiments concerned with the time problem. As mentioned in the introduction to this chapter, two principles may be used to get "time-slice" pictures of the continuous process of induction: the active and reactive tissue can be brought together experimentally, and one can either introduce variations in the time of contact or use tissues with some age discrepancy in order to study the time factor (e.g., Gallera, 1958, 1959, 1960; Johnen, 1956a, 1956b, 1961; Toivonen, 1958, 1961). On the other hand, the normal induction process can be divided into successive stages by isolating the normally induced ectoderm at different stages of the invagination, and culturing it to obtain the end result of the morphogenetic stimulation which has occurred (Mangold and von Woellwarth, 1950; von Woellwarth, 1951, 1952; Eyal-Giladi 1954).

As was seen in the previous chapter, we have today a relatively definite idea of the distribution of inductive activity in the normal archenteron roof forming obvious gradients. Moreover, we know the changes that occur in this distribution during development, but what we actually do not know, is the answer to the question, *when does induction occur?* This question can be sub-divided into a variety of more detailed questions:

— At which stage of gastrulation do the inductive stimuli reach the ectoderm?
— What is the time required for an inductive stimulus, and do there exist differences between the different types of induction?

— Do there occur successive waves of inductive stimuli during gastrulation responsible for certain cumulative, stabilizing and re-determinative processes?

— What is the role of the possible differences in the molecular size, diffusability, etc., of the different hypothetical inductive agents?

— What is the role of the changes in the competence of the ectoderm?

These questions show us how complicated the study of this dynamic process is, and how very difficult it is to carry out experiments in which all these factors can be taken into consideration, and to study only one or two of the factors by exclusion of the others. We will return to these questions after presentation of some experimental results.

The isolation experiments of von Woellwarth (1951, 1952) have already been described on page 175. After isolation of the presumptive neural plate at successive stages of gastrulation, he obtained neural differentiations in the following order: neural crest material—archencephalic structures—deuterencephalic structures. The results have more recently been confirmed by Eyal-Giladi (1954), who used a grafting method obviously inspired by the folds of Nieuwkoop *et al.* (1952): a transverse area of the presumptive neural plate ectoderm was removed at different stages of gastrulation, and cultured as a fold on the ventral side of the same embryo (figure 72). This method made it possible to follow with relative precision the effect of the invagination upon the determination of the overlying ectoderm. Eyal-Giladi (1954) noted that after the first contact with the archenteron roof, the ectoderm formed normal epidermis, and subsequently, after a somewhat prolonged contact, derivatives of the neural crest. The next step is definitely an archencephalic induction (activation), which can thus be demonstrated in the posterior part of the neural plate as a result of an early contact with the invaginating archenteron roof. During subsequent invagination, the "activated" or labile-determined part becomes "transformed" by the chordal area of the inductor tissue, and this leads to the formation of more caudal structures. The author discussed these results in the light of Nieuwkoop's (1952) hypothesis, and we will return to them after the presentation of some other experimental data. Her results may not be quite conclusive as regards the activation-transformation-hypothesis, but they have provided us with valuable information on the induction process related to the stage of invagination. The results of Eyal-Giladi (1954) hint at a progressive, two-wave-process which leads to the final regional differentiations of the central nervous system, and also to the determination of the tail. This does not seem to be in accordance with some of the observations made in very illustrative experiments by Waddington and Deuchar (1952). They first studied the effect of a prolonged induction on the determination of the medullary plate by transplanting this part from an old, "already induced" gastrula,

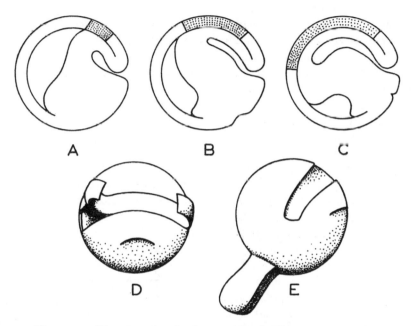

Figure 72. The operational scheme of Eyal-Giladi (*D* and *E*), and the different stages of gastrulation used in her experiments (*A* to *C*). The spotted areas show the distribution of contact between the inductive chordamesoderm and the reactive ectoderm at these stages. (After Eyal-Giladi, 1954.)

into the corresponding site in a much younger gastrula. Following invagination in the new host, the medullary plate was induced for a second time, but no definite effects were noted, and the embryo and its central nervous system developed normally. In a further experiment, the medullary plate was removed from late gastrulae, and substituted by vital-stained presumptive ectoderm from early gastrulae.

In cases where the operation was successful, complete normal embryos were developed, and the stain demonstrated that the whole neural axis was formed from the transplanted presumptive ectoderm. This convincing experiment demonstrated that it is not necessary for normal development that the presumptive ectoderm receives a continuous stimulation during invagination, but can be induced normally when all its parts are exposed for equal periods of time to the inductive stimuli of the archenteron roof. These results thus do not seem to corroborate the idea of Nieuwkoop *et al.* (1952), Eyal-Giladi (1954) and Sala (1956) suggesting that two successive waves are necessary for the induction process. Mrs. Eyal-Giladi (1954) made some criticisms of this experiment and its convincing nature, but we do not quite agree with her criticism. However, there is a great deal of evidence that in some experimental cases, and obviously also during normal development, archencephalic induction precedes the "transforming" stimulus (see below), but it does not appear to be a prerequisite for the latter.

Temporal relationships were further investigated by Johnen (1956a, 1956d, 1961), Toivonen (1958, 1961) and Gallera (1958, 1959, 1960), mainly in the same way, i.e. by experimental alterations of the time of contact between the inductor and the ectoderm. Johnen (1956a, 1956b), used Amblystoma and Triturus ectoderm in sandwich experiments, and the anterior notochordal region of the archenteron roof as inductor. The inductive stimulus was interrupted by removal of the inductor after different periods of time. The results show that the first reaction of the ectoderm always seems to be a formation of archencephalic structures, as might be suggested by the results of von Woellwarth (1951, 1952) and Eyal-Giladi (1954). However, a definite difference was noted between these two species: Amblystoma ectoderm became neuralized after an inductive stimulus lasting no more than 5 minutes, whereas in Triturus the minimum time of reaction seemed to be around 4 hours. (Similar data are reported by Denis (1957, 1958) for *Pleurodeles waltii*.) The "transforming" stimulus leading to the formation of deuterencephalic inductions, on the other hand, needed a much longer time—in Amblystoma about 10 hours, in Triturus somewhat longer. More recently Johnen (1961) extended her series and examined the inductive action of the middle chordal part of the archenteron roof after $\frac{1}{2}$, 1, 2, 4, 8, 12 and 16 hours of contact. The results demonstrate the differences in the time required for different regional types of induction (figure 73), but does not show that the "activation" is a prerequisite for the "transformation". It has to be noted that the time for activation in Amblystoma is unexpectedly short and does not appear to be quite in accordance with observations made on other species. It is not absolutely out of the question that the Amblystoma ectoderm, known to be extremely sensitive to different physical and chemical treatment, had been damaged so as to become auto-neuralized. In our experience, the sandwich technique and the subsequent removal of the inductor might suffice to stimulate an auto-neuralization such as is known to lead to the differentiation of archencephalic structures (see Chapter IV). This might also be true of

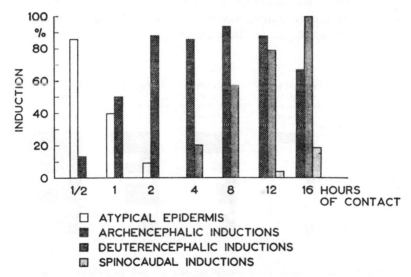

Figure 73. Percentage of archencephalic, deuterencephalic and spinocaudal inductions in series where archenteron roof was used as inductor and the time of contact varied between ½ and 16 hours. In the control series (right) the inductor was not removed. (After Johnen, 1961.)

some observations of Eyal-Giladi (1954) with the same species— she mentioned that also in her results, there were considerable differences between the two species.

Gallera (1959, 1960) used the same anterior notochordal (deuterencephalic) inductor in both implantation (1959) and explantation (1960) experiments, and noted that an archencephalic action could be

demonstrated only by dissociating it artificially from the deuterencephalic action. "This can be obtained by interrupting the induct-
ing contact sufficiently early and at the right moment" (Gallera,
1959).

Toivonen (1958) re-investigated the question of the minimum
time required for different types of inductive stimuli, and in these
experiments used a heterogenous inductor, the alcohol-treated bone-
marrow of guinea-pig. As can be seen in Table 1 (page 80), this
inductor was known to be a strong mesodermalizing inductor, and
both archencephalic and deuterencephalic inductions were completely lacking in the earlier series. As in the experiments of Johnen
(1956a, 1956b), the sandwich method was used, and the inductor
mechanically removed after different intervals of time. The results
are shown in figure 74. In this series, the minimum time for induc-

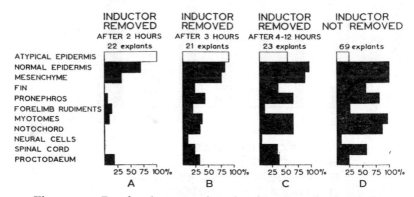

Figure 74. Results demonstrating the time-dependence of the
inductive effect. The inductor (alcohol-treated bone-marrow) was
removed after different periods of time (2 to 12 hours), and the
inductive effect indicated by the percentage of different structures
obtained in the ectodermal explants. (After Toivonen, 1958.)

tion was of the order of three hours, and a prolonged contact with the
inductor tissue did not essentially affect the induction produced. The
most interesting observation was that there could not be demonstrated
a preliminary "activation" of the ectoderm, but it was directly converted into mesodermal and spinocaudal formations. The obvious
discrepancy in the observations of Johnen (1956a, 1956b) and

Gallera (1959) might be explained by differences in the *release* of the inductively active agents from the living, normal inductor on the other hand, and the alcohol-treated, heterogenous inductor on the other: from the living inductor, the "activating" principle is liberated first, and only subsequently is the "transforming" agent, of larger molecules, released, whereas the alcohol-treated inductor releases both factors more rapidly. In any case, the result suggests that the "activating wave" might not be necessary for the determinative stimuli leading to the differentiation of more caudal structures.

This suggestion was subsequently tested experimentally by Gallera (1958) and by Toivonen (1961). The former isolated pieces of the rhombencephalic and spinal cord area of the neural plate of young neurula, and as in the experiments of von Woellwarth (1952), these differentiated into rhombencephalic brain vesicles when cultivated in isolation in Holtfreter solution. In contrast, if these grafts were put into contact with the prechordal plate at this early neurula stage, their prospective determination could be altered, and archencephalic brain portions developed.

Toivonen (1961) tested the temporal relationships of the two inductive waves, the activation and transformation respectively of the Dutch embryologists. This was done by employment of the sandwich methods and of two heterogenous inductors with different inductive action: the neuralizing guinea-pig bone-marrow, and HeLa-cells cultivated *in vitro* from which the mesodermalizing capacity had been inactivated by heat treatment, resulting in a purely archencephalic action. The competent ectoderm was first induced for three hours with the bone-marrow, following which this inductor was removed, and replaced by the heated HeLa-cells. As a result of these two successive inductive influences, a combined action was noted, in comparison with the results obtained by the two inductors separately (figure 75). These results indicate that the two waves of Nieuwkoop *et al.* (1952, 1955) and Eyal-Giladi (1954) can be produced in reversed order, i.e., a mesodermalizing "transformation" can precede a neuralizing "activation", thus confirming the results of Gallera (1958) mentioned above.

(c) *The role of competence.* In stating at the beginning of this chapter that competence of the presumptive ectoderm is uniform, and that its segregation into different types of neural structures must therefore be due to external stimuli, one most important reservation must be made. Temporal variations in this competence to react to external stimuli have to be borne in mind when discussing the induction process in the light of the data given above.

This point has recently been discussed by Kuusi (1961), and she has presented an interesting hypothesis on the role of these temporal variations of competence. She points out that there are obviously at least two different "competences"—the competence to react to neuralizing stimuli, and the capacity to respond to mesodermalizing influences (see Chapter IV). If some temporal differences in these

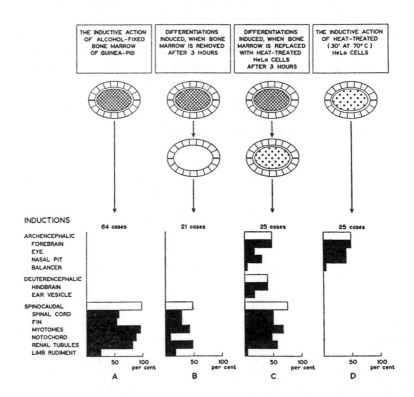

Figure 75. The "normal" sequence of neuralizing and mesodermalizing actions has been experimentally changed: ectodermal explants were first induced by mesodermalizing bone-marrow, and this was subsequently replaced by heat-treated, neuralizing HeLa-cells. The resulting inductive action was a combination of the two subsequent actions (C). (After Toivonen, 1961.)

competences exist, the quality of the induction will not only be dependent on the external stimuli, inductors, but also on these differences in the times of competence (figure 76). This hypothesis entails, in fact, that regional differentiation during gastrulation is actually controlled by the "intrinsic" properties of the reacting tissue,

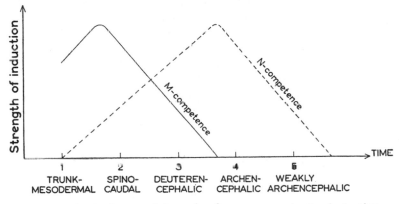

Figure 76. A theory of the role of competence in the induction process. (After Kuusi, 1961.)

and only to a lesser degree by the inductive stimuli. Accordingly, the results of Kuusi (1961) on the effect of denaturing the inductor tissue could be explained not as an inactivation of the inducing agent but as a delayed release of the agents. If a denaturing treatment (heat, alcohol, etc.) results in a delayed release of the active agents, these will not "reach" the reacting ectoderms until its mesodermal competence is lost, and all that remains is the capacity to react to neuralizing stimuli. Most of the results obtained by such treatment and leading to the "inactivation" of the mesodermalizing principle (see page 139) might be explained by means of this hypotheses, but it does not seem in accordance with certain observations on changes in competence. As described in Chapter IV, both the experiments of Borghese (1943) and of Nieuwkoop (1958) seem to indicate that *neural competence is lost first*, and the competence to react to mesodermalizing (transforming) stimuli lasts longer during normal gastrulation. The opposite results of Leikola (page 58) were attained after *in vitro* culture of isolated ectoderm, and thus might not be quite convincing when discussing normal development (cf. Spofford, 1953). The idea of

Kuusi (1961) may thus be too schematic, but it has the great merit of having focused our attention on the reacting tissue also in this connection.

(d) *Some remarks on the time factor*. At present, most embryologists seem to agree that there must be at least two different processes during induction, one leading to neuralization or activation, and the other to the segregation of the more caudal structures. Even Dalcq (1960) recently came to the same conclusion that there are "two different but genetically related inductors". After presenting data on the distribution of the active agents leading to these two processes, along with some data on the role played by time in this phenomenon, it is apposite to discuss the "time factor" in general. In other words, what is the temporal relationship between these two different processes or steps of induction, and can the different actions be explained as being due to differences in their time of action?

As a consequence of the mode of invagination of the inductor tissue, and of the distribution of inductive activity in the archenteror roof, there is a "time-gradient" of the inductive stimulus. The neuralizing (activating) influence has been exercised by the whole midline of the invaginating tissue, and thus is follows that during invagination the posterior part of the presumptive neural plate is exposed first and longest to this stimulus, and the cranial part, corresponding to the prechordal plate, not until the end of gastrulation. This is quite obviously followed by another external stimulus, located in the more posterior part of the invaginating archenteron roof and leading to the induction of more caudal neural structures, and also to the mesodermalization of the caudal fifth of the presumptive neural plate (see page 44). This second action can hardly be produced by a prolonged action of the first stimulus (neuralizing or activating principle). The experiments of Waddington and Deuchar (1952), already referred to, demonstrate that a prolonged contact with the inductor tissue does not alter the final determination of the reacting tissue, and a similar observation was made by Eyal-Giladi (1954) after an experimental blocking of invagination. Furthermore, in the experiments of Toivonen (1958) with heterogenous inductors, there were no qualitative changes in the results obtained with prolonged exposures of the inductor. In conclusion this concept cannot explain the results obtained with heterogenous inductors, in which the inductive activity of different tissues varies greatly, despite controlled experimental conditions. There thus seems to be every reason to suggest at least two processes stimulated by different active agents or factors.

The question now arises of whether these two actions are dependent on each other and actually successive, or whether there are two or more simultaneous, independent processes. As mentioned above, the theory of Nieuwkoop suggests an activation wave as being necessary for the subsequent transforming influence, whereas our idea has been that this activation is not a prerequisite for "transforming" influences, and that the ectoderm can be converted directly into mesoderm. The results of Nieuwkoop and his school have definitely shown that the stimulus leading to the formation of archencephalic structures precedes the "transforming" influence. Both in the ectodermal folds and in the flattened sandwiches the more peripheral parts differentiated into archencephalic structures, and only those areas close to the inductor tissue were transformed into more caudal neural structures (Nieuwkoop et al., 1952; Nieuwkoop and Nigtevecht, 1954). Moreover, during normal gastrulation the first result of contact between the ectoderm and the archenteron roof is an archencephalic induction (Eyal-Giladi, 1954), and when living inductor is used a much longer contact is necessary for the manifestation of "transforming" activity of the inductor. Nevertheless, we are inclined to explain all these results as a different release and diffusion rate for the two active agents or group of agents (see Toivonen and Saxén, 1955a; Dalcq, 1960). If the archencephalic or activating agent is of smaller molecular size (as is often suggested) it seems possible that it is released more rapidly from the living inductor, and subsequently diffuses more rapidly in the reacting tissue (e.g., folds or flattened ectoderms).

This concept of a "transforming" (our mesodermalizing) effect which is not dependent on a preceding activation is corroborated by some experimental data. The transplantation experiments of Waddington and Deuchar (1952) (page 195) demonstrated that when a piece of ectoderm from a young gastrula is transplanted in contact with the already invaginated archenteron roof, a normal segregation of the medullary plate is obtained, despite all of its parts having been exposed for an equal period of time to the inductive stimuli. Furthermore, the results of Gallera (1958) and Toivonen (1961) show that the normal sequence of "activating" and "transforming" influences could be changed experimentally, leading to neural "transformation" of mesodermally "activated" material. It thus seems very probable that the process leading to mesodermalization of the competent ecto-derm is an independent one, obviously occurring later than the first step of induction during normal development, but not being depen-dent on it. The regional differentiation of the central nervous system due to these two different processes seems to be a later step of differentiation, and will be discussed in conjunction with "late interactions".

4. Chemical data in the light of the theories

The extensive literature on the fractionation of inductively active tissues, the purification of active fractions, and the characterization of the chemical nature of the active compounds, has already been re-viewed in Chapter VII. There is no need for its repetition here, but after the presentation of the main theories of induction process, some of the principal results should be discussed in the light of these con-ceptions. The following observations may be mentioned:

(a) It has been shown that most of the inductively active tissues can be separated chemically into fractions yielding different in-ductive actions.

(b) Correspondingly, chemical analyses have shown that fractions which yield archencephalic inductions are chemically different from preparations inducing spinocaudal or mesodermal structures.

(c) Some chemical or physical treatments of "combined" induc-tors (deuterencephalic or spinocaudal) will always destroy selectively the capacity to induce caudal structures, and following these treat-ments the tissues yield a pure archencephalic inductive action.

Despite the large number of investigations of the chemical nature of inductively active compounds, it must be admitted that today we do not have the inductors "in our hands", though certain conclusions can be drawn as regards the general theories. The data summarized above can hardly be explained in terms of the original quantitative theory, and the single active compound which it postulated. More-over, in the light of these recent results, it seems highly improbable that the mesodermalizing activity can be a "mechanical" one resulting from certain movements during invagination, as was suggested in Yamada's (1950b) original theory. On the contrary, these data seem to be in accord with the qualitative theory of Chuang (1940) and Toivonen (1940), suggesting several, chemically distinct inductive agents of different morphogenetic activity. Recently the idea has been brought forward that one of these (two) active compounds, the mesodermalizing inductor, can be changed into the neuralizing or archencephalic agent (Yamada, 1958a, 1958b, 1959; Kawakami and Mifune, 1957; Dalcq, 1960). This idea has not yet been conclusively proved, and our group in particular has not been able to accept it (Kuusi, 1961; Saxén and Toivonen, 1961). We have to confess, however, that at present this idea cannot be completely excluded, and we lack definite counter-evidence against such transformation. (This question has already been dealt with on page 147.)

5. Experiments with combined inductors

Our modification of the two-gradient hypothesis was originally based on experiments in which two heterogenous inductors yielding different inductive actions were combined (Toivonen and Saxén, 1955a, 1955b). In suggesting that during normal induction such combined effects exist, it seems only natural to follow this line of experimentation, despite the fact that results obtained with heterogenous inductors have repeatedly been criticized as inadequate and not relevant to the normal induction process. We have already stressed the extreme improbability that the active agents in heterogenous inductors are the same as in normal inductor tissue, but the *reaction of the competent ectoderm is very much the same*, and for as long as we cannot perform similar experiments with a normal inductor, there seems to be every reason to study these reactions by means of "artificial stimulation".

Our original experiments with guinea-pig liver and bone-marrow tissue were later repeated by Kawakami and Yamana (1959), crude protein extracts of these tissues and of guinea-pig kidney being employed. Their results fully confirmed our observations, and in fact the conclusion drawn by the authors did not differ from ours. They suggested two active substances, one responsible for archencephalic induction (Ma), and the other possessing mesodermalizing inductive capacity (Mm). "The structural patterns which develop during embryogenesis are decided by these two inductive substances, Ma and Mm" (Kawakami and Yamana, 1959).

All these experiments were purely qualitative in nature. However, our original conception suggested some quantitative differences in these active principles as did most of the theories previously presented, and it was therefore desirable to make the approach to the study of this problem quantitative. The most satisfactory way would have been the use of chemical, purified fractions yielding different inductive actions and to mix these in different ratios. For several reasons, mainly technical, this approach was abandoned, and instead use was made of cells cultivated *in vitro*. HeLa-cells grown in fresh, nontreated human serum have proved to be strong spinocaudal-mesodermal inductors (Saxén and Toivonen, 1958a, 1958b), and after heat-treatment this action is changed into purely archencephalic (neuralizing) activity (page 89). Thus these cells were used with or without heat pretreatment, as implantation or explantation material, and mixed in different ratios in order to obtain mixtures containing different amounts of neuralizing and mesodermalizing "factors". Preliminary experiments showed that in mixing different amounts of homogenized suspensions of these cells, homogeneous implants were obtained with an even distribution of heated and nonheated cells (Toivonen, Saxén and Vainio, 1961). Subsequent control experiments with C-14 labelled cells proved this homogenicity of the implants (Saxén and Toivonen, 1961).

Heated and non-heated HeLa-cells were then mixed in different ratios, implanted, and their inductive activity tested. The results are shown in figures 77 and 78.

These results demonstrate that the inductive action of a heterogenous implant can be altered by varying the relative amounts of two components with a different inductive action. Starting from the purely archencephalic action of heated HeLa-cells, the inductive action of the implant is progressively shifted from this action through an activity which is mainly deuterencephalic into an action in which the spinocaudal activity dominates by adding increasing amounts of spinocaudal-inducing, non-heated cells. None of the mixtures of heated and untreated cells yielded an inductive action which was identical with those obtained when the two cell suspensions were tested separately. For example, the almost purely deuterencephalic action obtained with mixtures in ratios of 1 to 9 or 3 to 7 is a completely new type of induction when compared with the separate actions of the two components of this mixture. Thus the results cannot be explained as a simple competitive action on the competent ectoderm by the two components, but as a *combined action* whose quality is determined by *the relative amounts* of the two active components of the implant. It is interesting in this connection to note the similarity between these results and some of the observations following chemical or physical treatment of heterogenous inductors:

if an originally spinocaudal inductor is treated by denaturing agents (alcohol, heat), its spinocaudal activity is progressively shifted through a deuterencephalic action into a purely archencephalic effect (see Chapter VII, Engländer and Johnen, 1957, page 137). These

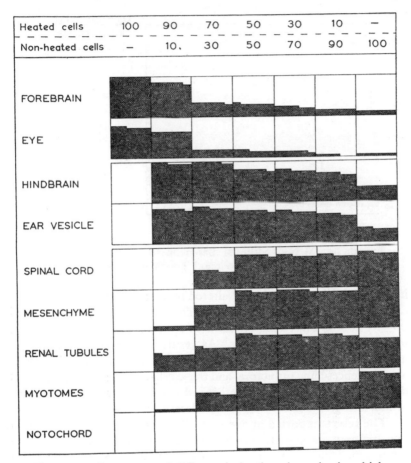

| Heated cells | 100 | 90 | 70 | 50 | 30 | 10 | — |
| Non-heated cells | — | 10. | 30 | 50 | 70 | 90 | 100 |

FOREBRAIN

EYE

HINDBRAIN

EAR VESICLE

SPINAL CORD

MESENCHYME

RENAL TUBULES

MYOTOMES

NOTOCHORD

Figure 77. Percentage of different inductions in series in which different mixtures of heated and non-heated HeLa-cells were used as inductors. (Results of Saxén and Toivonen, 1961, orig.)

results are very similar to ours if they are read from "right to left", that is, starting from the non-heated cells and following the effect of the addition of increasing amounts of heated, archencephalic-inducing cells. Furthermore, a very similar weakening of the spinocaudal

activity of HeLa-cells can be obtained during prolonged cultivation
in heated serum or in a protein-free culture medium (Saxén and
Toivonen, 1958a, 1958b, page 89). It might thus be stated that the
inductive action of spinocaudal-mesodermal-inducing heterogenous

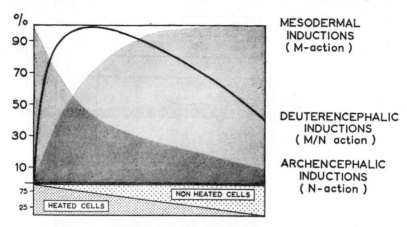

Figure 78. A schematic representation of the two-gradient
hypothesis (M/N-hypothesis) based on the results indicated in
Figure 77. (Saxén and Toivonen, 1961.)

inductors can be progressively altered by certain physical and chemical treatments, but that an opposite change can be artificially "built
up" by adding increasing amounts of spinocaudal-inducing material
to an archencephalic inductor. As regards HeLa-cells, this phenomenon is very definite: non-treated cells will gradually be shifted
into archencephalic inductors, and these cells can again be "activated"
through the same steps of different inductive activities by the addition
of increasing amounts of non-treated cells to them.

The results reported above were obtained by the employment of
two different inductors: one archencephalic, and one spinocaudal-
mesodermal inducing. These two effects seem to be close to the
"activation" and "transformation" of Nieuwkoop et al. (1952), but
both the more recent conceptions of Yamada (1958a, 1958b) and our
hypothesis (Toivonen and Saxén, 1955a, 1955b) include the idea of a
mesodermalizing principle, and according to our earlier ideas the spinocaudal effect of HeLa-cells is already a combined effect of this and the
neuralizing principle. As we did not employ a purely mesodermalizing inductor in the recent series involving HeLa-cells, we wish to add

our earlier results using bone-marrow to them (Toivonen and Saxén, 1955a, 1955b). In these spinocaudal activity comparable to that of non-treated HeLa cells was produced by a simultaneous implantation of mesodermalizing bone-marrow and neuralizing liver tissue. *These two series thus demonstrated an experimental production of all regional types of induction by the mixing of different types of inductors.*

In discussing the results obtained from the different mixtures of treated and non-treated HeLa-cells in the light of our mesodermaliz-ing/neuralizing-theory (M/N-hypothesis), and on the assumption that the neuralizing principle is not affected by short-term heat-treatment (Chapter VII), it becomes evident that the amount of the neuralizing factor(s) was constant in the different mixtures. The changes in the inductive action of the implants were thus consequent on the variations in the amount of the mesodermalizing factor(s). This, again, is exactly what was suggested as occurring in the different regions of the archenteron roof (figure 63): an evenly distributed archencephalic (neuralizing) activity in the midline of the roof, and a caudo-cranial gradient of the mesodermalizing activity.

Fully aware that we are drawing conclusions for which there is insufficient justification, we should like finally to compare these results with the observations of the inductive action of the different areas of the archenteron roof (Sala, 1955a, 1955b). This has been done in figure 79 where the four regions of Sala (1955a) are compared with our four mixtures (heated/non-heated in ratios 10 : 0, 9 : 1, 7 : 3 and 1 : 1). The results from these selected series are strikingly similar, and demonstrate that the normal inductive "field" of the archenteron roof can be imitated by an experimental combination of two inductors with different inductive action. Here again the criti-cism of results obtained with heterogenous inductors might be justi-fied, but the only point we wish to stress is that the reaction of the competent ectoderm is very similar in the two series. It is thus tempting to take this similarity as an evidence of the presence of similar "mixtures" of two active principles in the normal inductor tissue also.

Later in this chapter we will revert to these findings and to the possible mode of the "combined" action of the neuralizing and the mesodermalizing principle. At present, it appears to us that this could be explained not as a direct action of the "mixtures", but as a secondary interaction of the two types of tissue induced by these principles.

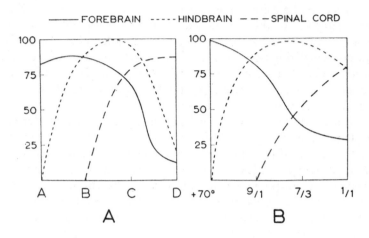

Figure 79. A comparison of the results of Sala (1955b) and Saxén and Toivonen (1961). Figure A indicates the percentage of forebrain, hindbrain and spinal cord inductions by different territories of the archenteron roof (Sala, 1955b); Figure B shows the corresponding percentages in series in which heated and nonheated HeLa-cells were used as inductor in ratios 1 to 0, 9 to 1, 7 to 3 and 1 to 1. (Saxén and Toivonen, 1961.)

6. *Primary stimulus and subsequent events*

(a) *Introduction.* As was stressed in the introduction to this chapter, the methods we have available for study of the initial stimuli to differentiation, the "primary induction", are limited. The results of these stimuli cannot be followed in the reactive tissue (with the expection of a few preliminary approaches employing histochemical or electron-microscopical methods) and only the end-result is to be observed. It is therefore obvious that there must be a long chain of subsequent events in the primarily-determined cells before we examine their morphological changes after several days of development. This has been known since the days of Spemann, and in addition to the classical case of lens-induction, we have today a variety of examples of secondary tissue interactions representing different steps in the chain of progressive determining stimuli during development, but these are still too often neglected. Consequently, many differentiation processes which obviously belong to this category have been considered as being due to the primary stimulus. In some way, it

appears unnatural for us to speak about archencephalic, deuterencephalic and spinocaudal inductors (as we ourselves have done), and
suggest that a magical factor could convert undifferentiated ectodermal cells directly into a hindbrain part, a spinal ganglion, etc.
The first step of differentiation can hardly be anything else than a
determination into neural or mesodermal, perhaps even in the neuro-
ectodermal and endodermal direction, and the whole complexity
of the organism cannot be determined at the time of primary
induction.

Looked at from the viewpoint of primary induction, our present
problem can be formulated as follows. During normal invagination
or under experimental conditions, a brief contact of the inductor
tissue and the competent ectoderm leads to a definite, but unknown,
change in the ectodermal cells. During subsequent development,
these changes are manifested in a progressive cytodifferentiation,
leading finally to the extreme complexity of the organism. There are,
however, various experiments which suggest that the first changes in
the ectoderm initiated by the inductive stimuli are not irreversible,
and thus there must be both stabilizing, and later, inductive stimuli
which control subsequent development, and as Grobstein (1955b)
says: ". . . we cannot safely assume that the source of the stabilization
revealed lies in intrinsic cellular changes alone".

The problems presented by later events may be divided, quite
schematically, into two categories: The first concerns the significance
of the mass of the cells initially determined, and the second the late
interactions between different cell and tissue types within this mass.
After presenting several examples of such effects, we will discuss them
in the context of primary induction and of theories on it.

(b) *Mass effect.* To start with a definition, or what is actually a
conclusion based on a variety of experimental results, there is a
"minimum mass effect", which means that the capacity of already
determined tissues to differentiate seems to depend on a certain
minimum mass which is essential for continued morphogenesis (see
Grobstein, 1955b). This phenomenon has been demonstrated in a
variety of species from Protozoa to mammals: In slime moulds
(Raper, 1941; Bonner, 1960), in sponges (Wilson, 1908; Brien, 1937),
in Hydrozoa (Child, 1928; Chalkley, 1945), in ascidians (Berrill,
1941a, 1941b), in fish (Trinkaus and Drake, 1956b), in amphibian
(Lopashov, 1935; Muchmore, 1957), in birds (Grobstein and
Zwilling, 1953) and in mammals (Grobstein, 1952). Some of these

experiments will be presented here (see also Holtfreter, 1951; Grobstein, 1955b).

Bonner (1960) studied the development of cellular slime moulds by time-lapse cinematography, and followed their differentiation in small aggregates. When such aggregates of *Dictyostelium mucoroides* were studied, two possible courses of development were noted: "they would either form a small fruiting body or, after the cells had remained in a tight central mass for a few hours, they would disperse and disintegrate." Figure 80 shows the relationship between the cell number of the aggregate and its future fate, and it is seen that, parallel to an increase in the cell number, there is a rise in the percentage of differentiated aggregates. The minimum mass or the minimum number of cells essential for normal development seems here to be about 200 cells—in aggregates consisting of less than 50 cells, a normal development was never observed.

Trinkaus and Drake (1956b) cultured blastoderms of *Fundulus heteroclitus* in nutrient media, and compared the differentiation of single or fused blastoderms with that of several blastoderms crowded together in a small amount of culture medium. Both a fusion of two blastoderms and the increase in the mass in small, crowded cultures led to a definite increase in differentiation. However, when crowded cultures were made in CO_2-free atmosphere, they showed no differentiation beyond that of the controls, and thus the stimulation of differentiation was due at least in part to an increased CO_2-tension, as was the case in some other experiments of the authors (Trinkaus and Drake, 1956a).

Before similar experiments with amphibian material are described, some experiments of Grobstein need mention (Grobstein, 1952, 1955b; Grobstein and Zwilling, 1953). He studied the effect of fragmentation of the presumptive neural plate on the subsequent differentiation of the central nervous system when the fragments were cultured *in vitro*. When shields of mouse embryonic tissue were cut into fragments from halves to sixteenths and subsequently cultured in close clusters, the differentiation of the central nervous system decreased progressively, despite the fact that the total amount of tissue was roughly constant. At a later medullary plate stage, similar fractionation failed to prevent the differentiation of the explants. Subsequently, this investigation was extended to chick material which has the advantage of better known fate maps and a larger medullary plate. A small area of $0 \cdot 25 \times 0 \cdot 25$ mm. was cut from the presumptive neural area of a definite primitive streak embryo. This piece was either cultured intact, or after fragmentation and re-combination of the fragments (Grobstein and Zwilling, 1953). The first interesting observation was that there was a tendency towards "cranialization" of the intact pieces of known prospective fate. Thus, when the explant was taken from a prospective hindbrain

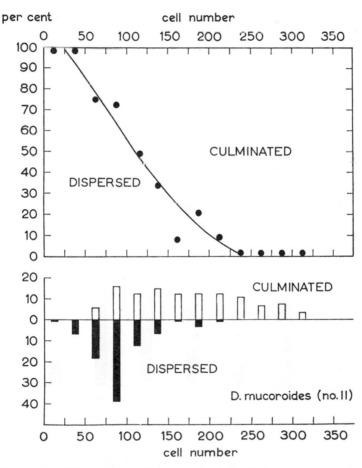

Figure 80. The relation of the number of cells in aggregates of *Dictyostelium mucoroides* to the culmination and differentiation of the aggregates. Upper part: percentage of the dispersed and cul-minated aggregates, lower part: the relation of frequency in the two types of aggregates. (After Bonner, 1960.)

P

region, for instance, prosencephalic structures were frequently noted. In addition, in these experiments the earlier observations with mouse material were confirmed. Fragmentation into eighths did not seem to affect the differentiation of the central nervous system, but when one-sixteenth fragments were cultured in clusters, nervous tissue was only occasionally noted (figure 81). These pieces of the chick

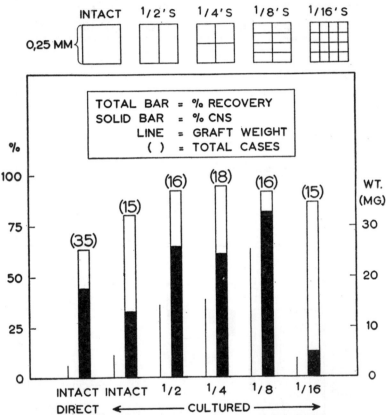

Figure 81. Percentage of differentiation of central nervous system (CNS) in cultures of different "masses" of presumptive neural tissue (scheme of fragmentation, above). (After Grobstein and Zwilling, 1953.)

blastoderm agreed roughly in size with that of the whole shield of the mouse tissue used in the previous investigations, and it thus appears that the essential point is not the relative amount of the presumptive neural plate tissue, but its absolute amount which was of the order of 0·1 mm square. Grobstein (1955b) pointed out that this amount of tissue seemed to be very close to the "limiting minimum mass" reported by Brien (1937) for the reconstruction of aggregates of sponges, and by Child (1928) for the lower limit of fragments of *Corymorpha* able to regenerate. It might be added that in these experiments with the presumptive neural tissue differentiation was not only dependent upon the size of the fragment but also on the "effective explant mass", i.e., the number of cells in a certain area (density of the cluster). Thus, if the explant was dispersed, the percentage of central nervous tissue formed was much less than in clusters which were originally of the same mass but explanted as a dense cluster.

These experiments of Grobstein (1952, 1955) and Grobstein and Zwilling (1953) clearly showed the existence of a "limiting minimum mass", and the fact that cells of the developing central nervous system are still determined in a labile fashion "despite the apparently high stability of the developing system of which they are part" (Grobstein and Zwilling, 1953). The significance of these observations in connection with the morphogenesis following inductive stimuli will be discussed below.

Similar experiments employing amphibian tissues were made by Lopashov (1935), who combined two to ten fragments cut from the presumptive head mesoderm area of young gastrulae (figure 82). Explants of a single fragment differentiated into striated muscle without notochord or other tissue components However, if two to four such fragments were combined, they formed a compact tissue mass which frequently showed notochordal differentiation A combination of four to five fragments led to the formation of muscle, notochord, together with epidermis; when six to ten fragments were combined, definite brain structures could be observed, usually at the other end of the explant. The results might thus be summarized as follows:

    1 fragment → muscle
   2–4 fragments → muscle + notochord
   4–5 fragments → muscle + notochord + epidermis
   6–10 fragments → muscle + notochord + epidermis + central nervous system

In his discussion of these results, Lopashov (1935) considered the area concerned in young gastrulae as an "ectomesoderm", "dessen Eigenschaften sich in Richtung von der Randzone zum Ektoderm ändern". There exists a certain balance between its ectodermal and mesodermal tendencies—an increase in the total amount of the presumptive mesodermal tissues leads to neuralization of the "overhead" tissue and to the attainment of normal proportions. In this connection, Lopashov referred to the defect experiments of Bruns (1931), in

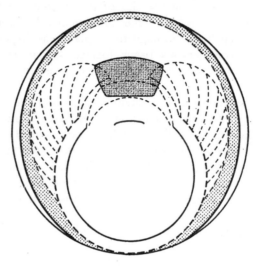

Figure 82. The operation scheme of Lopashov (1935). The dorsal lip fragment used in the experiments indicated by the dark area.

which removal of either presumptive mesodermal or ectodermal pieces led to normal tissue proportions, obviously through changes in the prospective determination of the component not removed. Whatever may be the mechanism of this phenomenon, the most interesting fact is the demonstration of neural tendencies in the presumptive mesodermal area which manifest themselves when the total mass is increased. In the connection we would refer to the theory of Takaya (1957), presented in the next section.

Experiments resembling those of Lopashov (1935) have been carried out more recently by Muchmore (1957), who combined fragments of axolotl presumptive somite material. The results, some of which are indicated in figure 83, again demonstrate the dependence of differentiation on the initial mass. In parallel with increasing mass (from one to ten fragments, each corresponding to the presumptive material of five somites) there was an increase in the percentage of cases with definite muscle, and at the same time the tissue became better organized. In addition to the "mass effect", these results indicate that the somite tissue is already determined at the neurula stage, and will continue its development in the absence of any other tissues.

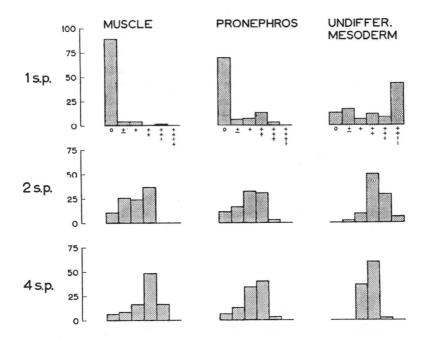

Figure 83. Differentiation percentages of muscle, and pronephros in explants of 1, 2 or 4 fragments of presumptive somite plates fused together. (O, no differentiation; + + + +, large masses of differentiated tissue.) (After Muchmore, 1957.)

As regards the presumptive neural tissue in amphibians, information is more scanty, but corroborates the observations made with mesodermal tissue. Damas (1947) and Gallera (1947) isolated small fragments of presumptive neural plate and grafted them on to the belly of normal hosts. However, the final differentiation of these grafts did not correspond to their original fate. Thus Damas (1947) obtained differentiation of neural crest derivatives when fragments of presumptive spinal cord were transplanted, and Gallera (1947) obtained similar results after transplantation of the presumptive eye region. It seems clear that here again, the changes in the presumptive determination can be considered as a lowering of the degree of differentiation capacity due to the small size of the transplanted fragments.

Finally, an account should be given of the recent experiments of Wilde (1961a). He studied disaggregated cells from Ambystoma neuroepithelium and archenetron roof, and cultured them in microdrop cultures. He first noted that a single cell would never differentiate under these conditions, but that when two cells were placed in the same drop, one of them would show differentiation. This would indicate the necessity for some type of interaction between these already determined cells for their subsequent development. Wilde (1961a) then devoted his attention to the visible extracellular material in his cultures, and succeeded in inhibiting differentiation by washing this material from the cells before cultivation. Only in larger cultures of 25 to 100 cells were any differentiated cells noted. In addition, "confused" cells were observed in these washed cultures showing simultaneous differentiation in several directions, e.g. cells with melanogenesis as well as the production of definite myofibrils (Plate 10.1). Some later experiments further demonstrated the significance of this extracellular material in differentiation, and Wilde (1961a) thus concluded that "the maintenance of discrete differentiative pathways is dependent upon further specific configurations of the molecular microenvironment which act to canalize the particular differentiative pathway into unique and exclusive biochemical and morphological differentiations". The importance of such extracellular materials has also been given repeated emphasis by other authors, especially by Moscona (1960, 1961).

(1) *Concluding remarks*. The presentation of these results might seem to be irrelevant in a discussion of the process of primary induction, particularly because we do not know the significance of the initial number of cells induced in a larger mass. Direct evidence of such significance may still be lacking, but it has to be borne in mind that in some of the experiments referred to above, such conditions were actually present. For instance, when Damas (1947) and Gallera (1947) transplanted already determined pieces of presumptive neural tissue on the belly side of normal embryos, the total mass was

not limited, and only the amount of "neuralized" cells in this mass was restricted. We may thus agree with Holtfreter and Hamburger (1955): "This reduction and final loss of patterning seems to show that the organological complexity of a neurogenic field depends primarily on the number of cells which have experienced stimulation. In other words, the size of the field appears to be a determining factor in its future organ pattern". Consequently, following the discussion in previous chapters of the quality of the inductive stimulus, its duration and distribution in embryos, and the role of the reactive tissue, there seems to be every reason to add one further factor to the already extremely complicated process, the significance of the initially determined mass. On the other hand, these findings may explain some of the observations with combined inductors in which very weak neural or mesodermal stimuli are not manifested—because the mass of tissue originally determined by them is too small. This suggestion will be dealt with in the discussion of this chapter.

(c) *Late interactions.* When recording the effect of a primary inductive stimulus by way of morphogenetic changes occurring during the 7–11 days following the stimulus itself, the question arises, which of the reaction products can really be due to the first stimuli, i.e., to primary induction. We know that the progressive differentiation of tissues and their increasing stability is due to a chain of inductive interactions, and there is accumulating evidence that such interactions between already determined tissues start very early after the first determining stimuli. In addition to the well known inductions of certain placodes, the interactions of tissue components in glandular tissues and regenerating limb rudiments, mention will be made of some interactions between the young tissue anlagen (the reader is referred to recent reviews by Grobstein, 1956b; Dalcq, 1960; Lopashov, 1961; and Mangold, 1961a).

(i) Interaction between the *neural plate* and the *underlying mesoderm* is discussed below in more detail.

(ii) The differentiation of *mesoderm* in neurulae is not independent of the other anlagen, and when transplanted alone, it will not develop in accordance with its prospective significance. Its differentiation can be stimulated by the neural plate, by the embryonic endoderm, and if lateral mesoderm is used, by the presence of notochord (Muratori, 1939; Yamada, 1940; Muchmore, 1951; Chuang and Tseng, 1956; Takaya, 1956c). Similarly, during later development the growth and differentiation of axial mesoderm is influenced by the spinal cord (Holtzer, Lash and Holtzer, 1956; Avery and Holtzer, 1958). Even inside the developing mesoderm, tissue interactions seem to occur, e.g., between limb bud and nephric tubules (Lopashov, 1941; Nieuwkoop, 1946; Muchmore, 1957).

(iii) The differentiation of the third embryonic layer, *the endoderm*, is also dependent on the other tissues, as demonstrated in particular in the experimental series of T. S. Okada (1953a, 1953b, 1954a, 1954b, 1955a, 1955b, 1957, 1960) and Takata (1960a, 1960b). Branchial, gastric or intestinal endodermal primordia of Triturus neurulae were explanted, in combination with ecto- or endomesodermal fragments from different regions. The results definitely showed that the differentiation of the endodermal primordium was dependent on the mesoderm, and mesodermal fragments from different regions had different effects. The mesodermal effect called "anteriorization" was strongest in the cranial mesectoderm, and gradually weakened in lateral and posterior directions (see page 49).

iv. Similar interaction has been demonstrated by several authors in the development of the *neural crest*. Recently, Seno and Nieuwkoop (1958) made experiments resembling those of Okada (1960) just mentioned: neural crest material from different regions (anterior head, posterior head, trunk) was grafted in sandwich form either alone or combined with neural plate, mesoderm or endoderm of the corresponding area. Although the series were relatively limited, some quite obvious interactions between these different components were noted.

These few examples demonstrate that even during early development of the embryos, a variety of morphogenetic interactions do exist between neural, mesodermal, endodermal and neural crest tissues. Most of these interactions occur soon after the first inductive stimulus of the archenteron roof, and thus experimental results in investigations dealing with this primary stimulus are, in fact, the results of a most complicated and partly unknown chain of morphogenetic stimuli. Consequently the mesoderm/neural interactions in particular have to be analyzed in more detail before there can be any final discussion of conceptions of primary induction.

(1) *Neural-mesodermal interaction.* A large number of experimental results have demonstrated that the development, differentiation and segregation of the central nervous system is a progressive phenomenon, and evidently a result of a variety of secondary interactions. Some of these results may be briefly summarized:

(i)   The determination of the neural plate is still labile at a young neurula stage, and removal of the underlying mesoderm or transplantation of the neural plate primordium leads to a lowering of its differentiative state (Mangold, 1929a; Mangold and von Woellwarth, 1960; Damas, 1947; Gallera, 1947, 1951).

(ii) At the visible neural plate stage, it is still partially dependent on the mesodermal tissue, and the removal of this, or treatment with compounds which disturb the development of the mesoderm, results in abnormalities in the central nervous system (Mangold, 1931a, 1936; Adelmann, 1934, 1937; Lehmann, 1933).

(iii) During neurulation, the neural plate gradually attains a certain stability and becomes independent of the underlying mesoderm (Nakamura, 1938; ter Horst, 1948; Kitchin, 1949; Gallera, 1951; von Woellwarth, 1951, 1952).

Having observed on the one hand this progressive nature of the segregation of the central nervous system, and on the other the fact that an inductive stimulus lasting a few hours will lead to the same final result (Johnen, 1956a, 1956b, 1961; Toivonen, 1958, 1961), there seems to be no doubt, that *in the development of the central nervous system the initial inductive stimuli are followed by a chain of secondary tissue interactions which lead to the final segregation of the tissue.* These secondary actions have been subjected to analysis, especially by Takaya (1953–1957), and his results will be reported in more detail.

In an excellent series of investigations, Takaya studied the neural-mesodermal interactions during the segregation of the central nervous system (Takaya, 1953a, 1953b, 1955a, 1955b, 1956a, 1956b, 1956c, 1957), and in his last paper of this series he presented a general two-gradient theory (unfortunately, in Japanese).

Takaya (1953a, 1953b) started investigation of the notochord-forming potencies of dorsal lip tissue by cultivating pieces of it, from gastrulae of different stages in ectodermal explants. He was able to show, that even the prechordal region was capable of forming notochord before its invagination, but that this potency disappeared after invagination. During the course of early gastrulation, the notochord-forming potency was even higher in the prechordal territory than in the areas corresponding to the presumptive notochord. It appeared that the potency to form notochord was highest at the margin of the blastopore lip just prior to invagination, and gradually decreased in the caudal direction. The results thus demonstrated the presence of a certain mesodermalization gradient (see below). The author compared these observations with the findings of Okada and Hama (1954a), demonstrating parallel changes in the inductive capacity of the invaginating dorsal lip tissue. These were confirmed in Takaya's (1953a, 1953b) experiments. Before invagination, the explanted tissue induced hindbrain and spinocaudal tissues, but after the notochord-forming potency had been lost, the inductive products were always of archencephalic type. Takaya (1953a, 1953b) assumed that the type of neural structures induced was dependent on the influence of the notochord (and perhaps also of the other mesodermal structures obtained in the explants). This assumption was tested by the culture of pieces of the branchial part of the neural plate in explants, and by removal of the underlying mesoderm in whole or in part (Takaya, 1955a). The results demonstrated that the type of neural differentiation in these cultures was again dependent on the presence of absence of the mesoderm: following its total removal, the neural plate tissue always developed into "neural vesicles or solid masses showing archencephalic character" despite its prospective significance (spinal cord). By contrast, when mesodermal tissues were present in the explant, neural tissue of deuterencephalic or spinal cord type was formed. Takaya (1953a) concluded that in the differentiation of the central nervous system two steps were clearly distinguishable: a general neuralization (evocation) induced by the underlying mesoderm, followed by a determination of the regional character of the induced tissue. In this second step, two kinds of factor may operate: "the internal factors involved in the neuralizing tissue itself, and the external factors issuing from the surrounding mesodermal tissues". As further evidence for these ideas, Takaya (1955b) presented some observations in which a mild heat-shock applied to the dorsal lip tissue resulted in a loss of both of its capacity to form muscle tissue and of its ability to induce other than archencephalic brain parts. In some cases where only forebrain structures were induced, a notochord was seen (but no muscle tissue), and Takaya (1955b) concluded that the determining tissue might in fact

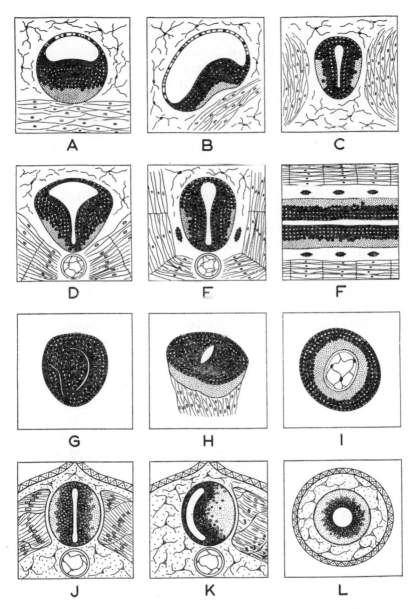

Figure 84. Different types of neural differentiations in explants in which neural tube had been combined with mesodermal tissues. (*A* to *F* after Takaya, 1956b; *G* to *I* after Takaya, 1956 a; *J* to *L*.) After Holtfreter and Hamburger, 1955.)

be the muscle tissue. The experiments were continued on similar lines, and by explantation of neural plate material with different amounts of mesodermal tissue (Takaya, 1956a, 1956b). These explants again showed different types of neural differentiation, and in the total absence of mesoderm, the neural plate material developed into archencephalic structures. In addition, and dependent on the amount, type and distribution of the mesodermal tissues, different types of neural structures were noted (figure 84), and the author explained these as being due to the growth-promoting effect of the muscle tissue. He concluded (1956b), that "in all probability, it is difference in degree of neural proliferation which determines the type of neural structure". It thus follows that the segregation of the neural tissue is not due to the initial inductive stimulus but to the effect of the neighbouring mesodermal tissues.

With these investigations as his main basis, Takaya (1957)* presented an interesting and important theory of neural and mesodermal differentiation during early development. The main points of his analysis are presented below.

Takaya (1957) suggested the presence of two gradients, a "mesodermization gradient" and a "neuralization gradient". The mesodermization gradient indicates the capacity of the dorsal lip tissue to become mesodermalized, and is based on his observations on the changes in the notochord-forming potency of this area. Takaya indicated the temporal variations in this gradient in a series of figures (figure 85). The gradient develops gradually during gastrulation and shows a strengthening in the cranio-caudal direction. The neuralization gradient in the ectoderm shows an opposite course weakening in the cranial direction (figures 86A and 86B). Takaya further suggested that the neuralization gradient might be due to a graded inductive action of the invaginated tissue, and opposite in sense to its mesodermalization gradient (figure 86c). As a result of secondary interactions of the neural and mesodermal structures determined by these gradients, the different parts of the central nervous system are developed, as demonstrated in earlier experiments made by the same author.

In making a comparison of these ideas with our two-gradient theory, Takaya (1957) pointed out that the main difference is the

---

* The authors are indebted to Dr. Yoshitaro Sakai, M.D., for the translation from Japanese of the comprehensive paper by Takaya (1957).

location of the two gradients suggested in both theories. If the neuralization gradient of Takaya is induced by a corresponding gradient in the archenteron roof, these parts of the conceptions seem

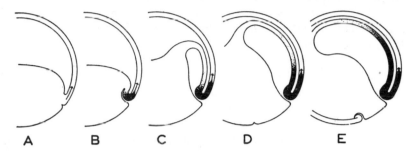

Figure 85. The "mesodermization gradient" at different stages of gastrulation. (After Takaya, 1957.)

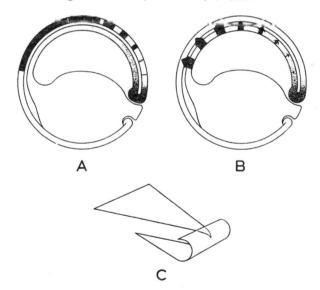

Figure 86. The neuralization gradient in the ectoderm and the mesodermalization gradient of the chordamesoderm (*A* and *C*), and neuralizing gradient of the latter. (After Takaya, 1957.)

similar. The main difference lies, however, in the mesodermization gradient. Our theory suggests that the posterior part of the neural plate is induced by an underlying mesodermalization gradient, whereas Takaya does not appear to hold this view. He suggests the existence of a substance leading to mesodermal differentiation, but this is located inside the developing mesoderm, and is normally not a transmittable, inductive agent. We return to this point below.

(2) *Concluding remarks on the late interactions.* After the presentation of these data, it may be briefly concluded that there is much to indicate that:

(i) After the first differentiation into different embryonic layers, the ecto- endo- and mesoderm, as well as the neural crest, are still only determined in a labile fashion, and remain competent to react to inductive or similar stimuli.

(ii) During subsequent development, their final fate is determined by a chain of interactions between different tissues.

(iii) As regards the segregation of the central nervous system, this is hardly due to the brief inductive stimuli occurring during gastrulation, but to subsequent interactions between the neuralized ectoderm and the underlying mesoderm.

Discussion. We have recently discussed the different conceptions of primary induction in the light of the above data on the mass effect and late interactions (Saxén and Toivonen, 1961). Some of the points may be repeated here.

Most of the present conceptions suggest, in addition to qualitatively different inductive agents, certain quantitative differences in their distribution and effect. However, in the reactive tissue each cell may respond only to one of these stimuli—a simultaneous response to several inductive stimuli seems very improbable, although not quite impossible, as indicated by the "confused" cells obtained by Wilde (1961a) under abnormal conditions (Plate 10.1). Following this, the reactive tissue after an initial stimulus by an inductor tissue containing both neuralizing and mesodermalizing inductive agents can be considered as a mass of intermingled cells already determined as becoming either neural or mesodermal. The relative amount of these cells depends on the ratio between mesodermalizing and neuralizing stimuli in the inductive tissue (as is suggested by our results with artificial mixtures of such inductive agents (Saxén and Toivonen, 1961)). The final fate of these cells might now be determined by several factors: these dispersed cells are under experimental conditions able to assume definite active organizing, selective aggregation, as shown by Townes and Holtfreter (1955), and it is not improbable that similar active "recombination" of similarly induced cells occurs after the first inductive stimuli, resulting in larger masses of neuralized and mesodermalized cells. During this process, it can quite hypothetically be suggested that the "minimum mass effect" already plays a role—e.g., a few neuralized cells scattered among a large number of mesodermalized cells, or even smaller islands of these cells, might not be able to continue their original line of differentiation like the small masses of prospective neural plate or somite tissue in the experiments of Damas (1947), Gallera (1947), Grobstein (1955b), and Muchmore (1957). This suggestion would furthermore explain the obvious fact that a very strong mesodermalizing effect can completely "mask" a weak neuralizing stimulus from the same inductor material (Yamada, 1959, see figure 50). This "minimum mass effect" might eliminate some of the determined cells, but evidently plays a role in the future development and morphogenesis of the "remaining" cells. Simultaneously, the tissue interactions between these originally determined cells will control their continued morphogenesis and organ formation, as in the experimental conditions of Takaya (1953–1957). Here the original ratio between the cells determined in different directions must again play a role, now as a quantitative ratio between the amount of the tissue types involved in the interactive processes (much mesoderm + neural → spinocaudal, less mesoderm + neural → deuterencephalic etc.). Following this line of more or less speculative thinking, the importance of masses and quantities can be traced back to the quantitative ratios of the first morphogenetic stimuli of primary induction.

7. *Discussion*

Following this presentation of the large amount of experimental data obtained in studies made to clarify the mechanism of the induction, there seems ample reason for discussing the information available in the light of the different concepts presented in Chapter IX. As was mentioned in the Introduction, no syntheses can yet be made; all that can be done is to group the data and see how far they are accommodated by the different theories.

The lively research work presented in this chapter was originally stimulated by two very different theories which were actually in opposition, the quantitative theory of Dalcq-Pasteels, and the concept of Chuang and Toivonen which suggested several active agents involved in the process of primary induction. Today it can be stated that both of these theories have undergone a certain metamorphosis. In his most recent discussion of the induction process, Dalcq (1960) seemed to accept the idea of a number, or at least of two different inductive agents (although closely related). Correspondingly, our qualitative theory has accepted the ideas of different gradients and "concentrations" originally included in the quantitative theory (see Toivonen and Saxén, 1955b, Saxén and Toivonen, 1961). It seems to us that at present the majority of embryologists, confused by the abundance of experimental data and the opposing ideas on primary induction, appear to agree on at least one point: induction can hardly be initiated by one single agent or group of agents, and at least two active principles (or types of reaction) can be distinguished, i.e., neuralization and mesodermalization, respectively (e.g., Yamada, 1958a, 1958b, 1961; Tiedemann, 1959; Dalcq, 1960; Kuusi, 1961; Saxén and Toivonen, 1961). There is no need once again to repeat the experimental evidence for this style of thought, but the chemical data presented in Chapter VII have provided strong evidence for the existence of a number of agents with different morphogenetic actions.

In the last chapter of our book, a great deal of space has been devoted to those investigations aimed at clarifying the distribution of these "inductive agents" in the normal embryo during early development. From the beginning it was noted that no specific distribution of the two (or more) active principles could be demonstrated in the organizer tissue, but that during invagination a definite segregation arose: the archenteron roof formed an inductive "model" corresponding to the future fate of the overlying ectoderm. The nature of this process of modification or maturation of the inductive activity of the organizer tissue is unknown. Some authors have suggested that a chemical transformation of the agents might occur; as another, purely tentative suggestion, we wish to present another explanation. The results of the differentiation of the ectodermal folds of Nieuwkoop et al. (1952) have been explained as different diffusion rates of the chemically separate inductive agents (Toivonen and Saxén, 1955b, Dalcq, 1960) in which small-molecule neuralizing agents diffuse more rapidly than the mesodermalizing agents of larger molecular size. The recent results of Johnen (1961) appear to corroborate this idea. There accordingly may be some possibility that these differences in diffusion rate play a role during the normal invagination of the dorsal lip, resulting in a graded distribution of the two principles of Okada and Hama (1945b). Furthermore, the staining experiments of Okada and Hama (1945b) demonstrated that the material of the territory close to the blastopore is distributed over a much wider area than that of the region corresponding to the future caudal part of the archenteron roof (the "mesodermalizing area"). This different distribution of the organizer material may further facilitate the formation of gradients in the two main principles. It may be stressed that the inductive action of the different territories of the archenteron roof obtained by Sala (1955a, 1955b) and ter Horst (1948) has recently been imitated in our experiments (Saxén and Toivonen, 1961). Here, similar inductors were produced by an experimental combination of two types of inductively active cells. Following the pretreatment of these cells, their difference in inductive action can only be explained as differences in their physico-chemical constitution. The statement might thus be made that the inductive action of the different archenteron roof territories *can be* imitated by the combination of two different inductors, and to us it seems very probable that this is also the case in normal development.

If we agree on this point, no further major controversy may be occasioned by the different conceptions presented. One such difference in opinion seems to be the question of two successive phases versus a simultaneous action of the different principles. This has already been discussed on page 203, but even this point might be of minor significance. As we have pointed out in several connections, it is not yet possible to distinguish between the *primary differentiating stimulus* and the long chain of *subsequent inductive interactions*. It seems quite obvious that many of the specific inductions traced back to the initial stimulus are, in fact, due to such secondary interactions as these demonstrated in the experiments of Takaya (1957).

Final Remarks

Despite the progress made in the study of the mechanism of primary induction presented in this monograph, and the convergence of the different concepts discussed in the last chapter, it must be said that we are still doing little more than scratching the surface of the problem. The demonstration of two main types of reaction in primary induction might constitute a basis of knowledge for subsequent studies, but it is far from what can in fact be termed the "mechanism" of induction. The chemistry of the more or less hypothetical agents is not fully understood, and in this field the

Q

findings are confusing. The physical properties of these agents are not well enough known, and our knowledge is based on data which are partly inconclusive. The role played by the reacting ectoderm is completely obscure, and finally our ideas of the "molecular level" of the transfer of inductive information from cell to cell are purely speculative.

It is fortunate that an increasing amount of information is being gained from interactive systems quite other than primary induction, and some day it might be possible to return to the "concepts on primary induction" from a basis quite different from the one we have today. Meanwhile, as we await information of this type from other fields, study of primary induction has to be continued by using all the possible tools of modern biological research, and our pessimistic attitude can be saved for the long hours of the night during the "operation season".

References

ADELMANN, H. B., 1934. A study of cyclopia in Amblystoma punctatum with special reference to the mesoderm. *J. exp. Zool.*, **67**, 219–281.

ADELMANN, H. B., 1937. Experimental studies on the development of the eye. IV. The effect of the partial and complete excision of the prechordal substrate on the development of the eyes of Amblystoma punctatum. *J. exp. Zool.*, **75**, 199–227.

D'AMELIO, V., and CEAS, M. P., 1957. Distribution of protease activity in the blastula and early gastrula of discoglossus pictus. *Experientia*, **13**, 152–153.

ATLAS, M., 1938. The rate of oxygen consumption of frogs during embryonic development and growth. *Physiol. Zoöl.*, **11**, 278–291.

AUERBACH, R., 1960. Morphogenetic interactions in the development of the mouse thymus gland. *Develop. Biol.*, **2**, 271–284.

AUERBACH, R., and GROBSTEIN, C., 1958. Inductive interaction of embryonic tissues after dissociation and reaggregation. *Exp. Cell Res.*, **15**, 384–397.

V. AUFSESS, A., 1941. Defekt- und Isolationsversuche an der Medullarplatte und ihrer Unterlagerung an Triton alpestris und Amblystoma-Keimen, mit besonderer Berücksichtigung der Rumpf- und Schwanzregion. *Arch. EntwMech Org.*, **141**, 248–339.

AVERY, G., and HOLTZER, H., 1958. Growth promoting activity of spinal cord on somite muscle. *Anat. Rec.*, **131**, 529.

BALINSKY, B. I., 1938. On the determination of endodermal organs in Amphibia. *C.R. Acad. Sci. U.R.S.S.*, **20**, 215–217.

BALINSKY, B. I., 1948. Korrelationen in der Entwicklung der Mund- und Kiemenregion und des Darmkanals bei Amphibien. *Arch. EntwMech. Org.*, **143**, 365–395.

BALINSKY, B. I., 1960. *An introduction to embryology.* Saunders, Philadelphia and London.

BARNES, M. R., 1944. The metabolism of the developing Rana pipiens as revealed by specific inhibitors. *J. exp. Zool.*, **95**, 399–417.

BARTH, L. G., 1934. The chemical nature of the amphibian organizer. I. The use of the cephalinfraction of mammalian brain as an inducing agent. *Biol. Bull.*, Wood's Hole, **67**, 244–249.

BARTH, L. G., 1939. (a) The chemical nature of the amphibian organizer. III. Stimulation of the presumptive epidermis of Amblystoma by means of cell extracts and chemical substances. *Physiol. Zoöl.*, **12**, 22–29.

BARTH, L. G., 1939 (b). Oxygen consumption of the parts of amphibian gastrula. *Proc. Soc. exp. Biol.*, New York, **42**, 744–746.

BARTH, L. G., 1941. Neural differentiation without organizer. *J. exp. Zool.*, **87**, 371–383.

231

BARTH, L. G., 1942. Regional differences in oxygen consumption of the amphibian gastrula. *Physiol. Zoöl.*, **15**, 30–46.

BARTH, L. G., 1946. Studies of the metabolism of development. The metabolic nature of the block to gastrulation in hybrid eggs. *J. exp. Zool.*, **103**, 463–486.

BARTH, L. G., and BARTH, L. J., 1954. *The energetics of development.* Colombia Univ. Press, New York.

BARTH, L. G., and BARTH, L. J., 1959. Differentiation of cells of the Rana pipiens gastrula in unconditioned medium. *J. Embryol. exp. Morph.*, **7**, 210–222.

BARTH, L. G., BARTH, L. J., and GOLDHOR, S., 1960. Factors influencing the expression of differentiation potencies of presumptive epidermis cultured in vitro. *Anat. Rec.*, **137**, 337.

BARTH, L. G., and GRAFF, S., 1938. The chemical nature of the amphibian organizer. *Cold. Spr. Harb. Symp. Quant. Biol.*, **6**, 385–391.

BARTH, L. G., and GRAFF, S., 1943. Effect of protein extracts of neural plate plus chordamesoderm on presumptive epidermis. *Proc. Soc. exp. Biol.*, New York, **54**, 118–121.

BARTH, L. J., BARTH, L. G., and NELSON, I., 1960. Induction of pigment cells from the presumptive epidermis of Rana pipiens gastrula. *Anat. Rec.*, **137**, 337–338.

BAUTZMANN, H., 1926. Experimentelle Untersuchungen zur Abgrenzung des Organisationszentrums bei Triton taeniatus. *Arch. EntwMech. Org.*, **108**, 283–321.

BAUTZMANN, H., 1932. Induktionsvermögen nach Abtötung durch Hitze. In: Bautzmann, H., Holtfreter, J., Spemann, H., and Mangold, O.: Versuche zur Analyse der Induktionsmittel in der Embryonalentwicklung. *Naturwissenschaften*, **20**, 971–972.

BAUTZMANN, H., HOLTFRETER, J., SPEMANN, H., und MANGOLD, O., 1932. Versuche zur Analyse der Induktionsmittel in der Embryonalentwicklung. *Naturwissenschaften*, **20**, 971–974.

BEATTY, R. A., de JONG, S., and ZIELINSKI, M. A., 1939. Experiments on the effect of dyes in induction and respiration in the amphibian gastrula. *J. Exp. Biol.* **16**, 150–154.

BECKER, U., 1955. Experimentelle Untersuchungen zum Kausalitätsproblem der Linsenbildung bei Triturus. *Diss. Naturwiss. Fak. Univ. Köln.* (Cited by Mangold, 1961.)

BECKER, U., 1959 (a). Die Bedeutung des reagierenden Gewebes für die Ausbildung von freien Linsengebilden bei Triturus vulgaris. *Arch. EntwMech. Org.*, **151**, 188–217.

BECKER, U., 1959 (b). Personal communication to the authors.

BECKER, U., 1960. Untersuchungen über die Abhängigkeit der Linsenbildung von der Wirtsregion bei Triturus vulgaris. *Arch. EntwMech. Org.*, **152**, 339–372.

BECKER, U., DOSTAL, V., TIEDEMANN, H., und TIEDEMANN, H., 1959. Über die Induktionswirkung verschiedener maligner Tumoren sowie normaler und maligner Gewebezellstämme bei der Implantation ins Blastocoël der Triturusgastrula. *Z. Naturf.*, **14b**, 260–264.

BECKER, U., TIEDEMANN, H., und TIEDEMANN, H., 1959. Versuche zur Determination von embryonalem Amphibiengewebe durch Induktionsstoffe in Lösung. Z. Naturf., 14b, 608–609.

BELL, E., 1960. Some observations on the surface coat and intercellular matrix material of the Amphibian ectoderm. Exp. Cell Res., 20, 378–383.

BELLAIRS, R., 1959. The development of the nervous system in chick embryos, studied by electron microscopy. J. Embryol. exp. Morph., 7, 94–115.

BENITEZ, H. H., MURRAY, M. R., and CHARGAFF, E., 1959. Heteromorphic change of adult fibroblasts by ribonucleoproteins. J. biophys. biochem. Cytol., 5, 25–34.

BENOIT, J. A. A., 1960. Induction de cartilage in vitro par l'extrait d'otocystes d'embryos de Poulet. J. Embryol. exp. Morph., 8, 33–38.

BERRILL, N. J., 1941 (a). Spatial and temporal growth patterns in colonial organisms. Growth (suppl.), 5, 89–111.

BERRILL, N. J., 1941 (b). Size and morphogenesis in the bud of Botryllus. Biol. Bull., Wood's Hole, 80, 185–193.

BERTOLINI, B., 1958. Sul comportamento del tappeto nero di embrioni di polls in particolari condizioni di impianto in allanto-corion. Riv. Biol. 50, 345–360.

BIJTEL, J H., 1931. Über die Entwicklung des Schwanzes bei Amphibien. Arch. EntwMech. Org., 125, 448–486.

BIJTEL, J. H., 1936. Die Mesodermbildungspotenzen der hinteren Medullarplattenbezirke bei Amblystoma mexicanum in Bezug auf die Schwanzbildung. Arch. EntwMech. Org., 134, 262–282.

BIJTEL, J. H., 1958. The mode of growth of the tail in urodele larvae. J. Embryol. exp. Morph., 6, 466–478.

BIJTEL, J. H., and WOERDEMAN, M. W., 1928. On the development of the tail in the amphibian embryo. Proc. roy. Acad. Sci., Amst., 31, 1030–1040.

BOELL, E. J., 1945. Functional differentiation in embryonic development. II. Respiration and cytochrome oxidase activity in Amblystoma punctatum. J. exp. Zool., 100, 331–352.

BOELL, E. J., 1948. Biochemical differentiation during amphibian development. Ann. N.Y., Acad. Sci., 49, 773–800.

BOELL, E. J., 1955. Energy exchange and enzyme development during embryogenesis. In: Analysis of development. Ed. by B. H. Willier, P. A. Weiss, and V. Hamburger. Saunders, Philadelphia and London. pp. 520–555.

BOELL, E. J., and WEBER, R., 1955. Cytochrome oxidase activity in mitochondria during amphibian development. Exp. Cell Res., 9, 559–567.

BONNER, J. T., 1960. Development in the cellular slime molds: The role of cell division, cell size, and cell number. In: Developing Cell Systems and their Control. Ed. by D. Rudnick. The Ronald Press Co., New York, pp. 3–20.

BORGHESE, E., 1943. Transplantation der Chorda von Neurulen unter die präsumptive Rumpfepidermis mittlerer und später Gastrulen in verschiedener Orientierung bei Triton. Arch. EntwMech. Org., 142, 53–82.

BRACHET, A., 1908. Recherches sur l'ontogénèse de la tête chez les Amphibiens. Arch. Biol., 23, 165–257.

BRACHET, A., 1927. Étude comparative des localisations germinales dans l'oeuf des amphibiens urodèles et anoures. *Arch. EntwMech. Org.*, **111**, 250–291.

BRACHET, J., 1934. Étude du métabolisme de l'œuf de grenouille (Rana fusca) au cours du développement. 1. La respiration et la glycolyse, de la segmentation a l'éclosion. *Arch. Biol.*, **45**, 611–727.

BRACHET, J., 1935. Étude du métabolisme de l'œuf de Grenouille (Rana fusca) au cours du développement. 3. Métabolisme respiratoire et "centre organisateur" de la gastrula. *Arch. Biol.*, **46**, 25-45.

BRACHET, J., 1940. Étude histochimique des protéins au cours du développement embryonnaire des Poissons, des Amphibiens et des Oiseaux. *Arch. Biol.*, **51**, 167–202.

BRACHET, J., 1941 (a). La localisation des acides pentosenucléiques dans les tissus animaux et les oeuf d'Amphibiens en voie de développement. *Arch. Biol.*, **53**, 207–257.

BRACHET, J., 1941 (b). La détection histochimique des acides pentosenucléiques (tissus animaux—développement embryonnaire des Amphibiens). *Enzymologia*, **10**, 87–96.

BRACHET, J., 1942. Le rôle des acides nucléiques dans l'induction chez les Amphibiens. *Acta biol. belg.*, **2**, 16–19.

BRACHET, J., 1943. Pentosenucleoproteides et induction neurale. *Bull. Acad. R. Sci. Belg.*, 5th Ser. , **29**, 707–718.

BRACHET, J., 1944. *Embryologie chimique*. Masson & Cie, Paris.

BRACHET, J., 1947. Nucleic acids in the cell and the embryo. *Symp. Soc. exp. Biol.*, **1**, 207-224.

BRACHET, J., 1948. Le rôle et la localisation des acides nucléiques au cours du développement embryonnaire. *C.R. Soc. Biol.*, Paris, **142**, 1241–1254.

BRACHET, J., 1950 (a). *Chemical embryology*. Interscience Publ., New York and London.

BRACHET, J., 1950 (b). Quelques observations sur le mode d'action de l'organisateur chez les Amphibiens. *Experientia*, **6**, 56–57.

BRACHET, J., 1957. *Biochemical cytology*. Acad. Press Inc., New York.

BRACHET, J., 1959. Tissue interactions: embryonic induction. Discussion. In: *Biological organization*. Ed. by C. H. Waddinton. Pergamon Press, London, pp. 225–230.

BRACHET, J., 1960 (a). *The biochemistry of development*. Pergamon Press, London.

BRACHET, J., 1960 (b). Nucleic acids and growth. In: *Fundamental aspects of normal and malignant growth*. Ed. by W. Nowinski. Elsevier, Amsterdam, pp. 260–304.

BRACHET, J., and HUGON DE SCOEUX, F., 1949. Remarques sur le mode d'action de l'organisateur chez les Amphibiens. *J. Cyto-Embryol. belgonéerl*, 56- 60.

BRACHET, J., KUUSI, T. et GOTHIE, S., 1952. Une étude comparative du pouvoir inducteur en implantation et en micro-injection des acides nucléiques et des constituants cellulaires nucléoprotéiques. *Arch. Biol.*, **63**, 429–440.

BRACHET, J., and SHAVER, J. R., 1949. The injection of embryonic microsomes into early amphibian embryos. *Experientia*, **5**, 204–205.

BRAHMA, S. K., 1957. Induction through the surface coat ectoderm. *Proc. zool. Soc. Beng. Moorkerjee Memor. Vol.*, 155–163.

BRAHMA, S. K., 1958. Experiments on the diffusibility of the Amphibian evocator. *J. Embryol. exp. Morph.*, **6**, 418–423.

BRIEN, P., 1937. La réorganisation de l'éponge après dissociation par filtration et phénomènes d'involution chez Ephydatia fluviatilis. *Arch. Biol.*, **48**, 185.

BRIGGS, R., and KING, T., 1952. Transplantation of living nuclei from blastula cells into enucleated frogs' eggs. *Proc. nat. Acad. Sci.*, Wash., **38**, 455–463.

BRIGGS, J., and KING, T., 1955. Specificity of nuclear function in embryonic development. In: *Biological specificity and Growth*, Ed. by E. G. Butler, Univ. Press, Princeton, pp. 207–228.

BRUNS, E., 1931. Experimente über das Regulationsvermögen der Blastula von Triton taeniatus und Bombinator pachypus. *Arch. EntwMech. Org.*, **123**, 682–718.

BYTINSKI-SALZ, H., 1929. Untersuchungen über die Determination und die Induktionsfähigkeit einiger Keimbezirke der Anuren. *Arch. EntwMech. Org.*, **118**, 121 163.

CAMPENHOUT, E. VAN, 1930. Contribution to the problem of the development of the sympathetic nervous system. *J. exp. Zool.*, **56**, 295–320.

CASPERSSON, T., 1941. Studien über den Eiweissumsatz der Zelle. *Naturwissenschaften*, **29**, 33–43.

CÉAS, M. P., and NASELLI, A., 1958. Incorporation of S^{35}-methionine in developmental stages of Discoglossus pictus. *Acta. embryol. morph. exp.*, **1**, 207–210.

CHALKLEY, H. W., 1945. Quantitative relation between the number of organized centres and tissue volume in regenerating masses of minced body sections of Hydra. *J. nat. Cancer Inst.*, **6**, 191–195.

CHEN, P. S., 1960. Changes in DNA and RNA during embryonic urodele development. *Exp. Cell Res.*, **21**, 523–534.

CHEN, P. S., and RICKENBACHER, J., 1954. Concerning the free amino acids in Amphibian development. *Experientia*, **10**, 182–183.

CHILD, C. M., 1928. Axial development in aggregates of dissociated cells from Corymorpha palma. *Physiol. Zoöl.*, **1**, 419.

CHILD, C. M., 1929. Physiological dominance and physiological isolation in development and reconstitution. *Arch. EntwMech. Org.*, **117**, 21–66.

CHILD, C. M., 1941. *Patterns and problems of development*. Univ. Press, Chicago.

CHILD, C. M., 1948. Patterns of indicator oxidation in Triturus development. *J. exp. Zool.*, **109**, 79–108.

CHUANG, H-H., 1938. Spezifische Induktionsleistungen von Leber und Niere im Explantationsversuch. *Biol. Zbl.*, **58**, 472–480.

CHUANG, H-H., 1939. Induktionsleistungen von frischen und gekochten Organteilen (Niere, Leber) nach ihrer Verpflanzung in Explantate und verschiedene Wirtsregionen von Tritonkeimen. *Arch. EntwMech. Org.*, **139**, 556–638.

CHUANG, H-H., 1940. Weitere Versuche über die Veränderung der Induktionsleistungen von gekochten Organteilen. *Arch. EntwMech. Org.*, **140**, 25–38.

CHUANG, H-H., 1947. Defekt- und Vitalfärbungsversuche zur Analyse der Entwicklung der kaudalen Rumpfabschnitte und des Schwanzes bei Urodelen. *Arch. EntwMech. Org.*, **143**, 19–125.

CHUANG, H-H., 1955. Untersuchungen über die Reaktionsfähigkeit des Ektoderms mittels sublethaler Cytolyse. (Chinese text with German summary.) *J. Acad. Sinica*, **4**, 151–186.

CHUANG, H-H., and TSENG, M-P., 1956. An experimental analysis of the determination and differentiation of the mesodermal structures of neurula in urodeles. *Scientia Sinica*, **6**, 669–708.

CLARKE, W. M., and FOWLER, I. 1960. The inhibition of lens-inducing capacity of the optic vesicle with adult lens antisera. *Develop. Biol.*, **2**, 155–172.

CLAYTON, R. M., 1953. Distribution of antigens in the developing newt embryo. *J. Embryol. exp. Morph.*, **1**, 25–42.

CLAYTON, R. M., and ROMANOVSKY, A., 1959. Passage of antigenic material between inductor and ectoderm. *Exp. Cell Res.*, **18**, 410–412.

COHEN, S., 1954. The metabolism of $C^{14}O_2$ during amphibian development. *J. biol. Chem.*, **211**, 337–354.

COOPER, R. S., 1948. A study of frog egg antigens with serum-like reactive groups. *J. exp. Zool.*, **107**, 397–438.

DALCQ, A., 1941. *L'Oeuf et son dynamisme organisateur*. Michel, Paris.

DALCQ, A., 1947. Recent experimental contributions to brain morphogenesis in Amphibians. *Growth* (suppl.), **10**, 85–119.

DALCQ, A., 1960. Germinal organization and induction phenomena. In: *Fundamental aspects of normal and malignant growth*. Ed. by W. W. Nowinski. Elsevier, Amsterdam, pp. 305–494.

DALCQ, A., et PASTEELS, J., 1937. Une conception nouvelle des bases physiologiques de la morphogénèse. *Arch. Biol.*, **48**, 669–710.

DALCQ, A., et PASTEELS, J., 1938. Potentiel morphogénétique, régulation et "Axial gradients" de child. Mireau point des bases physiologiques de la morphogénèse. *Bull. Acad. Méd. Belg.*, 6ᵉ sér. **3**, 261–308.

DAMAS, H., 1947. Effet de la suspension précoce du flux inducteur sur la détermination du neurectoblaste médullaire. *Arch. Biol.*, **58**, 15–57.

DENIS, H., 1957. Influence du facteur temps sur la determination de la plaque neurale chez les Amphibiens. *Ann. Soc. zool. Belg.*, **87**, 501–536.

DENIS, H., 1958. Influence de la méthode d'élevage sur la différenciation nerveuse d'un fragment d'ectoblaste. *J. Embryol. exp. Morph.*, **6**, 444–447.

DETWILER, S. R., 1937. Observations upon the migration of neural crest cells, and upon the development of the spinal ganglia and vertebral arches in Amblystoma. *Amer. J. Anat.*, **61**, 63–94.

DETWILER, S. R., and VAN DYKE, R. H., 1953. The induction of neural retina from the pigment epithelial layer of the eye. *J. exp. Zool.*, **122**, 367–383.

DETWILER, S. R., and VAN DYKE, R. H., 1954. Further experimental observations on retinal inductions. *J. exp. Zool.*, **126**, 135–155.

DEUCHAR, E. M., 1953. The regional properties of Amphibian organizer tissue after disaggregation of its cells in alkali. *J. exp. Biol.*, **30**, 18–43.

DEUCHAR, E. M., 1956. Amino acids in developing tissues of Xenopus laevis. *J. Embryol. exp. Morph.*, **4**, 327–346.

DEUCHAR, E. M., 1958. Regional differences in catheptic activity in Xenopus laevis embryos. *J. Embryol. exp. Morph.*, **6**, 223–237.

VAN DOORENMALEN, W. J., 1958. Histo-serological demonstration of the localization of lens-antigens in the embryonic chick-lens. *Acta Morph. neerl.-scand.*, **2**, 1–12.

DORRIS, F., 1938. Differentiation of the chick eye *in vitro*. *J. exp. Zool.*, **78**, 385–407.

DRAGOMIROW, N., 1936. Über Induktion sekundärer Retina in transplantierten Augenbechern bei Triton und Pelobates. *Arch. EntwMech. Org.*, **134**, 716–737.

DRIESCH, H., 1897. Betrachtungen über die Organisation des Eies und ihre Genese. *Arch. EntwMech. Org.*, **4**, 75–124.

DUESBERG, J., 1910. Les chondriosomes des cellules embryonnaires du poulet, et leur rôle dans la genèse des myofibrilles, avec quelques observations sur le developpement des fibres musculaires striées. *Arch. Zellforsch.*, **4**, 602–671.

DÜRCKEN, B., 1926. Das Verhalten embryonaler Zellen im Interplantat. Mit Berücksichtigung des Geschwulstproblems. *Arch. EntwMech. Org.*, **107**, 727–828.

DUSHANE, G. P., 1939. Neural fold derivatives in the Amphibia: Pigment cells, spinal ganglia and Rohon-Beard cells. *J. exp. Zool.*, **78**, 485–503.

EAKIN, R. M., 1939. Further studies in regulatory development of Triturus torosus. *Univ. California Publ. Zool.*, **43**, 185–210.

EAKIN, R. M., 1949. The nature of the organizer. *Science*, **109**, 195–197.

EAKIN, R. M., 1957. An electronmicroscopic study of amphibian ectoderm. *Anat. Rec.* **129**, 532.

EAKIN, R. M., BERG, W. E., and KUTSKY, P. B., 1950. Studies in protein metabolism of the Amphibian embryo. II. Free amino acids. *Proc. Soc. exp. Biol.*, New York, **75**, 32–34.

EAKIN, R. M., KUTSKY, P. B., and BERG, W. E., 1951. Protein metabolism of Amphibian embryo. III. Incorporation of methionine into protein of gastrulae. *Proc. Soc. exp. Biol.*, New York, **78**, 502–504.

EAKIN, R. M., and LEHMANN, F. E., 1957. An electronmicroscopic study of developing amphibian ectoderm. *Arch. EntwMech. Org.*, **150**, 177–198.

EBERT, J. D., 1959 (a). The acquisition of biological specificity. In: *The Cell*, Ed. by J. Brachet and A. E. Mirsky. Acad. Press, New York, pp. 619–693.

EBERT, J. D., 1959 (b). The formation of muscle and muscle-like elements in the chorioallantoic membrane following inoculation of a mixture of cardiac microsomes and Rous sarcoma virus. *J. exp. Zool.*, **142**, 587–622.

EBERT, J. D., and WILT, F. H., 1960. Animal viruses and embryos. *Quart. Rev. Biol.*, **35**, 261–312.

EDDS, M. V., Jr. (Ed.), 1958 (a). *Immunology and development.* A report from the developmental biology confer. ser., 1956. Univ. Press, Chicago.

EDDS, M. V., Jr., 1958 (b). Origin and structure of intercellular matrix. In: *A symposium on the chemical basis of development*. Ed. by W. D. McElroy and B. Glass. The John Hopkins Press, Baltimore, pp. 157–173.

EKMAN, G., 1921. Experimentelle Beiträge zur Entwicklung des Bombinator Herzens. *Övers. Finska Vetenskapssoc. Förh.*, **63**, A. No. 5, 1–37.

EKMAN, G., 1924 (a). Über die Explantation von Herzanlagen der Amphibien. *Ann. Soc. zool.-bot. fenn.*, Vanamo, **2**, No. 3, 1–5.

EKMAN, G., 1924 (b). Neue experimentelle Beiträge zur frühesten Entwicklung des Amphibienherzens. *Soc. Sci. Fennica, Comment. Biol.*, **1**, No. 9, 1–36.

EKMAN, G., 1936. Beobachtungen über den Bau durch halbseitige obere Urmundlippe induzierter Embryonen bei Triton. *Ann. Acad. Sci. fenn.*, **45**, No. 4, 1–100.

EKMAN, G., 1937. Zwei bemerkenswerte induzierte Embryonen (ein sehr vollständiger und ein zweiköpfiger) bei Triton. *Acta Soc. Fauna Flora fenn.*, **60**, 113–128.

ENDRES, H., 1895. Über Anstick- und Schnürversuche an Eiern von Triton taeniatus. *Schles. Ges. Vaterländ. Kultur*, 73.

ENGLÄNDER, H., JOHNEN, A. G., 1957. Experimentelle Beiträge zu einer Analyse der spezifischen Induktionsleistung heterogener Induktoren. *J. Embryol. exp. Morph.*, **5**, 1–31.

ENGLÄNDER, H., JOHNEN, A. G. und VAHS, W., 1953. Untersuchungen zur Klärung der Leistungsspezifität verschiedener abnormer Induktoren bei der Embryonalentwicklung der Urodelen. *Experientia*, **9**, 100–101.

EYAL-GILADI, H., 1954. Dynamic aspects of neural induction in Amphibia. *Arch. Biol.*, **65**, 179–259.

FELL, H. B., 1953. The effect of excess vitamin A on the differentiation of chick ectoderm in culture. *J. Embryol. exp. Morph.*, **1**, 287–288.

FELL, H. B., 1957. The future of tissue culture in relation to morphology. *J. nat. Cancer Inst.*, **19**, 643–662.

FELL, H. B., and MELLANBY, E., 1953. Metaplasia produced in cultures of chick ectoderm by high vitamin A. *J. Physiol.*, London, **119**, 470–488.

FERRIS, W., and BAGNARA, J. T., 1960. Electron microscope observations of the optic vesicle-lens epithelium relationship in the chick embryo. *Anat. Rec.*, **137**, 355.

FICQ, A., 1954 (a). Analyse de l'induction neurale par autoradiographia. *Experientia*, **10**, 20–21.

FICQ, A., 1954 (b). Analyse de l'induction neurale chez les Amphibiens au moyen d'organisateurs marqués. *J. Embryol. exp. Morph.*, **2**, 194–203.

FISCHER, F. G., 1935. Zur chemischen Kenntnis der Induktionsreize in der Embryonal-Entwicklung. *Verh. dtsch. zool. Ges.* (Zool. Anz. Suppl.), **37**, 171–176.

FISCHER, F. G. und HARTWIG, H., 1936. Die Vitalfärbung von Amphibien-keimen zur Untersuchung ihrer Oxydation-Reduktions-Vorgänge. *Z. vergl. Physiol.*, **24**, 1–13.

FISCHER, F. G. und HARTWIG, H., 1938. Vergleichende Messungen der Atmung des Amphibien-Keimes und seiner Teile während der Entwicklung. *Biol. Zbl.*, **58**, 567–589.

FISCHER, F. G. und WEHMEIER, E., 1933. Zur Kenntnis der Induktions-mittel in der Embryonalentwicklung. *Naturwissenschaften*, **21**, 518.

FISCHER, F. G., WEHMEIER, E., LEHMANN, H., JÜHLING, L. und HULTZSCH, K., 1935. Zur Kenntnis der Induktionsmittel in der Embryonal-Ent-wicklung. *Ber. dtsch. chem. Ges.*, **68**, 1196–1199.

FLICKINGER, R. A., 1954. Utilization of $C^{14}O_2$ by developing amphibian embryos, with special reference to regional incorporation into individual embryos. *Exp. Cell Res.*, **6**, 172–180.

FLICKINGER, R. A., 1958 (a). Regional localization of neural and lens antigens in the frog embryo in relation to induction. *Biol.*, *Bull.*, Wood's Hole, **115**, 201–208.

FLICKINGER, R. A., 1958 (b). Induction of neural tissue in ventral explants from frog gastrulae by carbon dioxide shock. *Science*, **127**, 145–146.

FLICKINGER, R. A., and BLOUNT, R. W., 1957. The relation of natural and imposed electrical potentials and respiratory gradients to morphogenesis. *J. cell. comp. Physiol.*, **50**, 403–422.

FLICKINGER, R. A., HATTON, E., and ROUNDS, D. E., 1959. Protein transfer in chimaeric Taricha-Rana explants. *Exp. Cell Res.*, **17**, 30–34.

FLICKINGER, R. A., and NACE, G. W., 1952. An investigation of proteins during the development of the amphibian embryo. *Exp. Cell Res.*, **3**, 393–405.

FORD, P., 1950. The origin of the segmental musculature of the tail of the Axolotl (Amblystoma). *Proc. zool. Soc.*, Lond., **119**, 609–632.

GALLERA, J., 1947. Effects de la suspension précoce de l'induction normale sur la partie préchordale de la plaque neurale chez les Amphibiens. *Arch. Biol.*, **58**, 221–264.

GALLERA, J., 1949. Transplantations de matériel inducteur céphalique du Triton prélévé durant la gastrulation et les premiers stades de la neurula-tion. *Arch. Anat.*, Strasbourg, **32**, 121–172.

GALLERA, J., 1951, Contribution a l'etude expérimentale de la morphogénèse de l'arcencéphale chez les amphibiens. *Arch. EntwMech. Org.*, **145**, 143–173.

GALLERA, J., 1952. Inductions céphaliques dans l'ectoblaste vieilissant (Triturus alpestris). *Arch. EntwMech. Org.*, **146**, 21–67.

GALLERA, J., 1958. L'action inductrice de la plaque préchordale sur de l'ectoblaste qui était auparavant influencé par la chorde (Triturus alpes-tris). *Acta anat.*, **35**, 47–62.

GALLERA, J., 1959. La facteur "temps" dans l'action inductrice du chordo-mesoblaste et l'âge de l'ectoblaste réagissant. *J. Embryol. exp. Morph.*, **7**, 487–511.

GALLERA, J., 1960. L'action inductrice du chordo-mésoblaste au cours de la gastrulation et de la neurulation et les effets de la culture *in vitro* sur les manifestations. *J. Embryol. exp. Morph.*, **8**, 477–494.

GEINITZ, B., 1925. Embryonale Transplanatation zwischen Urodelen und Anuren. *Arch. EntwMech. Org.*, **106**, 357–408.

GOERTTLER, K., 1927. Die Bedeutung gestaltender Bewegungsvorgänge beim Differenzierungsgeschehen. (Transplantationsexperimente an Uro-delenkeimen zur Frage der Differenzierung des Medullarmaterials.) *Arch. EntwMech. Org.*, **112**, 517–576.

GOLDBERG, B., and GREEN, H., 1960. Immune cytolysis. I. The release of ribonucleoprotein particles. II. Membrane-bounded structures arising during cell fragmentation. *J. biophysic. biochem. Cytol.*, **7**, 645–650.

GRANT, P., 1958. The synthesis of deoxyribonucleic acid during early embryonic development of Rana pipiens. *J. cell. comp. Physiol.*, **52**, 227–247.

GRÄPER, L., 1929. Die Primitiventiwicklung des Hühnchens nach stereo-kinematographischen Untersuchengen, kontrolliert durch vitale Farb-markierung und verglichen mit der Entwicklung anderer Wirbeltiere. *Arch. EntwMech. Org.*, **116**, 382–429.

GREGG, J. R., 1948. Carbohydrate metabolism of normal and of hybrid amphibian embryos. *J. exp. Zool.*, **109**, 119–134.

GREGG, J. R., and LØVTRUP, S., 1950. Biochemical gradients in the Axolotl gastrula. *C.R. Lab.*, Carlsberg (sér. chim.), **27**, 307–324.

GREGG, J. R., and LØVTRUP, S., 1955. Synthesis of desoxyribonucleic acid in lethal Amphibian hybrids. *Biol. Bull.*, Wood's Hole, **108**, 29–34.

GROBSTEIN, C., 1952. Effect of fragmentation of mouse embryonic shields on their differentiative behavior after culturing. *J. exp. Zool.*, **120**, 437–456.

GROBSTEIN, C., 1953. Morphogenetic interaction between embryonic mouse tissues separated by a membrane filter. *Nature*, London, **172**, 869.

GROBSTEIN, C., 1955 (a). Tissue interaction in the morphogenesis of mouse embryonic rudiments *in vitro*. In: *Aspects of synthesis and order in growth*. Ed. by D. Rudnick, Univ. Press, Princeton, pp. 233-256.

GROBSTEIN, C., 1955 (b). Tissue disaggregation in relation to determination and stability of cell type. *Ann. N.Y. Acad. Sci.*, **60**, 1095–1106.

GROBSTEIN, C., 1956 (a), Trans-filter induction of tubules in mouse meta-nephrogenic mesenchyme. *Exp. Cell Res.*, **10**, 424–440.

GROBSTEIN, C., 1956 (b). Inductive tissue interaction in development. *Advanc. Cancer Res.*, **4**, 187–236.

GROBSTEIN, C., 1957. Some transmission characteristics of the tubuleinduc-ing influence on mouse metanephrogenic mesenchyme. *Exp. Cell Res.*, **13**, 575–587.

GROBSTEIN, C., 1959 (a), Differentiation of vertebrate cells. In: *The Cell*. Ed. by J. Brachet, and A. Mirsky. Acad. Press, New York, pp. 437–496.

GROBSTEIN, C., 1959 (b). Autoradiography of the interzone between tissues in inductive interaction. *J. Exp. Zool.*, **142**, 203–213.

GROBSTEIN, C., 1961 (a). Cell contact in relation to embryonic induction. *Exp. Cell Res.* (suppl.), **8**, 234–245.

GROBSTEIN, C., 1961 (b). Passage of radioactivity into a membrane filter from spinal cord pre-incubated with tritiated amino acids or nucleosides. In: *Actes du colloque international sur "La culture organotypique. Associa-tions et dissocciations d'organes en culture in vitro"*. Ed. by M. E. Wolff. Éditions du centre national de la recherche scientifique. Paris, pp. 169–182.

GROBSTEIN, C., and DALTON, A. J., 1957. Kidney tubule induction in mouse metanephrogenic mesenchyme without cytoplasmic contact. *J. exp. Zool.*, **135**, 57–73.

GROBSTEIN, C., and PARKER, G., 1954. *In vitro* induction of cartilage in mouse somite mesoderm by embryonic spinal cord. *Proc. Soc. exp. Biol.*, New York, **85**, 477-481.

GROBSTEIN, C., and ZWILLING, E., 1953. Modification of growth and differentiation of chorio-allantoic grafts of chick blastoderm pieces after cultivation at a glass-clot interface. *J. exp. Zool.*, **122**, 259–284.

GUSTAFSON, T., and LENICQUE, P., 1952. Studies on mitochondria in the developing sea urchin egg. *Exp. Cell Res.*, **3**, 251–274.

HAGUEANAU, F., 1958. The ergastoplasm: Its history, ultrastructure and biochemistry. *Int. Rev. Cytol.*, **7**, 425–483.

HALL, E. K., 1937. Regional differences in the action of the organization center. *Arch. EntwMech. Org.*, **135**, 671–688.

HAMA, T., 1944. On the inductive specificity of fresh and boiled tissues of vertebrate kidney and liver. *Annot. zool. jap.*, **22**, 165–172.

HAMA, T., 1947. Interchange between head organizer and trunk organizer. (Japanese text with English summary.) *Zool. Mag.*, Tokyo, **57**, 137-140.

HAMA, T., 1949. Explantation of the urodelen organizer and the process of morphological differentiation attendant upon invagination. *Proc. imp. Acad.*, Japan, **25**, No. 9, 4–11.

HAMA, T., 1950 (a). Induction as it is affected by variously paired head and trunk organizers. *Annot. zool., jap.*, **23**, 49–57.

HAMA, T., 1950 (b). Differences in results obtained by different manner of transplantation of the head organizer. *Annot. zool. jap.*, **23**, 191–193.

HARRISON, R. G., 1924/25. Neuroblast versus sheath cell in the development of peripheral nerves. *J. comp. Neurol.*, **37**, 123–194.

HARRISON, R. G., 1933. Some difficulties in the determination problem. *Amer. Nat.*, **67**, 306–321.

HAYASHI, Y., 1955. Inductive effect of some fractions of tissue extracts after removal of pentose nucleic acid, tested on the isolated ectoderm of Triturus gastrula. *Embryologia*, **2**, 145–162.

HAYASHI, Y., 1956. Morphogenetic effects of pentose nucleoprotein from the liver upon the isolated ectoderm. *Embryologia*, **3**, 57–67.

HAYASHI, Y., 1958. The effects of pepsin and trypsin on the inductive ability of pentose nucleoprotein from guinea pig liver. *Embryologia*, **4**, 33–53.

HAYASHI, Y., 1959 (a). The effect of ribonuclease on the inductive ability of liver pentose nucleoprotein. *Develop. Biol.*, **1**, 247–268.

HAYASHI, Y., 1959 (b). Significance of lipids in induction by tissue and by a pentose nucleoprotein sample isolated from tissue. *Develop. Biol.*, **1**, 343–363.

HAYASHI, Y., and TAKATA, K., 1958. Morphogenetic effects of subfractions of pentose nucleoprotein from the liver separated by means of ultracentrifugation. *Embryologia*, **4**, 149–160.

HEATLEY, N. G., and LINDAHL, P. E., 1937. Studies on the nature of the Amphibian organization centre. V. The distribution and nature of glycogen in the Amphibian embryo. *Proc. Roy. Soc.*, London, s.B, **122**, 395–402.

HERLITZKA, A., 1897. Sullo sviluppo di embrioni completi da blastomeri isolati di uova di tritone (Molge cristata). *Arch. EntwMech. Org.*, **4**, 624–658.

HERMANN, H., 1960. Molecular mechanisms of differentiation. An inquiry into the protein forming system of developing cells. In: *Fundamental aspects of normal and malignant growth*. Ed. by W. W. Nowinski, Elsevier, Amsterdam, pp. 494–545.

HOFF-JØREGENSEN, E., 1954. Desoxyribonucleic acid in some gametes and embryos. In: *Recent developments in cell physiology*. Ed. by J. A. Kitching, Butterworths, Sci. Publ., London, pp. 79–90.

HOFF-JØRGENSEN, E., and ZEUTHEN, E., 1952. Evidence of cytoplasmic desoxyribosides in the frog's egg. *Nature*, London, **169**, 245–246.

HOLTFRETER, J., 1929. Über die Aufzucht isolierter Teile des Amphibien-keimes. I. Methode einer Gewebezüchtung *in vivo*. *Arch. EntwMech. Org.*, **117**, 422–510.

HOLTFRETER, J., 1931. Über die Aufzucht isolierter Teile des Amphibien-keimes. II. Züchtung von Keimen und Keimteilen in Salzlösung. *Arch. EntwMech. Org.*, **124**, 404–466.

HOLTFRETER, J., 1933 (a). Eigenschaften und Verbreitung induzierender Stoffe. *Naturwissenschaften*, **21**, 766–770.

HOLTFRETER, J., 1933 (b). Nachweis der Induktionsfähigkeit abgetöteter Keimteile. Isolations- und Transplantationsversuche. *Arch. EntwMech. Org.*, **128**, 584–633.

HOLTFRETER, J., 1933 (c). Der Einfluss von Wirtsaltter und verschiedenen Organbezirken auf die Differenzierung von angelagertem Gastrulaekto-derm. *Arch. EntwMech. Org.*, **127**, 619–775.

HOLTFRETER, J., 1933 (d). Organisierungsstufen nach regionaler Kombination von Entomesoderm mit Ektoderm. *Biol. Zbl.*, **53**, 404–431.

HOLTFRETER, J., 1933 (e). Die totale Exogastrulation, eine Selbstablösung des Ektoderms von Entomesoderm. Entwicklung und funktionelles Verhalten nervenloser Organe. *Arch. EntwMech. Org.*, **129**, 669–793.

HOLTFRETER, J., 1934. Über die Verbreitung induzierender Substanzen und ihre Leistungen im Triton-Keim. *Arch. EntwMech. Org.*, **132**, 307–383.

HOLTFRETER, J., 1935. Morphologische Beeinflussung von Urodelenektoderm bei xenoplastischer Transplantation. *Arch. EntwMech. Org.*, **133**, 367–426.

HOLTFRETER, J., 1936. Regionale induktionen in xenoplastisch zusammen-gesetzten explantaten. *Arch. EntwMech. Org.*, **134**, 466–550.

HOLTFRETER, J., 1938 (a). Veränderungen der Reaktionsweise im alternden isolierten Gastrulaektoderm. *Arch. EntwMech. Org.*, **138**, 163–196.

HOLTFRETER, J., 1938 (b). Differenzierungspotenzen isolierter Teile der Urodelengastrula. *Arch. EntwMech. Org.*, **138**, 522–656.

HOLTFRETER, J., 1938 (c). Differenzierungspotenzen isolierter Teile der Anurengastrula. *Arch. EntwMech. Org.*, **138**, 657–738.

HOLTFRETER, J., 1939 (a). Studien zur Ermittlung der Gestaltungsfaktoren in der Organentwicklung der Amphibien. I. Dynamisches Verhalten isolierter Furchungszeller und Entwicklungsmechanik der Entodermor-gane. *Arch. EntwMech. Org.*, **139**, 110–190.

HOLTFRETER, J., 1939 (b). Gewebeaffinität, ein Mittel der embryonalen Formbildung. *Arch. Zellforsch.*, **23**, 169–209.

HOLTFRETER, J., 1943 (a). Properties and functions of the surface coat in amphibian embryos. *J. exp. Zool.*, **93**, 251–323.

HOLTFRETER, J., 1943 (b). A study of the mechanics of gastrulation. I. *J. exp. Zool.*, **94**, 261–318.

HOLTFRETER, J., 1944 (a). A study of the mechanics of gastrulation. II. *J. exp. Zool.*, **95**, 171–212.

HOLTFRETER, J., 1944 (b). Neural differentiation of ectoderm through exposure to saline solution. *J. exp. Zool.*, **95**, 307–340.

HOLTFRETER, J., 1944 (c). Experimental studies on the development of the pronephros. *Rev. canad. biol.*, **3**, 220–250.

HOLTFRETER, J., 1945. Neuralization and epidermization of gastrula ectoderm. *J. exp. Zool.*, **98**, 161–209.

HOLTFRETER, J., 1946. Structure, motility and locomotion in isolated embryonic amphibian cells. *J. Morph.*, **79**, 27–62.

HOLTFRETER, J., 1947 (a). Observations on the migration, aggregation and phagocytosis of embryonic cells. *J. Morph.*, **80**, 25–55.

HOLTFRETER, J., 1947 (b). Changes of structure and the kinetics differentiating embryonic cells. *J. Morph.*, **80**, 57–92.

HOLTFRETER, J., 1947 (c). Neural induction in explants which have passed through a sublethal cytolysis. *J. exp. Zool.*, **106**, 197–222.

HOLTFRETER, J., 1948 (a). Concepts on the mechanism of embryonic induction and its relation to parthenogenesis and malignancy. *Symp. Soc. exp., Biol.* **2**, 17–48.

HOLTFRETER, J., 1948 (b). Significance of the cell membrane in embryonic process. *Ann. N.Y. Acad. Sci.*, **49**, 709–760.

HOLTFRETER, J., 1951. Some aspects of embryonic induction. *Growth* (suppl.), **10**, 117–152.

HOLTFRETER, J., 1955. Studies on the diffusibility, toxicity and pathogenic properties of "inductive" agents derived from dead tissues. *Exp. Cell Res.*, (suppl.), **3**, 188–209.

HOLTFRETER, J., and HAMBURGER, V., 1955. Embryogenesis: Progressive differentiation. Amphibians. In: *Analysis of Development*. Ed. by B. H. Willier, P. A. Weiss, and V. Hamburger. Saunders, Philadelphia and London, pp. 230–296.

HOLTZER, H., LASH, J., and HOLTZER, S., 1956. The enchancement of somitic muscle maturation by the embryonic spinal cord. *Biol. Bull.*, Wood's Hole, **11**, 303.

HOLTZER, H., MARSHALL, J. M., Jr., and FINCK, H., 1957. An analysis of myogenesis by the use of fluorescent antimyosin. *J. biochem. biophys. Cytol.*, **3**, 705–724.

HORI, R., and NIEUWKOOP, P. D., 1955. Induction phenomena with denatured inductor. *Proc. Acad. Sci. Amst.*, ser. C., **58**, 266–272.

HORST, J. TER, 1948. Differenzierungs- und Induktionsleistungen verscheidener Abschnitte der Medullarplatte und des Urdarmdasches von Triton im Kombinat. *Arch. EntwMech. Org.*, **143**, 275–303.

HÖRSTADIUS, S., 1950. *The neural crest*. Oxford Univ. Press, London.

HÖRSTADIUS, S., und SELLMAN, S., 1946. Experimentelle Untersuchungen über die Determination des knorpeligen Kopfskelettes bei Urodelen. *Nova Acta Soc. Sci. Upsal. Ser. IV*, **13**, No. 8, 1-170.

HUNT, H., 1961. A study of the fine structure of the optic vesicle and lens placode of the chick embryo during induction. *Develop. Biol.*, **3,** 175–209.

IKEDA, Y., 1937. Über die Bildung akzessorischer Retina aus dem Tapetum bei Hynobius. *Arch. EntwMech. Org.*, **136,** 676–680.

JOHNEN, A. G., 1956 (a). Experimental studies about the temporal relationships in the induction process. I. Experiments on Amblystoma mexicanum. *Proc. Acad. Sci. Amst.*, ser. C., **59,** 554–561.

JOHNEN, A. G., 1956 (b). Experimental studies about the temporal relationships in the induction process. II. Experiments on Triturus vulgaris. *Proc. Acad. Sci. Amst.*, ser. C., **59,** 652–660.

JOHNEN, A. G., 1961. Experimentelle Untersuchungen über die Bedeutung des Zeitfaktors beim Vorgang der neuralen Induktion. *Arch. EntwMech. Org.*, **153,** 1–13.

KARASAKI, S., 1957 (a). Changes of cell components during embryonic development. (In Japanese with English summary.) *Symp. Soc. cell Chem.* (Japan), **6,** 77–88.

KARASAKI, S., 1957 (b). On the mechanism of the dorsalization in the ectoderm of Triturus gastrulae caused by precytolytic treatments. I. Cytolytical and morphogenetic effects of various injurious agents. *Embryologia*, **3,** 317–334.

KARASAKI, S., 1957 (c). On the mechanism of the dorsalization in the ectoderm of Triturus gastrulae caused by precytolytic treatments. II. The suppression of dorsalization by treatments with sucrose, glucose and 2,4-dinitrophenol. *Embryologia*, **3,** 335–341.

KARASAKI, S., 1959 (a). Electron microscopic studies on cytoplasmic structures of ectoderm cells of the Triturus embryo during the early phase of differentiation. *Embryologia*, **4,** 247–272.

KARASAKI, S., 1959 (b). Changes in fine structure of the nucleus during early development of the ectoderm cells of the Triturus embryo. *Embryologia*, **4,** 273–282.

KARASAKI, S., and YAMADA, T., 1955. Morphogenetic effects of centrifugation on the isolated ectoderm and whole embryo of some anurans. *Experientia*, **11,** 1–9.

KAWAKAMI, I., 1958. Inductive effect of rat ascites hepatoma on the Amphibian competent ectoderm. *Gann*, **49,** 177–191.

KAWAKAMI, I., IYEIRI, S., and SASAKI, N. 1960. Analysis of inductive agents in chick embryo extract using Triturus gastrula ectoderm as reactor. *J. exp. Zool.*, **144,** 33–42.

KAWAKAMI, I., and MIFUNE, S., 1955. Studies on the inductive effects on the amphibian embryos of fresh mouse tissues. I. Specificities of the inductive effects of the normal fresh tissues. *Mem. Fac. Sci. Kyushu Univ.*, ser E., **2,** 21–30.

KAWAKAMI, I., and MIFUNE, S., 1957. Studies on the inductive effects on amphibian embryos of fresh mouse tissues. II. Modification of the inductive effects of tissues by total-body X-irradiation. *Mem. Fac. Sci. Kyushu Univ.*, ser. E., **2,** 141–147.

KAWAKAMI, I., and YAMANA, K., 1959. Studies on the inductive capacities of the combined proteins from bone marrow, kidney and liver of guinea-pig. *Mem. Fac. Sci. Kyushu Univ.*, ser. E., **2**, 171–182.

KAWAKAMI, I. K., 1959. Mesodermal inductive capacity of retinal tissue. *Mem. Fac. Sci. Kyushu Univ.*, ser. E., **3**, 1–11.

KAWAKAMI, I. K., 1960. Successive alterations in inductive capacity of retinal tissue in chick embryo. *J. Exp. Zool.*, **143**, 47–55.

KING, T. J., and BRIGGS, J., 1955. Changes in the nuclei of differentiating gastrula cells, as demonstrated by nuclear transplantation. *Proc. nat. Acad. Sci.*, Wash., **41**, 321–325.

KITCHIN, I. C., 1949. The effects of notochordectomy in Amblyostoma mexicanum. *J. exp. Zool.*, **112**, 393–416.

KOHONEN, J., 1962. On the thermolability of embryonic inductive action of mouse spleen. *Arch. Soc. zool.-bot. fenn. Vanamo* (in press).

KRIEGEL, H., 1956. Über die Induktionwirkung fixierter Oocytenkerne bei Triton alpestris. *Naturwissenschaften*, **43**, 185–186.

KRUGELIS, E. J., NICHOLAS, J. S., and VOSGIAN, M. E., 1952. Alkaline phosphatase activity and nucleic acids during embryonic development of Amblystoma punctatum at different temperatures. *J. exp. Zool.*, **121**, 489–504.

KUTSKY, P. B., 1950, Phosphate metabolism in the early development of Rana pipiens. *J. exp. Zool.*, **115**, 429–466.

KUTSKY, P. B., EAKIN, R. M., BERG, W. E., and KAVANAU, J. L., 1953. Protein metabolism of amphibian embryo. IV. Quantitative changes in free and non-protein amino acids. *J. exp. Zool.*, **124**, 263–277.

KUUSI, T., 1951 (a). Über die chemische Natur de Induktionsstoffe im Implantatversuch bei Triton. *Experientia*, **7**, 299–300.

KUUSI, T., 1951 (b). Über die chemische Natur der Induktionsstoffe mit besonderer Berücksichtigung der Rolle der Proteine und der Nuklein-säuren. Diss., Helsinki. *Ann. Soc. zool.-bot. fenn. Vanamo*, **14**, No. 4, 1–98.

KUUSI, T., 1953. Sur les effets des acides nucléiques et des protéines dans l'induction hétérogène. *Arch. Biol.*, **64**, 189–226.

KUUSI, T., 1957 (a). On the properties of the mesoderm inductor. I. *Arch. Soc. zool.-bot. fenn. Vanamo*, **11**, No. 2, 136–148.

KUUSI, T., 1957 (b). On the properties of the mesoderm inductor. II. *Arch. Soc. zool.-bot. fenn. Vanamo*, **12**, No. 7, 75–93.

KUUSI, T., 1959. The mesoderm induction process in Amphibians, studied with the aid of radioactive tracers. I. Experiments with glycine-1-C[14]. *Arch. Soc. zool.-bot. fenn. Vanamo*, **13**, 97–105.

KUUSI, T., 1960. The mesoderm induction process in Amphibians, studied with the aid of radioactive tracers. II. Experiments with $Na_2S^{35}O_4$ and methionine-S[35]. *Arch. Soc. zool.-bot. fenn. Vanamo*, **14**, 4–28.

KUUSI, T., 1961. The effect of urea denaturation on the inductor properties of a protein fraction of the bone-marrow. *Acta embryol., morph. exp.* **4**,18–39.

LALLIER, R., 1950. Etude de l'induction primaire chez les Amphibiens. *Experientia*, **6**, 92–93.

LANGMAN, J., SCHALEKAMP, M. A. D. H., KUYKEN, M. P. A., and VEEN, R. 1957. Seroimmunological aspects of lens development in chick embryos. *Acta Morph. neerl.-scand.*, **2**, 142–154.

R

LASH, J., HOLTZER, S., and HOLTZER, H. 1957. An experimental analysis of the development of the spinal column. VI. Aspects of cartilage induction. *Exp. Cell Res.*, **13**, 292–303.

LEHMANN, F. E., 1928. Die Entwicklung der Differenzierungspotenzen im Ectoderm der Triton-Gastrula. *Verh. dtsch. zool. Ges. (Zool. Anz. suppl.*), **32**, 267–272.

LEHMANN, F. E., 1929. Die Entwicklung des Anlagenmusters im Ektoderm der Tritongastrula. *Arch. EntwMech. Org.*, **117**, 312–383.

LEHMANN, F. E., 1932. Die Beteilung von Implantats- und Wirtsgewebe bei der Gastrulation und Neurulation induzierter Embryonalanlagen. *Arch. EntwMech. Org.*, **125**, 566–639.

LEHMANN, F. E., 1933. Die Augen- und Linsenbildung von Amphibien-embryonen unter dem Einfluss chemischer Mittel. *Rev. suisse Zool.*, **40**, 251–264.

LEHMANN, F. E., 1938. Regionale Verschiedenheiten des Organisators von Triton, insbesondere in der vorderen und hinteren Kopfregion, nachge-wiesen durch phasenspezifische Erzeugung von Lithiumbedingten und operativ bewirkten Regionaldefekten. *Arch. EntwMech Org.*, **138**, 106–158.

LEHMANN, F. E., 1945. Einführung in die physiologische Embryologie. Birkhäuser, Basel.

LEHMANN, F. E., 1950. Die Morphogenese in ihrer Abhängigkeit von ele-mentaren biologischen Konstituenten des Plasmas. *Rev. suisse Zool.*, **57**, suppl. 1, 141–151.

LEHMANN, H., 1938. Zur chemische Kenntnis der Induktionsmittel in der Embryonalentwicklung von Amphibien. *Diss., Freiburg i. Br.*

LOPASHOV, G. V., 1935. Die Entwicklungsleistungen des Gastrulaekto-derms in Abhängigkeit von Veränderungen der Masse. *Biol. Zbl.*, **55**, 606–615.

LOPASHOV, G. V., 1939. On the character of cell changes in neural plate induction. *C.R. Acad. Sci. U.R.S.S.*, **24**, 205–208.

LOPASHOV, G. V., 1941. Formbildungsfelder des Mesoderms bei Amphi-bienkeimen. *C.R. Acad. Sci. U.R.S.S.*, **30**, 770–774.

LOPASHOV, G. V., 1959. Comparative studies of the transformation capacity of the eye layers at various stages of development in vertebrates. *XVth Int. Congr. Zool. Sect. VII*, Paper 14, 1–3.

LOPASHOV, G. V., 1961. The development of the vertebrate eye in relation to the problem of embryonic induction. *Ann. Soc. zool.-bot. fenn. Vanamo*, 22, No. 6, 1–17.

LOPASHOV, G. V., and STROEVA, O. G., 1961. Morphogenesis of the verte-brate eye. *Advanc. Morph.* **1**, 331–377.

LØVTRUP, S., 1953. Energy sources of amphibian embryogenesis. *C.R. Lab. Carlsberg*, sér chim., **28**, 371–399.

LØVTRUP, S., 1955. Chemical differentiation during embryogenesis. *C.R. Lab. Carlsberg*, sér. chim., **29**, 261–314.

MACHEMER, H., 1932. Experimentelle Untersuchung über die Induktions-leistungen der oberen Urmundlippe in älteren Urodelenkeimen. *Arch. EntwMech. Org.*, **126**, 391–456.

McKEEHAN, M. S., 1951. Cytological aspects of embryonic lens induction in the chick. *J. exp. Zool.*, **117**, 31–64.

McKEEHAN, M. S., 1956. The relative ribonucleic acid content of lens and retina during lens induction in the chick. *Amer. J. Anat.*, **99**, 131–156.

McKEEHAN, M. S. 1958. Induction of the portions of chick lens without contact with the optic cup. *Anat. Rec.*, **132**, 297–305.

McLOUGHLIN, C. B., 1961. Metaplasia of epidermis transplanted into different types of mesenchyme in the chick. In: *Actes du colloque international sur "La culture organotypique: Associations et dissociations d'organes en culture in vitro"*. Ed. by M. E. Wolff. Editions du centre national de la recherche scientifique, Paris, pp. 145–154.

MANGOLD, O. 1923. Transplantationsversuche zur Frage der Spezifizität und der Bildung der Keimblätter. *Arch. EntwMech. Org.*, **100**, 198–301.

MANGOLD, O., 1925. Die Bedeutung der Keimblätter in der Entwicklung. *Naturwissenschaften*, **13**, 213–218, 231–237.

MANGOLD, O., 1928. Das Determinationsproblem. I. Das Nervensystem und die Sinnesorgane der Seitenlinie unter spezieller Berücksihtigung der Amphibien. *Ergeb. Biol.*, **3**, 151–227.

MANGOLD, O., 1929 (a). Die Induktionsfähigkeit der Medullarplatte und ihrer Bezirke. *Verh. dtsch. zool. Ges. (Zool. Anz. suppl.)*, 166–173.

MANGOLD, O., 1929 (b). Experimente zur Analyse der Determination und Induktion der Medullarplatte. *Arch. EntwMech. Org.*, **117**, 586–696.

MANGOLD, O., 1931 (a). Das Determinationsproblem. III. Das Wirbeltierauge in der Entwicklung und Regeneration. *Ergebn. Biol.*, **7**, 193–403.

MANGOLD, O., 1931 (b). Versuche zur Analyse der Entwicklung des Haftfadens bei Urodelen, ein Beispiel für die Induction artfremder Organe. *Naturwissenschaften*, **19**, 905–911.

MANGOLD, O., 1932. Ist das Induktionsmittel diffusionsfähig? In: Bautzmann, H., Holtfreter, J., Spemann, H. und Mangold, O.: Versuche zur Analyse der Induktionsmittel in der Embryonalentwicklung. *Naturwissenschaften*, **20**, 971–974.

MANGOLD, O., 1933 (a). Isolationsversuche zur Analyse der Entwicklung bestimmter Kopforgane. *Naturwissenschaften*, **21**, 394–397.

MANGOLD, O., 1933 (b). Über die Induktionsfähigkeit der verschiedenen Bezirke der Neurula von Urodelen. *Naturwissenschaften*, **21**, 761–766.

MANGOLD, O., 1936. Experimente zur Analyse der Zusammenarbeit der Keimblätter. *Naturwissenschaften*, **24**, 753–760.

MANGOLD, O., 1937. Isolationsversuche zur Analyse der Entwicklung der Gehör-, Kiemen- und Extremitätenregion bei Urodelen. *Acta Fauna Flora fenn.* **60**, 1–44.

MANGOLD, O., 1961 (a). Grundzüge der Entwicklungsphysiologie der Wirbeltiere mit besonderer Berücksichtigung der Missbildungen auf grund experimenteller Arbeiten an Urodelen. *Acta genet. med. et gemel.*, **10**, 1–49.

MANGOLD, O., 1961 (b). Molchlarven ohne Zentralnervensystem und ohne Ektomesoderm. *Arch. EntwMech. Org.*, **152**, 725–769.

MANGOLD, O. und SPEMANN, H., 1927. Über Induktion von Medullarplatte

248   PRIMARY EMBRYONIC INDUCTION

durch Medullarplatte im jüngeren Keim, ein Beispiel homoögenetischer oder assimilatorischer Induktion. *Arch. EntwMech. Org.*, **111**, 341–422.

MANGOLD, O. und VON WOELLWARTH, C., 1950. Das Gehirn von Triton. Ein experimenteller Beitrag zur Analyse seiner Determination. *Naturwissenschaften*, **37**, 365–372, 390–395.

MASSUI, Y., 1956. Effect of LiCl upon the organizer and the presumptive ectoderm. *Annot. zool. jap.*, **29**, 75–78.

MASUI, Y., 1959. Induction of neural structures under the influence of lithium chloride. *Annot. zool. jap.*, **32**, 23–30.

MASUI, Y., 1960 (a). Differentiation of the prechordal tissue under influence of lithium chloride. *Mem. Konan Univ.*, Sci. ser. No. **4**, 65–78.

MASUI, Y., 1960 (b). Alteration of the differentiation of gastrula ectoderm under influence of lithium chloride. *Mem. Konan Univ.*, Sci. ser. No. **4**, 79–102.

MASUI, Y., 1960 (c). Effect of lithium chloride upon differentiation of the neural-plate ectoderm of head area. *Mem. Konan Univ.*, Sci. ser. No. **4**, 103–114.

MAYER, B., 1935. Über das Regulations- und Induktionsvermögen der halbseitigen oberen Urmundlippe von Triton. *Arch. EntwMech. Org.*, **133**, 518–581.

MEVES, F., 1908. Die Chondriosomen als Träger erblicher Anlagen; cytologische Studien am Hühnerembryo. *Arch. mikr. Anat.*, **72**, 816–867.

MIFUNE, S., 1955. Regional differences in inductive capacity of mouse organs. I. Studies on kidney. *Mem. Fac. Sci. Kyushu Univ.* ser. E., **2**, 13–19.

MIFUNE, S., 1957. Studies on the inductive effects on Amphibian embryos of mouse tissues. III. Modification of the inductive effects of tissues by injecting nitrogen Mustard-N-Oxide. *Mem. Fac. Sci. Kyushu Univ.*, ser E., **2**, 149–158.

MIFUNE, S., 1959. Studies on the inductive effects of mammalian bone marrow in explantation experiments with embryos of Triturus. *Mem. Fac. Sci. Kyushu Univ.*, ser. E., **3**, 33–41.

MOOG, F., 1944., The chloretone sensitivity of frogs' eggs in relation to respiration and development. *J. cell. comp. Physiol.*, **23**, 131–155.

MOORE, J. A., 1947. Studies in the development of frog hybrids. II. Competence of the gastrula ectoderm of Rana pipiens ♀ x Rana sylvatica ♂ hybrids. *J. exp. Zool.*, **105**, 349–370.

MOORE, J. A., 1955. Abnormal combinations of nuclear and cytoplasmic systems in frogs and toads. *Advanc. Genet.*, **7**, 139–182.

MOORE, J. A., 1958. Transplantation of nuclei between Rana pipiens and Rana sylvatica. *Exp. Cell. Res.*, **14**, 532–540.

MOSCONA, A., 1956. Development of heterotypic combinations of dissociated embryonic chick cells. *Proc. Soc. exp. Biol.*, New York, **92**, 410–416.

MOSCONA, A., 1957 (a). The development *in vitro* of chimeric aggregates of dissociated embryonic chick and mouse cells. *Proc. nat. Acad. Sci.*, Wash., **42**, 184–194.

MOSCONA, A., 1957 (b). Formation of lentoids by dissociated retinal cells of the chick embryo. *Science*, **125**, 598–599.

MOSCONA, A., 1960. Patterns and mechanisms of tissue reconstruction from dissociated cells. In: *Developing cell systems and their control*. Ed. by D. Rudnick. The Ronald Press, New York, pp. 45–70.

MOSCONA, A., 1961. Environmental factors in experimental studies on histogenesis. In: *Actes du colloque international sur "La culture organo-typique. Associations et dissociations d'organes en culture in vitro"*. Ed. by M. E. Wolff. Editions du centre national de la recherche scientifique. Paris, pp. 155–168.

MOSCONA, A., and MOSCONA, H., 1952. The dissociation and aggregation of cells from organ rudiments of the early chick embryo. *J. Anat.*, **86**, 287–301.

MOSCONA, A., and MOSCONA, H., 1953. Development *in vitro* of embryonic organ rudiments on heterologous adult tissue derivatives. *Bull. Res. Counc. Israel*, **3**, 197–200.

MUCHMORE, W. B., 1951. Differentiation of the trunk mesoderm in Amblystoma maculatum. *J. exp. Zool.*, **118**, 137–186.

MUCHMORE, W. B., 1957. Differentiation of the trunk mesoderm in Amblystoma maculatum. II. Relation of the size of presumptive somite explants to subsequent differentiation. *J. exp. Zool.*, **134**, 293–310.

MURATORI, G., 1939. Explantate von Mesoderm mit und ohne Chorda-material gezüchtet in Ektodermhülle (in Triton alpestris). *Verh. anat. Ges. (Anat. Anz. suppl.)*, **87**, 430–433.

NACE, G. W., 1955. Development in the presence of antibodies. *Ann. N.Y. Acad. Sci.*, **60**, 1038–1055.

NACE, G. W., and CLARKE, W. M., 1958. Immuno-histological localization of one or more transistory antigens in the optic cup and lens of Rana pipiens. In: *A symposium on the chemical basis of development*. Ed. by W. D. McElroy and B. Glass. The John Hopkins Press, Baltimore, pp. 546–561.

NACE, G. W., and INOUE, K., 1957. Cytolysis versus differentiation in anti-neurula serum. *Science*, **126**, 259–261.

NAKAMURA, O., 1938. Tail formation in the urodele. *Zool. Mag.*, Tokyo, **50**, 442–446.

NAKAMURA, O., 1942. Die Entwicklung der hinteren Körperhälfte bei Urodelen. *Annot. zool. jap.*, **21**, 169–236.

NAKAMURA, O., 1952. Extirpation experiments of the presumptive rudiments in the caudal region of the newt. *Annot. zool. jap.*, **25**, 105–112.

NEEDHAM, J., 1931. *Chemical embryology*. I-III. Univ. Press, Cambridge.

NEEDHAM, J., 1942. *Biochemistry and morphogenesis.*, Univ. Press, Cambridge.

NEEDHAM, J., 1950. *Biochemistry and morphogenesis.*, Univ. Press, Cambridge.

NEEDHAM, J., WADDINGTON, C. H., and NEEDHAM, D. M., 1934. Physico-chemical experiments on the amphibian organizer. *Proc. roy. Soc.*, London, ser. B., **114**, 393–422.

NIEUWKOOP, P. D., 1946. Experimental investigations on the origin and the determination of the germ cells, and on the development of the lateral plates and germ ridges in Urodeles. Diss. Utrecht. *Arch. Néerl. Zool.*, **8**, 1–205.

NIEUWKOOP, P. D., 1950. Neural competence and neural fields. *Rev. suisse Zool.*, **57**, suppl. 1, 23–40.

NIEUWKOOP, P. D., 1955 (a). Independent and dependent development in the formation of the central nervous system in Amphibians. *Exp. Cell Res.* (suppl.), **3**, 262–273.

NIEUWKOOP, P. D., 1955 (b). Die neurale Induktion bei Amphibien. Autonomie und Abhängigkeit als Leitprincipien. *Rev. suisse Zool.*, **62**, 367–371.

NIEUWKOOP, P. D., 1958. Neural competence of the gastrula ectoderm in Amblystoma mexicanum. An attempt at quantitative analysis of morphogenesis. *Acta embryol. morph. exp.*, **2**, 13–53.

NIEUWKOOP, P. D., 1959. Discussion in: *Biological Organization. Cellular and sub-cellular*. Ed. by C. H. Waddington. Pergamon Press, London, pp. 212–230.

NIEUWKOOP, P. D., et al., 1952. Activation and organization of the central nervous system in Amphibians. I. Induction and activation. II. Differentiation and organization. III. Synthesis of a new working hypothesis. *J. exp. Zool.*, **120**, 1–108.

NIEUWKOOP, P. D., et al., 1955. Origin and establishment of organization patterns in embryonic fields during early development in amphibians and birds, in particular in the nervous system and its substrate. I and II. *Proc. Acad. Sci. Amst.*, ser. C., **58**, 219–227, 356–367.

NIEUWKOOP, P. D., and NIGTEVECHT, G. V., 1954. Neural activation and transformation in explants of competent ectoderm under the influence of fragments of anterior notochord in Urodeles. *J. Embryol. exp. Morph.* **2**, 175–193.

NIU, M. C., 1953. *In vitro* study of induction. *Anat. Rec.*, **117**, 560.

NIU, M. C., 1955. Identification of the organizing substance. *Anat. Rec.*, **122**, 420.

NIU, M. C., 1956. New approaches to the problem of embryonic induction. In: *Cellular mechanisms in differentiation and growth*. Ed. by D. Rudnick, Univ. Press, Princeton, pp. 155–171.

NIU, M. C., 1958 (a). The role of ribonucleic acid in embryonic differentiation. *Anat. Rec.*, **131**, 585.

NIU, M. C., 1958 (b). Thymus ribonucleic acid and embryonic differentiation. *Proc. nat. Acad. Sci.*, Wash., **44**, 1264–1274.

NIU, M. C., 1960. Personal communication to the authors.

NIU, M. C., and TWITTY, V. C., 1953. The differentiation of gastrula ectoderm in medium conditioned by axial mesoderm. *Proc. nat. Acad. Sci.*, Wash., **39**, 985–989.

OGAWA, Y., 1958. Development of skeletal muscle protein. *Nature*, London, **182**, 1312–1313.

OGI, K., 1961. Vegetalization of the presumptive ectoderm of the Triturus-gastrula by exposure to lithium chloride solution. *Embryologia*, **5**, 384–396.

OKADA, T. S., 1953 (a). Rôle of the mesoderm in the differentiation of endodermal organs. *Mem. Coll. Sci. Univ. Kyoto*, ser. B., **20**, 157–162.

OKADA, T. S., 1953 (b). Regulative power of the endoderm in Urodele. (In Japanese with English summary.) *Zool. Mag.*, Tokyo, **62**, 288–291.

OKADA, T. S., 1954 (a). Experimental studies on the differentiation of the endodermal organs in Amphibia. I. Significance of the mesenchymatous tissue to the differentiation of the presumptive endoderm. *Mem. Coll. Sci. Univ. Kyoto*, ser. B., **21**, 1–6.

OKADA, T. S., 1954 (b). Experimental studies on the differentiation of the endodermal organs in Amphibia. II. Differentiating potencies of the presumptive endoderm in the presence of the mesodermal tissues. *Mem. Coll. Sci. Univ. Kyoto*, ser. B., **21**, 7–14.

OKADA, T. S., 1955 (a). Experimental studies on the differentiation of the endodermal organs in Amphibia. III. The relation between the differentiation of pharynx and head-mesenchyme. *Mem. Coll. Sci. Univ. Kyoto.*, ser. B , **22**, 17–22.

OKADA, T. S., 1955 (b). Experimental studies on the differentiation of the endodermal organs in Amphibia. IV. The differentiation of the intestine from the fore-gut. *Annot. zool. jap.*, **28**, 210–214.

OKADA, T. S., 1957. The pluripotency of the pharyngeal primordium in Urodelan neurulae. *J. Embryol. exp. Morph.*, **5**, 438–448.

OKADA, T. S., 1960. Epithelio-mesenchymal relationships in the regional differentiation of the digestive tract in the Amphibian embryo. *Arch. EntwMech. Org.*, **152**, 1–21.

OKADA, Y. K., 1938. Neural induction by means of inorganic implantation. *Growth*, **2**, 49–53.

OKADA, Y. K., 1948. Induction of notochord by frog ventral skin and the organizing effect of such a notochord. *Proc. imp. Acad. Japan*, **24**, No. 10, 22–29.

OKADA, Y. K., and HAMA, T., 1943. Examination of regional differences in the inductive activity of the organizer by means of transplantation into ectodermal vesicles. *Proc. imp. Acad. Japan*, **19**, No. 1, 48–53.

OKADA, Y. K., and HAMA, T., 1944. On the different effects of the Amphibian organizer following culture, transplantation and heat treatment. *Proc. imp. Acad. Japan*, **20**, No. 1, 36–40.

OKADA, Y. K., and HAMA, T., 1945 (a). Regional differences in the inductive capacity of the dorsal roof of the archenteron of the Urodele, Triturus pyrrhogaster. *Proc. imp. Acad. Japan*, **21**, 240–247.

OKADA, Y. K., and HAMA, T., 1945 (b). Prospective fate and inductive capacity of the dorsal lip of the blastopore of the Triturus gastrula. *Proc. imp. Acad. Japan*, **21**, 342–348.

OKADA, Y. K., and HAMA, T., 1948. Induction of sensory organs by the uninvaginated portion of the dorsal lip of the amphibian gastrula. *Proc. imp. Acad. Japan*, **24**, 30–34.

OKADA, Y. K., and TAKAYA, H., 1942 (a). Experimental investigation of regional differences in the inductive capacity of the organizer. *Proc. imp. Acad. Japan*, **18**, 505–513.

OKADA, Y. K., and TAKAYA, H., 1942 (b). Further studies upon the regional differentiation of the inductive capacity of the organizer. *Proc. imp. Acad. Japan*, **18**, 514–519.

OKANO, H., 1957. On the neuralization of the presumptive epidermis of Amphibian embryo by lactic acid solution (Japanese). *Zool. Mag.*, Tokyo, **66**, 49.

OKANO, H., and KAWAKAMI, I., 1959. Studies on neuralizing effects of acid solution with and without lithium ion on Triturus presumptive ectoderm. *Mem. Fac. Sci., Kyushu Univ.*, ser. E., **2**, 183–201.

OKAZAKI, R., 1955. A critical study on the inducing capacity of the devitalized organizer. *Exp. Cell Res.*, **9**, 579–599.

OPPENHEIMER, J. M., 1959 (a). Extraembryonic transplantation of fragmented shield grafts in Fundulus. *J. exp. Zool.*, **142**, 441–460.

OPPENHEIMER, J. M., 1959 (b). Embryology and evolution: Nineteenth century hopes and twentieth century realities. *Quart. Rev. Biol.*, **34**, 271–277.

PALADE, G. E., 1955. A small particulate component of the cytoplasm. *J. biophys. biochem. Cytol.*, **1**, 59–68.

PASTEELS, J., 1933. La gastrulation et la répartition des territoires dans la moitié dorsale du blastodisque de Truite (Salmo iridaeus). *C.R. Soc. Biol.*, Paris, **113**, 425–428.

PASTEELS, J., 1934. Répartition des territoires et mouvements morphogénétiques de la gastrulation de l'oeuf de Truite ("Salmo iridaeus"). *C.R. Ass. Anat.*, Paris, **29**, 451–458.

PASTEELS, J., 1935. Les mouvements morphogénétiques de la gastrulation chez les Tortues. *Bull. Acad. Belg. Cl. Sci.*, **21**, 88–103.

PASTEELS, J., 1936. Analyse des mouvements morphogénétiques de gastrulation chez les Oiseaux. *Bull. Acad. Belg., Cl. Sci.*, **22**, 737–752.

PASTEELS, J., 1937 (a). Etudes sur la gastrulation des vertébrés méroblastiques. II. Reptiles. *Arch. Biol.*, **48**, 105–184.

PASTEELS, J., 1937 (b). Etudes sur la gastrulation des vertébrés méroblastiques. III. Oiseaux. IV. Conclusions générales. *Arch. Biol.*, **48**, 381–488.

PASTEELS, J., 1938. Recherches sur les facteurs initiaux de la morphogénèse chez les Amphibiens anoures. I. Résultats de l'expérience de Schultze et leur inteprétation. *Arch. Biol.*, **49**, 629–667.

PASTEELS, J., 1939 (a). Sur l'origine du matériel caudal des Urodèles. *Bull. Acad. Belg. Cl. Sci.*, **25**, 660–666.

PASTEELS, J., 1939 (b). La formation de la queue chez les vertébrés. *Ann. Soc. zool. Belg.*, **70**, 33–51.

PASTEELS, J., 1939 (c). Recherches sur les facteurs initiaux de la morphogénèse chez les Amphibiens anoures. II. Lèvres blastoporales successives dans un même œuf. *Arch. Biol.*, **50**, 291–320.

PASTEELS, J., 1940. Recherches sur les facteurs initiaux de la morphogénèse chez les Amphibiens anoures. IV. Centrifugation axiale de l'œuf fécondé et insegmenté. *Arch. Biol.*, **51**, 335–386.

PASTEELS, J., 1942. New observations concerning the maps of presumptive areas of the young Amphibian gastrula (Amblystoma and Discoglossus). *J. exp. Zool.*, **89**, 255–282.

PASTEELS, J., 1943. Proliferations et croissance dans la gastrulation et la formation de la queue des vertébrés. *Arch. Biol.*, **56**, 105–183.

PASTEELS, J., 1947 (a). Sur l'apparition d'organes variés dans l'ectoblaste, à la suite de la centrifugation de la blastula et de la gastrula chez les Amphibiens. *Experientia*, **3**, 30–32.

PASTEELS, J., 1947 (b). Sur la localisation du pronephros des anoures à

REFERENCES 253

propos d'expériences de centrifugation de la gastrula chez Rana temporaria. *Acta anat.*, **4**, 219–224.

PASTEELS, J., 1947 (c). Sur les interactions entre l'axe embryonnaire normal et les formations secondaires produites par la centrifugation de la blastula et de la gastrula chez les Amphibiens. *Experientia*, **3**, 73–74.

PASTEELS, J., 1953 (a). Les effets de la centrifugation sur la blastula et la jeune gastrula des Amphibiens. I. Mécanisme de la formation des organes secondaires aux dépens de l'ectoblaste. *J. Embryol. exp. Morph.*, **1**, 5–24.

PASTEELS, J., 1953 (b). Les effets de la centrifugation sur la blastula et la gastrula des Amphibiens. II. Étude comparative de la sensibilité en fonction des stades et des espéces. *J. Embryol. exp. Morph.*, **1**, 125–145.

PASTEELS, J., 1954. Les effets de la centrifugation sur la blastula et la jeune gastrula des Amphibiens. III. Interactions entre ébauches primaires et secondaires. IV. Discussion générale et conclusions. *J. Embryol. exp. Morph.*, **2**, 122–148.

PENNERS, A., 1929. Schultzescher Umdrehungsversuch an ungefurchten Froscheiern. *Arch. EntwMech. Org.*, **116**, 53–103.

PENNERS, A. und SCHLEIP, W., 1928 (a). Die Entwicklung der Schultzeschen Doppelbindungen aus dem Ei von Rana fusca. I–IV. *Z. wiss. Zool.*, **130**, 305–454.

PENNERS, A. und SCHLEIP, W., 1928 (b). Die Entwicklung der Schultzeschen Doppelbildungen aus dem Ei von Rana fusca. V–VI. *Z. wiss. Zool.*, **131**, 1–156.

PENTTINEN, K., SAXÉN, E., SAXÉN, L., TOIVONEN, S., and VAINIO, T., 1958. The importance of the growth medium on the morphological behavior, inductive action and immunology of cells. *Ann. Med. exp. Fenn.*, **36**, 27–46.

PERLMANN, P., 1953. Soluble antigens in sea urchin gametes and developmental stages. *Exp. Cell Res.*, **5**, 394–399.

PEARLMANN, P., 1954. Study on the effect of antisera on unfertilized sea urchin eggs. *Exp. Cell. Res.*, **6**, 485–490.

PERLMANN, P., and GUSTAFSON, T., 1948. Antigens in the egg and early developmental stages of the sea-urchin. *Experientia*, **4**, 481–483.

PERLMANN, P., and PERLMANN, H., 1957(a). Analysis of the surface structures of the sea urchin egg by means of antibodies. II. The J- and A-antigens. *Exp. Cell Res.*, **13**, 454–474.

PERLMANN, P., and PERLMANN, H., 1957(b). Analysis of the surface structures of the sea urchin egg by means of antibodies. III. The C- and F-antigens. *Exp. Cell Res.*, **13**, 475–487.

PFAUTSCH, M.-E., 1960. Utersuchung des Nukleinsäurengehaltes in verschiedenen Keimregionen bei der frühen Gastrula und Neurula von Triturus alphestris (Laur) und Amblystoma mexicanum (Cope). *Embryologia*, **5**, 139–169.

PIEPHO, H., 1938. Über Oxydation-Reduktionsvorgänge im Amphibienkeim. *Biol. Zbl.*, **58**, 90–117.

RAGOSINA, M. N., 1936. Induzierende Einwirkung von Pflanzengeweben auf das Gastrulaektoderm. (Russian text with German summary.) *Biol. Zh.*, **5**, 1073–1082.

RAGOSINA, M. N., 1937. Die Induktionswirkung pflanzlicher Gewebe auf das Ektoderm der Gastrula. *Arch. EntwMech. Org.*, **137**, 317-326.

RANZI, S., 1952. The biochemical and structural basis of morphogenesis. Proteins, protoplasmic structure and determination. *Arch. néerl. Zool.*, **10**, 92–107.

RANZI, S., and CITTERIO, P., 1955. The proteins in the Rana esculenta embryo in normal development and in experimental conditions. *Exp. Cell Res.* (suppl.), **3**, 287–293.

RANZI, S., CITTERIO, P., COPES, M. V., and SAMUELLI, C., 1957. Proteine e determinazione embrionale nella Rana, nel riccio di mare e negli incroci dei rospi. *Acta embryol. morph. exp.*, **1**, 78–98.

RAPER, K. B., 1941. Developmental patterns in simple slime molds. *Growth* (suppl.), **5**, 41–76.

RAUNICH, L., 1940. Sulle proprieta induttrici del cordomesoderma negli embrioni di Anuri (Discoglossus pictus e Bufo viridis). *Riv. Biol.*, **30**, 1–30.

RAUNICH, L., 1942. Die Reaktionsleistung des verschieden alten Gastrulaektoderms von Urodelen- und Anurenkeimen auf aspezifische Induktoren. *Naturwissenschaften*, **30**, 709–711.

RAVEN, C. P., 1931. Zur Entwicklung der Ganglienleiste. I. Die Kinematik der Ganglienleistenentwicklung bei der Urodelen. *Arch. EntwMech. Org.*, **125**, 210–292.

RAVEN, C. P., 1933. Experimentelle Untersuchungen über den Glykogenstoffwechsel des Organisationszentrums in der Amphibiengastula. I. *Proc. Acad. Sci. Amst.*, **36**, 566–569.

RAVEN, C. P., 1935 (a). Experimentelle Untersuchungen über den Glykogenstoffwechsel des Organizationszentrums in der Amphibiengastrula, II. *Proc. Acad. Sci. Amst.*, **38**, 1107–1109.

RAVEN, C. P., 1935 (b). Zur Entwicklung der Ganglienleiste. IV. Untersuchungen über Zeitpunkt und Verlauf der "materiellen Determination" des präsumptiven Kopfganglienleistenmaterials der Urodelen. *Arch. EntwMech. Org.*, **132**, 509–575.

RAVEN, C. P., 1936. Zur Entwicklung der Ganglienleiste. V. Über die differenzierung des Rumpfganglienleistenmaterials. *Arch. EntwMech. Org.*, **134**, 122-146.

RAVEN, C. P., 1938. Über die Potenz von Gastrulaektoderm nach 24-stündigem Verweilen im äusseren Blatt der dorsalen Urmundlippe. *Arch. EntwMech. Org.*, **137**, 661–713.

RAVEN, C. P., and KLOOS, J., 1945. Induction by medial and lateral pieces of the archenteron roof with special reference to the determination of the neural crest. *Acta neerl. morph.*, **4**, 348–362.

REYER, R. W., 1948. An experimental study of lens regeneration in Triturus viridescens viridescens. I. Regeneration of a lens after lens extirpation in embryos and larvae of different ages. *J. exp. Zool.*, **107**, 217–268.

ROLLHÄUSER-TER HORST, J., 1953. Die Induktionsleistung verschiedener Tritonkeimteile nach Denaturierung. *Arch. EntwMech. Org.*, **146**, 183–200.

ROTMANN, E., 1935. Reiz und Reizbeantwortung in der Amphibienentwicklung. *Verh. dtsch. zool. Ges.* (*Zool. Anz. Suppl.*), pp. 76–83.

ROTMANN, E., 1942 (a). Zur Frage der Leistungsspezifität abnormer Induktoren. *Naturwissenschaften*, 30, 60–62.

ROTMANN, E., 1942 (b). Über den Auslösungscharakter des Induktionsreizes bei der Linsentwicklung. *Biol. Zbl.*, 62, 154–170.

ROTMANN, E., 1943. Entwicklungsphysiologie. *Fortschr. Zool.*, N.F., 7, 167–255.

ROUNDS, D. E., and FLICKINGER, R. E., 1958. Distribution of ribonucleoprotein during neural induction of the frog embryo. *J. exp. Zool.*, 137, 479–500.

ROUX, W., 1888. Zur Frage der Axenbestimmung des Embryo im Froschei. *Biol. Zbl.*, 8, 399–413.

ROUX, W., 1894. Die Methode zur Erzeugung halber Froschembryonen und zum Nachweis der Beziehung der ersten Furchungscbcnen des Froscheies zur Medianebene des Embryo. *Anat. Anz.*, 9, 248–283.

SALA, M., 1955 (a). Influenze attivanti e caudalizzanti lungo la linea madiana del tetto dell'archenteron nell'induzione del sistcma nervoso di Anfibi Urodeli. *Comment. Pont. Ac. Sci.*, 16, 241–295.

SALA, M., 1955 (b). Distribution of activating and transforming influences in the archenteron roof during the induction of nervous system in Amphibians. *Proc. Acad. Sci. Amst.*, ser. C., 58, 635–647.

SASAKI, N., 1960. Inductive ettects of the chick embryo extract on the presumptive epidermis of Amphibian embryo. *Kumamoto J. Sci.*, ser. B., 5, 89–99.

SASAKI, N., KAWAKAMI, I., MIFUNE, S., and TAMANOI, I. 1957. The lens induction by a crude protein extracted from rabbit bone-marrow. *Mem. Fac. Sci. Kyushu Univ.*, ser. E., 2, 159–162.

SASAKI, N., KAWAKAMI, I., and OKANO, H., 1957. Embryonic inductions by chick embryo extract and its nucleoprotein. *Zool. Mag.*, Tokyo, 66, 58.

SAXÉN, E., and PENTTINEN, K., 1956. Factors in serum affecting the growth of HeLa cells. *Ann. Med. exp. Fenn.*, 34, 396–401.

SAXÉN, E., and PENTTINEN, K., 1961. Host factors in cell culture. Further studies of the growth controlling action of fresh human serum. *J. nat. Cancer Inst.*, 26, 1367–1379.

SAXÉN, L., 1961. Transfilter neural induction of Amphibian ectoderm. *Develop. Biol.*, 3, 140–152.

SAXÉN, L., and TOIVONEN, S., 1956. Inductive action of normal and leukemic bone-marrow of the rat. Experiments with Amphibian embryos. *Ann. Med. exp. Fenn.*, 34, 235–241.

SAXÉN, L., and TOIVONEN, S., 1957. The embryonic inductive action of normal and regenerating rat liver. *Embryologia*, 3, 353–360.

SAXÉN, L., and TOIVONEN, S., 1958 (a). Relationship between the growth medium and the embryonic induction capacity of HeLa cells. In: Penttinen, K., Saxén, E., Saxén, L., Toivonen, S., and Vainio, T., Importance of the growth medium on the morphological behaviour, inductive action and immunology of cells. *Ann. Med. exp. Fenn.*, 36, 27–46.

SAXÉN, L., and TOIVONEN, S., 1958 (b). The dependence of the embryonic inductive action of HeLa cells on their growth media. *J. Embryol. exp. Morph.*, 6, 616–633.

SAXÉN, L., and TOIVONEN, S., 1961. The two-gradient hypothesis in primary induction. The combined effect of two types of inductors mixed in different ratios. *J. Embryol. epx. Morp.*, **9**, 514–533.

SAXÉN, L., TOIVONEN, S., and VAINIO, T., 1961. The embryonic inductive action of cells cultivated *in vitro*. *Acta path. microbiol. scand. suppl.*, **144**, 163–164.

SCHECHTMAN, A. M., 1938. Competence for neural plate formation in Hyla regilla and the so-called nervous layer of the ectoderm. *Proc. Soc. exp. Biol.*, New York, **38**, 430–433.

SCHECHTMAN, A. M., 1942. The mechanism of amphibian gastrulation. I. *Univ. Calif. Publ. Zool.*, **51**, 1–40.

SENGEL, P., 1961. Action morphogène du système nerveux et de divers extraits de cerveau sur la peau d'embryon de Poulet cultivée *in vitro*. *Actes du colloque international sur "La culture organotypique: Associations et dissociations d'organes en culture* in vitro". Ed. by M. Wolff. Éditions du centre national de la recherche scientifique. Paris, pp. 95–116.

SENO, T., and NIEUWKOOP, P. D., 1958. The autonomous and dependent differentiations of the neural crest in Amphibians. *Proc. Acad. Sci. Amst.*, ser. C, **61**, 489–498.

SHAY, H., GRUENSTEIN, M., MARX, H. E., and GLASER, L., 1951. The development of lymphatic and myelogenous leukemia in Wistar rats following gastric instillation of methylcholanthrene. *Cancer Res.*, **11**, 29–34.

SHEN, S. C., 1939. A quantitative study of Amphibian neural tube induction with a water-soluble hydrocarbon. *J. exp. Biol.*, **16**, 143–149.

SHEN, S. C., 1942. Neural induction in epidermal explants in liquid medium. *J. exp. Biol.*, **19**, 5–10.

SIRLIN, J. L., 1955. Nuclear uptake of methionine-S_{35} in the newt embryo. *Experientia*, **11**, 112–113.

SIRLIN, J. L., and BRAHMA, S. K., 1959. Studies on embryonic induction using radioactive tracers. II. The mobilization of protein components during induction of the lens. *Develop. Biol.*, **1**, 234–246.

SIRLIN, J. L., BRAHMA, S. K., and WADDINGTON, C. H., 1956. Studies on embryonic induction using radioactive tracers. *J. Embryol. exp. Morph.*, **4**, 248–253.

SMITH, A. E. S., and SCHECHTMAN, A. M., 1954. Studies of induction by modified tissues. I. Absence of neural induction by dead organizer in two species of anurans. II. Analysis of the effects of formaldehyde- and alcohol-treated tissues upon the gastrular ectoderm of two species of anurans. *J. exp. Zool.*, **125**, 265–284.

SMITHBERG, M., 1954. The origin and development of the tail in the frog Rana pipiens. *J. exp. Zool.*, **127**, 397–425.

SPEMANN, H., 1901. Entwicklungsphysiologische Studien am Triton-Ei. I. *Arch. EntwMech. Org.*, **12**, 224–264.

SPEMANN, H., 1902. Entwicklungsphysiologische Studien am Triton-Ei. II. *Arch. EntwMech. Org.*, **15**, 448–534.

SPEMANN, H., 1903. Entwicklungsphysiologische Studien am Triton-Ei. III. *Arch. EntwMech. Org.*, **16**, 551–631.

SPEMANN, H., 1912. Zur Entwicklung des Wirbeltierauges. *Zool. Jber.* (*Abt. Zool. Phys.*), **32**, 1–98.

SPEMANN, H., 1916. Über Transplantationen an Amphibienembryonen im Gastrulastadium. *S.B. Ges. naturf. Fr. Berl.*, No. **9**, 306–320.

SPEMANN, H., 1918. Über die Determination der ersten Organanlagen des Amphibienembryo. I–VI. *Arch. EntwMech. Org.*, **43**, 448–555.

SPEMANN, H., 1919. Experimentelle Forschungen zum Determinations- und Individualitätsproblem. *Naturwissenschaften*, **7**, 581–591.

SPEMANN, H., 1921. Die Erzeugung tierischer Chimären durch heteroplastiche embryonale Transplantation zwischen Triton cristatus und taeniatus. *Arch. EntwMech. Org.*, **48**, 533–570.

SPEMANN, H., 1927. Neue Arbeiten über Organisatoren in der tierischen Entwicklung. *Naturwissenschaften*, **15**, 946–951.

SPEMANN, H., 1931. Über den Anteil von Implantat und Wirtskeim an der Orientierung und Beschaffenheit der Induzierten Embryonalanlage. *Arch. EntwMech. Org.*, **123**, 389–517.

SPEMANN, H., 1936. *Experimentelle Beiträge zu einer Theorie der Entwicklung.* Springer, Berlin.

SPEMANN, H., 1938. *Embryonic development and induction.* Yale Univ. Press, New Haven, Connecticut.

SPEMANN, H. und MANGOLD, H., 1924. Über Induktion von Embryonalanlagen durch Implantation artfremder Organisatoren. *Arch. EntwMech. Org.*, **100**, 599–638.

SPEMANN, H., und SCHOTTÉ, O., 1932. Über xenoplastische Transplantation als Mittel zur Analyse der embryonalen Induktion. *Naturwissenschaften*, **20**, 463–467.

SPIEGEL, M., 1954 (a). The role of specific surface antigens on cell adhesion. Pt. I. The reaggregation of sponge cells. *Biol. Bull.*, Wood's Hole, **107**, 130–148.

SPIEGEL, M., 1954 (b). The role of specific surface antigens on cell adhesion. Pt. II. Studies on embryonic amphibian cells. *Biol. Bull.*, Wood's Hole, **107**, 149–155.

SPIEGEL, M., 1955. The reaggregation of dissociated sponge cells. *Ann. N.Y. Acad. Sci.*, **60**, 1056–1078.

SPIEGELMAN, S., and MOOG, F., 1945. A comparison of the effects of cyanide and azide on the development of frogs' eggs. *Biol. Bull.*, Wood's Hole, **89**, 122–130.

SPIEGELMAN, S., and STEINBACH, H. B., 1945. Substrate-enzyme orientation during embryonic development. *Biol. Bull.*, Wood's Hole, **88**, 254–268.

SPOFFORD, W. R., 1945. Observations on the posterior parts of the neural plate in Amblystoma. I. The prospective significance of the posterior neural plate. *J. exp. Zool.*, **99**, 35–53.

SPOFFORD, W. R., 1948. Observations on the posterior parts of the neural plate in Amblystoma. II. The inductive effect of the intact posterior part of the chorda-mesodermal axis on competent prospective ectoderm. *J. exp., Zool.*, **107**, 123–164.

SPOFFORD, W. R., 1953. Observations on the posterior part of the neural plate in Amblystoma. III. The differentiation of neural plate grafts after translocation of mesodermal and neural primordia. *Arch. Biol.*, **64**, 439–493.

SPRATT, N. T., Jr., 1954. Physiological mechanisms in development. *Physiol. Rev.*, **34**, 1–24.

STABLEFORD, L. T., 1948. The potency of the vegetal hemisphere of the Amblystoma punctatum embryo. *J. exp. Zool.*, **109**, 385–427.

STEINERT, M., 1951. La synthese de l'acide ribonucléique au cours du développement embryonnaire des Batraciens. *Bull. Soc. Chim. biol.*, Paris, **33**, 549–554.

STEINERT, M., 1953. Métabolisme de l'acide ribonucléique dans l'œuf d'amphibien traité au dinitrophénol. *Biochem. & Biophys. Acta.*, **10**, 427–431.

STÖHR, P., Jr., 1924. Experimentelle Studien an embryonalen Amphibien-herzen. I. Über Explantation embryonaler Amphibienherzen. *Arch. EntwMech. Org.*, **102**, 426–451.

STÖHR, P., Jr., 1926. Zwei neue experimentelle Resultate zur Herzentwick-lung bei Amphibien. *Verh. anat. Ges.*, suppl., **61**, 151–154.

STONE, L. S., 1948. Neural retina degeneration followed by regeneration from surviving pigment cells in grafted adult salamander eyes. *Anat. Rec.*, **106**, 89–110.

STONE, L. S., 1950. The role of retinal pigment cells in regenerating neural retinae of adult salamander eyes. *J. exp. Zool.*, **113**, 9–26.

SUZUKI, S., 1940. Defektversuche über die Schwanzenentwicklung der Urodelen. *Jap. J. med. Sci., Anat.*, **8**, 50–51.

SZE, L. C., 1953. Respiration of the parts of the Rana pipiens gastrula. *Physiol. Zoöl.*, **26**, 212–223.

TAKATA, C., 1960 (a). The differentiation *in vitro* of the isolated endoderm under the influence of the mesoderm in Triturus pyrrhogaster. *Embryologia*, **5**, 38–70.

TAKATA, C., 1960 (b). The differentiation *in vitro* of the isolated endoderm in the presence of the neural fold in Triturus pyrrhogaster. *Embryologia*, **5**, 194–205.

TAKATA, C., and YAMADA, T., 1960. Endodermal tissues developed from the isolated newt ectoderm under the influence of guinea pig bone marrow. *Embryologia*, **5**, 8–20.

TAKATA, K., 1950. On the distribution of RNA within the Amphibian embryo. (Japanese text.) *Zool. Mag.*, Tokyo, **59**, 28.

TAKATA, K., 1953. Quantitative study on the distribution of pentose nucleic acid in the gastrula and neurula of Triturus. *Biol., Bull.*, Wood's Hole, **105**, 348–353.

TAKAYA, H., 1953 (a). On the notochord-forming potency of the prechordal plate in Triturus gastrulae. *Proc. imp. Acad.*, Japan, **29**, 374–380.

TAKAYA, H., 1953 (b). On the loss of notochord forming potency in the pre-chordal plate of the Triturus gastrula. *Annot. zool. jap.*, **26**, 202–207.

TAKAYA, H., 1955 (a). Formation of the brain from the prospective spinal cord of Amphibian embryos. *Proc. imp. Acad.*, Japan, **31**, 360–365.

TAKAYA, H., 1955 (b). Thermal influence upon the inducing specificity of the organizer. *Proc. imp. Acad.*, Japan, **31**, 366–371.

TAKAYA, H., 1956 (a). Two types of neural differentiation produced in connection with mesenchymal tissue. *Proc. imp. Acad.*, Japan, **32**, 282–286.

TAKAYA, H., 1956 (b). On the types of neural tissue developed in connection with mesodermal tissue. *Proc. imp. Acad.*, Japan, **32**, 288–292.

TAKAYA, H., 1956 (c). Notochordal influence upon the differentiation and segmentation of muscle tissue. *Annot. zool. jap.*, **29**, 133–137.

TAKAYA, H., 1957. Regionalization of the central nervous system in Amphibian embryo. (Japanese text.) *Jap. J. Exp. Morph.*, **11**, 1–24.

TAMANOI, I., and KAWAKAMI, I., 1959. The effect of LiCl on the yolk granules of Triturus embryos. *Mem. Fac. Sci., Kyushu Univ.*, ser. E., **2**, 163–169.

TEN CATE, G., 1953. The intrinsic development of amphibian embryos. Diss., Amsterdam.

TEN CATE, G., and VAN DOORENMAALEN, W. J., 1950. Analysis of the development of the eye-lens in chicken and frog embryos by means of the precipitin reaction. *Proc. Acad. Sci. Amst.*, ser. C., **53**, 894–909.

TENCER, R., 1958. Étude autoradiographique de l'incorporation de $^{14}CO_2$ dans des gastrulas d'Axolotl. *J. Embryol. exp. Morph.*, **6**, 117–123.

TIEDEMANN, H., 1959(a). Ein Verfahren zur gleichzeitigen Gewinnung deuterencephaler und mesodermaler Induktionsstoffe aus Hühnerembryonen. *Z. Naturf.*, **14**, 610–611.

TIEDEMANN, H., 1959 (b). Neue Ergebnisse zur Frage nach der chemischen Natur der Induktionsstoffe beim Organisatoreffekt Spemanns. *Naturwissenschaften*, **46**, 613–623.

TIEDEMANN, H. und TIEDEMANN, H., 1955. Induktionsstoffe aus Embryonalextrakt bei der Pepsinhydrolyse. *Naturwissenschaften*, **42**, 560.

TIEDEMANN, H. und TIEDEMANN, H., 1956. Isolierung von Ribonucleinsäure und Nucleotiden aus Embryonalextrakt und Leber und ihr Verhalten im Induktionsversuch. *Hoppe-Sey. Z.*, **306**, 132–142.

TIEDEMANN, H. und TIEDEMANN, H., 1957. Zur Gewinnung von Induktionsstoffen aus Hühnerembryonen. *Experientia*, **8**, 320.

TIEDEMANN, H. und TIEDEMANN, H., 1959 (a). Wirkungsabnahme eines spinocaudalen Induktionsstoffes nach Acetylierung. *Hoppe-Sey. Z.*, **314**, 90–94.

TIEDEMANN, H., und TIEDEMANN, H., 1959 (b). Versuche zur Gewinnung eines mesodermalen Induktionsstoffes aus Hühnerembryonen. *Hoppe-Sey. Z.*, **314**, 156–176.

TIEDEMANN, H., TIEDEMANN, H. und KESSELRING, K., 1960. Versuche zur Kennzeichnung von Iduktionsstoffen aus Hühnerembryonen. I. Abbau durch Trypsin und Carboxypeptidase. II. Verhalten bei der Dialyse. *Z. Naturf.*, **15**, 312–319.

TIEDEMANN-WAECHTER, H., 1960. Die Selbstdifferenzierungsfähigkeit und Induktionsfähigkeit medianer und lateraler Teile der Rumpfmedullarplatte bei Urodelen. *Arch. EntwMech. Org.*, **152**, 303–338.

TOIVONEN, S., 1938 (a). Über das Verhalten des Gastrulaektoderms von Triton taeniatus bei anwendung von pflanzlichen Implantaten. *Ann. Soc. zool.-bot. fenn., Vanamo*, **5**, No. 8, 1–12.

TOIVONEN, S., 1938 (b). Spezifische Induktionsleistungen von abnormen

Induktoren im Implantatversuch. *Ann. Soc. zool.-bot. fenn. Vanamo*, **6**, No. 5, 1–12.

TOIVONEN, S., 1940. Über die Leistungsspezifität der abnormen Induktoren im Implantatversuch bei Triton. Diss. Helsinki. *Ann. Acad. Sci. fenn.*, ser. A., IV, **55**, No. 6, 1–150.

TOIVONEN, S., 1945. Zur Frage der Induktion selbständiger Linsen durch abnorme Induktoren im Implantatversuch bei Triton. *Ann. Soc. zool.-bot. fenn. Vanamo.*, **11**, No. 3, 1–28.

TOIVONEN, S., 1949 (a). Zur Frage der Leistungsspezifität abnormer Induktoren. *Experentia*, **5**, 323–325.

TOIVONEN, S., 1949 (b). Die Induktionswirkung von leistungsspezifischen heterogenen Induktoren nach Behandlung mit verschiedenen Eingriffen (Temperatur, Lösungsmitteln u.dgl.m.) im Implantationsversuch bei Triton. *Arch. Soc. zool.-bot. fenn. Vanamo*, **4**, No. 1, 28–34.

TOIVONEN, S., 1950. Stoffliche Induktoren. *Rev. suisse Zool.*, **57**, suppl. 1, 41–56.

TOIVONEN, S., 1951. Verschiedenheit der Induktionsleistungen des Lebergewebes von hungerndem und gut ernährtem Meerschweinchen im Implantatversuch bei Triton. *Arch. Soc. zool.-bot. fenn. Vanamo*, **6**, No. 1, 63–71.

TOIVONEN, S., 1952. Die regionale Verschiedenheit der Induktionsleistungen des Lebergewebes von gut ernährten und hungernden Meerschweinchen im Implantatversuch. *Experientia*, **8**, 120.

TOIVONEN, S., 1953 (a). Knochenmark als mesodermaler Induktor im Implantatversuch bei Triturus. *Arch. Soc. zool.-bot. fenn. Vanamo*, **7**, No. 2, 113–121.

TOIVONEN, S., 1953 (b). Bone-marrow of the Guinea-pig as a mesodermal inductor in implantation experiments with embryos of Triturus. *J. Embryol. exp. Morph.*, **1**, 97–104.

TOIVONEN, S., 1954 (a). Über die Induktion des Mesoderms mit abnormen Induktoren. *Ann. Acad. Sci. fenn.*, ser. A, IV, **22**, 1–10.

TOIVONEN, S., 1954 (b). The inducing action of the bone-marrow of the Guinea-pig after alcohol and heat treatment in implantation and explantation experiments with embryos of Triturus. *J. Embryol. exp. Morph.*, **2**, 239–244.

TOIVONEN, S., 1958. The dependence of the cellular transformation of the competent ectoderm on temporal relationships in the induction process. *J. Embryol. exp. Morph.*, **6**, 479–485.

TOIVONEN, S., 1961. An experimentally produced change in the sequence of neuralizing and mesodermalizing inductive actions. *Experientia*, **17**, 87.

TOIVONEN, S., and KUUSI, T., 1948. Implantationsversuche mit in verschiedener Weise vorbehandelten abnormen Induktoren bei Triton. *Ann. Soc. zool.-bot. fenn. Vanamo*, **13**, No. 3, 1–19.

TOIVONEN, S. und SAXÉN, L. 1955 (a). Über die Induktion des Neuralrohrs bei Trituruskeimen als simultane Leistung des Leber- und Knochenmarkgewebes vom Meerschweinchen. *Ann. Acad. Sci. fenn ser.*, A, IV, **30**, 1–29.

TOIVONEN, S., and SAXÉN, L., 1955 (b). The simultaneous inducing action of liver and bone-marrow of the Guinea-pig in implantation and explantation experiments with embryos of Triturus. *Exp. Cell Res.* (suppl.), **3**, 346–357.

TOIVONEN, S., and SAXÉN, L., 1957. Embryonic inductive action of normal and leukemic bone marrow of the rat. *J. nat. Cancer Inst.*, **19**, 1095–1104.

TOIVONEN, S., SAXÉN, L., and VAINIO, T., 1960. The effect of heat treatment of growth media on the differentiating properties of continuous amniotic line cells. *Acta embryol. morph. exp.*, **3**, 23–34.

TOIVONEN, S., SAXÉN, L., and VAINIO, T., 1961. Quantitative evidence for the two-gradient hypothesis in the primary induction. *Experientia*, **17**, 86–87.

TOWNES, P. I., and HOLTFRETER, J., 1955. Directed movements and selective adhesion of embryonic Amphibian cells. *J. exp. Zool.*, **128**, 53–120.

TRINKAUS, J. P., 1956. The differentiation of tissue cells. *Amer. Nat.*, **90**, 273–289.

TRINKAUS, J. P., 1961. Affinity relationships in heterotypic cell aggregates. *Actes du colloque internatiol sur "La culture organotypique: Associations et dissociations d'organes en culture in vitro".* Ed. by M. E. Wolff. Éditions du centre national de la recherche scientifique. Paris, pp. 209–225.

TRINKAUS, J. P., and DRAKE, J. W., 1956 (a). Exogenous controls of morphogenesis in isolated Fundulus blastoderms by nutrient chemical factors *J. exp. Zool.*, **132**, 311–342.

TRINKAUS, J. P., and DRAKE, J. W., 1956 (b). Significance of mass of tissue and volume of medium in the differentiation of isolated Fundulus blastoderms. *Anat. Rec.*, **124**, 375.

TRINKAUS, J. P., and GROVES, P. W., 1955. Differentiation in culture of mixed aggregates of dissociated tissue cells. *Proc. nat. Acad. Sci.*, Wash., **41**, 787–795.

TSENG, M-P., 1956. The transplantation of embryonic tissue to adult abdominal cavity in urodeles. (Chinese text with English summary.) *Acta exp. biol. Sinica*, **5**, 51–73.

TWITTY, V. C., 1936. Correlated genetic and embryological experiments on Triturus. I. Hybridization: development of the three species of Triturus and their hybrid combinations. II. Transplantation: the embryological basis of species differences in pigment pattern. *J. exp. Zool.*, **74**, 239–302.

TWITTY, V. C., 1945. The developmental analysis of specific pigment patterns. *J. exp. Zool.*, **100**, 141–178.

TWITTY, V. C., 1955. Special vertebrate organogenesis: Eye. In: *Analysis of Development.* Ed. by B. H. Willier, P. A. Weiss and V. Hamburger. Saunders, Philadelphia and London, pp. 402–414.

TWITTY, V. C., and BODENSTEIN, D., 1939. Correlated genetic and embryological experiments on Triturus. III. Further transplantation experiments in pigment development. IV. The study of pigment cell behavior *in vitro*. *J. exp. Zool.*, **81**, 357–398.

TWITTY, V. C., and NIU, M. C., 1948. Causal analysis of chromatophore migration. *J. exp. Zool.*, **108**, 405–437.

TYLER, A., 1955. Special vertebrate organogenesis: Ontogeny of immunological properties. In: *Analysis of development.* Eds., B. H. Willier,

s

262 PRIMARY EMBRYONIC INDUCTION

P. A. Weiss and V. Hamburger. Saunders, Philadelphia and London. pp. 556–573.

UMANSKI, E., 1932. Uber die Induktion der Medullarplatte bei Triton taeniatus durch Implantation von Regenerationsblastem in die Blastula. *Zool. Anz.*, **97**, 286–287.

URBANI, E., 1955. Gli enzimi proteolitici nella cellula, e nell'embrione. *Experientia*, **11**, 209–218.

URBANI, E., 1957 (a). Sul comportamento dei glucidi nello sviluppo embrionale degli Anfibi anuri. *Ric Sci.*, **27**, 1549–1558.

URBANI, E., 1957 (b). Studi di embriologiae zoologia chimica degli anfibi. R.C. *Ist. lombardo, B.*, **92**, 69–179.

VAHS, W., 1955. Untersuchungen am Triturus-Keim über die Existenz spezifischer Induktionsstoffe in abnormen Induktoren. *Z. Naturf.*, **10**, 412–416.

VAHS, W., 1957 (a). Experimentelle Untersuchungen am Triturus-Keim über die stofflichen Mittel abnormer Induktoren. *Arch. EntwMech. Org.*, **149**, 339–364.

VAHS, W., 1957 (b). Über Induktionswirkungen von Bakterienagglomeraten im Triturus-Keim und die chemische Natur des wirksamen Stoffes. *Embryologia*, **3**, 201–219.

VAINIO, T., 1956. The antigenic properties of the blastoporal lip of the Triturus gastrula. *Ann. Med. exp. Fenn.*, **34**, 71–77.

VAINIO, T., 1957. An experimental study of the complementariness of heterogenous embryonic inductive agents. Diss. Helsinki. *Ann. Acad. Sci. Fenn.*, ser. A, IV, **35**, 1–94.

VAINIO, T., 1958. An approach to the problem of embryonic induction. *Exp. Cell Res.*, **15**, 184–190.

VAINIO, T., SAXÉN, L., and TOIVONEN, S., 1960. Transfer of the antigenicity of Guinea pig bone marrow implants to the graft tissue in explantation experiments. *Experimentia*, **16**, 27–28.

VAINIO, T., TOIVONEN, S., and SAXÉN, L., 1958. Embryonic inductive capacity of the blood and its constituents. *Ann. Med. exp. Fenn.*, **36**, 285–291.

VOGT., W., 1922. Operativ bewirkte "Exogastrulation" bei Triton und ihre Bedeutung für die Theorie der Wirbeltiergastrulation. *Verh. anat. Ges.* (*Anat. Anz. suppl.*), **55**, 53–64.

VOGT., W., 1923 (a). Eine Methode lokalizierter Vitalfärbung an jungen Amphibienkeimen. *Münch. med. Wschr.*, I, 861.

VOGT., W., 1923 (b). Weitere Versuche mit vitaler Farmarkierung und farbiger Transplantation zur Analyse der Primitiventwicklung von Triton. *Verh. anat. Ges.* (*Anat. Anz. suppl.*), **57**, 30–38.

VOGT, W., 1924. Morphogische und physiologische Fragen der Primitiventwicklung, Versuche zu ihrer Lösung mittels vitaler Farbmarkierung. *S.B. Ges. Morph. Physiol. Münch.*, **35**, 22–32.

VOGT., W., 1925. Gestaltungsanalyse am Amphibienkeim mit örtlicher Vitalfärbung. Vortwort über Wege und Ziele. I. Teil: Methodik und Wirkungsweise der örtlichen Vitalfärbung mit Agar als Farbträger. *Arch. EntwMech. Org.*, **106**, 542–610.

VOGT, W., 1926. Über Wachstum und Gestaltungsbewegungen am hinteren Körperende der Amphibien. *Vehr. anat. Ges. (Anat. Anz. suppl.)*, **61**, 62–75.

VOGT, W., 1929. Gestaltungsanalyse am Amphibienkeim mit örtlicher Vitalfärbung. II. Gastrulation und Mesodermbildung bei Urodelen und Anuren. *Arch. EntwMech. Org.*, **120**, 384–706.

WADDINGTON, C. H., 1932. Experiments on the development of chick and duck embryos, cultivated *in vitro*. *Phil. Trans.*, London, **221**, 179–230.

WADDINGTON, C. H., 1936. The origin of competence for lens formation in the Amphibia. *J. exp. Biol.*, **13**, 86–91.

WADDINGTON, C. H., 1938. Evocation by some further chemical compounds. *Proc. roy. Soc.*, London, ser. B., **125**, 365–372.

WADDINGTON, C. H., 1939. Order of magnitude of morphogenetic forces. *Nature*, London, **144**, 637.

WADDINGTON, C. H., 1941. Translocation of the organizer in the gastrula Discoglossus. *Proc. zool. Soc.*, London, ser. A., **111**, 189–198.

WADDINGTON, C. H. (Ed.), 1959. *Biological organization. Cellular and subcellular* Proc. symp. at the Univ. Edinburgh, 1957. Pergamon Press, London.

WADDINGTON, C. H., and DEUCHAR, E. M., 1952. The effect of type of contact with the organizer on the nature of the resulting induction. *J. exp. Biol.*, **29**, 496–510.

WADDINGTON, C. H., and MULHERKAR, L., 1957. The diffusion of substances during embryonic induction in the chick. *Proc. Zool. Soc.*, Calcutta, Mookerjee Memor. Vol., pp. 141–147.

WADDINGTON, C. H., and NEEDHAM, J., 1936. Evocation, individuation and competence, in amphibian organizer action. *Proc. Acad. Sci.*, Amst., **39**, 887–891.

WADDINGTON, C. H., NEEDHAM, J., and BRACHET, J., 1936. Studies on the nature of the amphibian organization centre. III. The activation of the evocator. *Proc. roy. Soc.*, London, ser. B., **120**, 173–198.

WADDINGTON, C. H., NEEDHAM, J., and NEEDHAM, D. M., 1933 (a). Physico-chemical experiments of the Amphibian organizer. *Nature*, London, **132**, 239.

WADDINGTON, C. H., NEEDHAM, J., und NEEDHAM, D. M., 1933 (b). Beobachtungen über die physikalisch-chemische Natur des Organisators. *Naturwissenschaften*, **21**, 771–772.

WADDINGTON, C. H., NEEDHAM, J., NOWINSKI, W. W., NEEDHAM, D. M., and LEMBERG, R., 1934. Active principle of the Amphibian organization centre. *Nature*, London, **134**, 103.

WADDINGTON, C. H., NEEDHAM, J., NOWINSKI, W. W., NEEDHAM, D. M. and LEMBERG R. 1935. Studies on the nature of the amphibian organization centre. I. Chemical properties of the evocator. *Proc. roy. Soc.*, London, ser. B, **117**, 289–310.

WADDINGTON, C. H., and SIRLIN, J. L., 1954. The incorporation of labelled amino acids into Amphibian embryos. *J. Embryol. exp. Morph.*, **2**, 340–347.

WADDINGTON, C. H., and SIRLIN, J. L., 1955. Studies in Amphibian embryogenesis using labelled grafts. *Proc. roy. phys. Soc.*, **24**, 28–31.

WADDINGTON, C. H., and YAO, T., 1950. Studies on regional specificity within the organization centre of the Urodeles. *J. exp. Biol.*, **27**, 126–144.

WAECHTER, H., 1951. Implantation von indifferentem embryonalem Gewebe in die Leibeshöhle erwachsener Molche. *Arch. EntwMech. Org.*, **144**, 572–617.

WAECHTER, H., 1953. Die Induktionsfähigkeit der Gehirnplatte bei Urodelen und ihr median-laterales Gefälle. *Arch. EntMech. Org.*, **146**, 201–274.

WEISS, P., 1939. *Principles of development.* Holt & Co., New York.

WEISS, P., 1945. Experiments on cell and axon orientation *in vitro*: the role of colloidal exudates in tissue organization. *J. exp. Zool.*, **100**, 353–386.

WEISS, P., 1947. The problem of specificity in growth and development. *Yale J. Biol. Med.*, **19**, 235–278.

WEISS, P., 1949. Nature of vertebrate individuality. The problem of cellular differentiation. *Proc. First nat. Cancer Conf.*, pp. 50–60.

WEISS, P., 1950. Perspectives in the field of morphogenesis. *Quart. Rev. Biol.*, **25**, 177–198.

WEISS, P., 1953. Some introductory remarks on the cellular basis of differentiation. *J. Embryol. exp. Morph.*, **1**, 181–211.

WEISS, P., 1955. Specificity in growth control. In: *Biological specificity and growth.* Ed. by E. G. Butler. Univ. Press, Princeton, New Jersey, pp. 195–206.

WEISS, P., 1958 (a). Cell contact. *Int. Rev. Cytol.*, **7**, 391–423.

WEISS, P., 1958 (b). Discussion in: *A symposium on the chemical basis of development.* Ed. by W. D. McElroy and B. Glass. The John Hopkins Press, Baltimore, pp. 259–260.

WEISS, P., 1959. Discussion in: *Biological organization. Cellular and subcellular.* Proc. Symp. at the Univ. Edinburgh, 1957. Ed. by C. H. Waddington. Pergamon Press, London, p. 231.

WEISS, P., and JAMES, R., 1954. Vitamin A and skin keratinization *in vitro*: Experimental dissociation of induction and realization phases in cytodifferentiation. *Science*, **119**, 587.

WEISS, P., and JAMES, R., 1955. Skin metaplasia *in vitro* induced by brief exposure to vitamin A. *Exp. Cell. Res.* (suppl.), **3**, 381–394.

WEISSENBERG, R., 1929 (a). Vitalmarkierung mit Bismarkbraun und ihre Konservierung zwecks Untersuchung auf Paraffinschnitten. *Arch. EntwMech. Org.*, **118**, 485–498.

WEISSENBERG, R., 1929 (b). Die feinere Lokalisation der Vitalfarbmarkierung am Neunaugenkeim und ihre Konservierung für Schnittpräparate, *S.B. Ges. naturf. Fr. Berl.*, Nr. 4–7, 225–243.

WEISSMANN, A., 1892. *Das Keimplasma. Eine Theorie der Vererbung.* Fischer, Jena.

WETZEL, R., 1929 (a). Neue Experimente zur Frühentwicklung des Huhnes. *Verh. anat. Ges. (Anat. Anz. suppl.)*, **67**, 76–84.

WETZEL, R., 1929 (b). Untersuchungen am Hühnchen. Die Entwicklung des

Keims während der ersten beiden Bruttage. *Arch. EntwMech. Org.*, **119**, 188–321.

WETZEL, R., 1931. Urmund und Primitivstreifen. *Z. ges. Anat.*, *Abt. III*, **29**, 1–24.

WILDE, C. E., Jr., 1955(a). The urodele neuroepithelium. II. The relationship between phenylalanine metabolism and the differentiation of neural crest cells. *J. Morph.*, **97**, 313–344.

WILDE, C. E., Jr., 1955 (b). The urodele neuroepithelium. I. The differentiation *in vitro* of the cranial neural crest. *J. exp. Zool.*, **130**, 573–596.

WILDE, C. E., Jr., 1956. The urodele neuroepithelium. III. The presentation of phenylalanine to the neural crest by archenteron roof mesoderm. *J. exp. Zool.*, **133**, 409–440.

WILDE, C. E., Jr., 1959. Differentiation in response to the biochemical environment. In: *Cell, organism and milieu.* Ed. by D. Rudnick. Ronald Press, New York, pp. 3–43.

WILDE, C. E., Jr., 1961 (a). Factors concerning the degree of cellular differentiation in organotypic and disaggregated tissue cultures. *Actes du colloque international sur "La culture organotypique: Associations et dissociations d'organes en culture* in vitro". Ed. by M. E. Wolff. Éditions du centre national de la recherche scientifique. Paris, pp. 183–198.

WILDE, C. E., Jr., 1961(b). The differentiation of vertebrate pigment cells. *Advanc. Morph.*, **1**, 267–300.

WILLIS, R. A., 1958. *The borderland of embryology and pathology.* Butterworth and Co., London.

WILLMER, E. N., 1951. Some aspects of evolutionary cytology. In: *Cytology and cell physiology.* 2nd ed. Ed. by G. H. Bourne, Clarendon Press, Oxford, pp. 11, 444.

WILSON, H. V., 1908. On some phenomena of coalescence and regeneration in sponges. *J. exp. Zool.*, **5**, 245–258.

WILT, F. H., 1959. The differentiation of visual pigments in metamorphosing larvae of Rana catesbeiana. *Develop. Biol.*, **1**, 199–233.

VON WOELLWARTH, C., 1951. Die Entwicklung der Determination des Wirbeltiergehirns. *Vehr. dtsch. Zool. Ges.* (*Zool. Anz. suppl.*), pp. 102–109.

VON WOELLWARTH, C., 1952. Die Induktionsstufen des Gehirns. *Arch. EntwMech. Org.*, **145**, 582–668.

VON WOELLWARTH, C., 1956 (a). Entwicklungsphysiologie der Wirbeltiere. *Fortschr. Zool.*, N.F., **10**, 458–560.

VON WOELLWARTH, C., 1956 (b). Die induzierenden Wirkung von rohem, flüssigem Hühnerembryonalextrakt auf Gastrula-Ektoderm von Triton. *Arch. EntwMech. Org.*, **148**, 504–517.

WOERDEMAN, M. W., 1930. Versuche zur Verringerung der Sterblichkeit nach mikrochirurgischen Eingriffen an Amphibienkeimen. *Arch. Entw-Mech. Org.*, **121**, 524–532.

WOERDEMAN, M. W., 1933 (a). Über Glykogenstoffwechsel des Organisationszentrums in der Amphibiengastrula. *Proc. Acad. Sci. Amst.*, **36**, 189–193.

WOERDEMAN, M. W., 1933 (b). Über den Glykogenstoffwechsel tierischer "Organisatoren". *Proc. Acad. Sci. Amst.*, **36**, 423–426.

WOERDEMAN, M. W., 1933 (c). Über die chemischen Prozesse bei der embryonalen Induktion. *Proc. Acad. Sci. Amst.*, **36**, 842–849.

WOERDEMAN, M. W., 1933 (d). Over glycolyse en embryonale inductie. *Ned. Tijdschr. Geneesk.*, **77**, 3621–3624.

WOERDEMAN, M. W., 1933 (e). Embryonale Induktion durch Geschwulstgewebe. *Proc. Acad. Sci. Amst.*, **36**, 477–481.

WOERDEMAN, M. W., 1953. Serological methods in the study of morphogenesis. *Arch. Nederl. Zool.*, **10**, suppl., **1**, 144–159.

WOERDEMAN, M. W., 1955. Immunological approach to some problems of induction and differentiation. In: *Biological specificity and growth*. Ed. by E. G. Butler, Univ. Press, Princeton, New Jersey, pp. 33–53.

YAMADA, T., 1939 (a). Über den Einfluss von Wirtsalter auf die Differenzierung von verpflanztem Ursegmentmaterial des Molchembryos. *Jap. J. exp. Zool.*, **8**, 265–283.

YAMADA, T., 1939 (b). Über bedeutungsfremde Selbstdifferenzierung der präsumptiven Rückenmuskulatur des Molchkeimes bei Isolation. *Okajimas Fol. anat. jap.*, **18**, 565–568.

YAMADA, T., 1940. Beeinflussung der differenzierungsleistung des isolierten Mesoderms von Molchkeimen durch zugefügtes Chorda- und Neuralmaterial. *Okajimas Fol. anat. jap.*, **19**, 131–197.

YAMADA, T., 1947. An extension of the potential theory of the morphogenesis (in Japanese). *Zool. Mag.*, Tokyo, **57**, 124–126.

YAMADA, T., 1950 (a). Dorsalization of the ventral marginal zone of the Triturus gastrula. I. Ammonia-treatment of the medio-ventral marginal zone. *Biol. Bull.*, Wood's Hole, **98**, 98–121.

YAMADA, T., 1950 (b). Regional differentiation of the isolated ectoderm of the Triturus gastrula induced through a protein extract. *Embryologia*, **1**, 1–20.

YAMADA, T., 1958 (a). Induction of specific differentiation by samples of proteins and nucleoproteins in the isolated ectoderm of Triturus-gastrulae. *Experientia*, **14**, 81–87.

YAMADA, T., 1958 (b). Embryonic induction. In: *A symposium on chemical basis of development*. Ed. by W. McElroy and B. Glass. John Hopkins Press, Baltimore, pp. 217–238.

YAMADA, T., 1959. A progressive change in regional inductive effects of the bone-marrow caused by heat-treatment. *Embryologia*, **4**, 175–190.

YAMADA, T., 1961. A chemical approach to the problem of the organizer. *Advanc. Morph.*, **1**, 1–53.

YAMADA, T., HAYASHI, Y., and TAKATA, K., 1958. Results published by Yamada (1958 (b).)

YAMADA, T., and KARASAKI, S., 1958. An electron microscopic study of the developing cells of the amphibian embryo. (In Japanese with English summary.) *Symp. Cell. Chem.* (Japan), **7**, 153–158.

YAMADA, T., and TAKATA, K. 1955 (a). An analysis of spino-caudal induction by the guinea pig kidney in the isolated ectoderm of the Triturus-gastrula. *J. exp. Zool.*, **128**, 291–332.

YAMADA, T., and TAKATA, K., 1955 (b). Effect of trypsin and chymotrypsin on the inducing ability of the kidney and its fractions. *Exp. Cell Res.*, **3**, 402–413.

YAMADA, T., and TAKATA, K. 1956. Spino-caudal induction by pentose nucleo-protein isolated from the kidney. *Embryologia*, **3**, 69–79.

YAMADA, T., TAKATA, K., and OSAWA, S., 1954. A test of the inductive effect of pentose nucleic acid of the kidney on the isolated ectoderm. *Embryologia*, **2**, 123–132.

ZELLER, C., 1956. Über den Ribonukleinsäure-Stoffwechsel des Bastardmerogons Triton palmatus (♀) Triton cristatus ♂. *Arch. EntwMech. Org.*, **148**, 311–335.

Index